# THE PEARSON CUSTOM LIBRARY FOR THE
# BIOLOGICAL SCIENCES

Des Moines Area Community College
Principles of Biology

**PEARSON**

ISBN 10: 1-269-28504-1
ISBN 13: 978-1-269-28504-9

# Laboratory Safety: General Guidelines

1. Notify your instructor immediately if you are pregnant, color blind, allergic to any insects or chemicals, taking immunosuppressive drugs, or have any other medical condition (such as diabetes, immunologic defect) that may require special precautionary measures in the laboratory.

2. Upon entering the laboratory, place all books, coats, purses, backpacks, etc. in designated areas, not on the bench tops.

3. Locate and, when appropriate, learn to use exits, fire extinguisher, fire blanket, chemical shower, eyewash, first aid kit, broken glass container, and cleanup materials for spills.

4. In case of fire, evacuate the room and assemble outside the building.

5. Do not eat, drink, smoke, or apply cosmetics in the laboratory.

6. Confine long hair, loose clothing, and dangling jewelry.

7. Wear shoes at all times in the laboratory.

8. Cover any cuts or scrapes with a sterile, waterproof bandage before attending lab.

9. Wear eye protection when working with chemicals.

10. Never pipet by mouth. Use mechanical pipeting devices.

11. Wash skin immediately and thoroughly if contaminated by chemicals or microorganisms.

12. Do not perform unauthorized experiments.

13. Do not use equipment without instruction.

14. Report all spills and accidents to your instructor immediately.

15. Never leave heat sources unattended.

16. When using hot plates, note that there is no visible sign that they are hot (such as a red glow). Always assume that hot plates are hot.

17. Use an appropriate apparatus when handling hot glassware.

18. Keep chemicals away from direct heat or sunlight.

19. Keep containers of alcohol, acetone, and other flammable liquids away from flames.

20. Do not allow any liquid to come into contact with electrical cords. Handle electrical connectors with dry hands. Do not attempt to disconnect electrical equipment that crackles, snaps, or smokes.

21. Upon completion of laboratory exercises, place all materials in the disposal areas designated by your instructor.

22. Do not pick up broken glassware with your hands. Use a broom and dustpan and discard the glass in designated glass waste containers; never discard with paper waste.

23. Wear disposable gloves when working with blood, other body fluids, or mucous membranes. Change gloves after possible contamination and wash hands immediately after gloves are removed.

24. The disposal symbol indicates that items that may have come in contact with body fluids should be placed in your lab's designated container. It also refers to liquid wastes that should not be poured down the drain into the sewage system.

25. Leave the laboratory clean and organized for the next student.

26. Wash your hands with liquid or powdered soap prior to leaving the laboratory.

27. The biohazard symbol indicates procedures that may pose health concerns.

The caution symbol points out instruments, substances,  and procedures that require special attention to safety. These symbols appear throughout this manual.

# Measurement Conversions

**Metric to American Standard**

**American Standard to Metric**

## Length

| | |
|---|---|
| 1 mm = 0.039 inches | 1 inch = 2.54 cm |
| 1 cm = 0.394 inches | 1 foot = 0.305 m |
| 1 m = 3.28 feet | 1 yard = 0.914 m |
| 1 m = 1.09 yards | 1 mile = 1.61 km |

## Volume

| | |
|---|---|
| 1 mL = 0.0338 fluid ounces | 1 fluid ounce = 29.6 mL |
| 1 L = 4.23 cups | 1 cup = 237 mL |
| 1 L = 2.11 pints | 1 pint = 0.474 L |
| 1 L = 1.06 quarts | 1 quart = 0.947 L |
| 1 L = 0.264 gallons | 1 gallon = 3.79 L |

## Mass

| | |
|---|---|
| 1 mg = 0.0000353 ounces | 1 ounce = 28.3 g |
| 1 g = 0.0353 ounces | 1 pound = 0.454 kg |
| 1 kg = 2.21 pounds | |

## Temperature

To convert temperature:

$$°C = \frac{5}{9}(F - 32) \qquad °F = \frac{9}{5} + 32$$

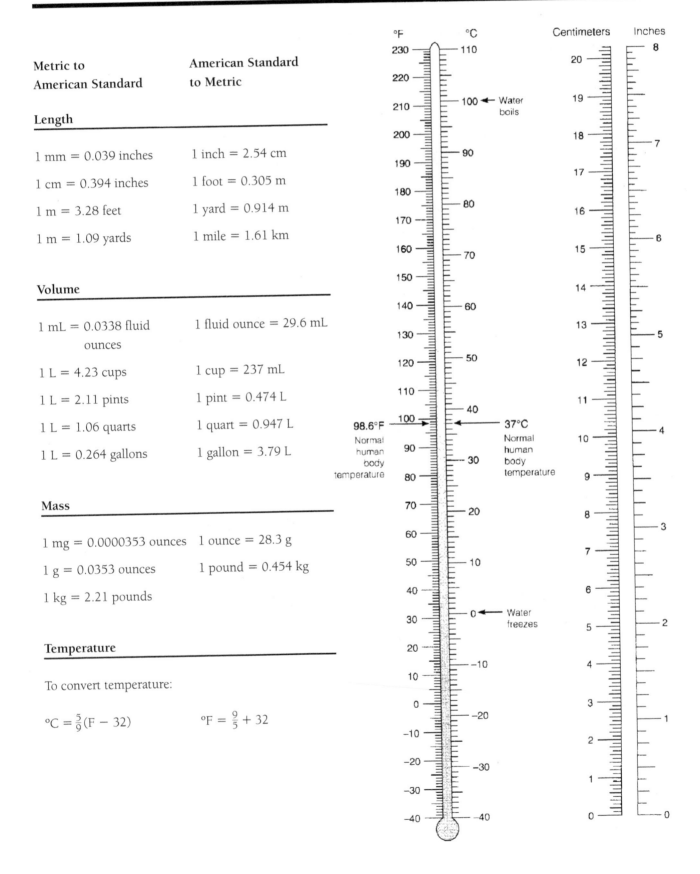

# Table of Contents

# Color Appendix

# Protists and Fungi

 This lab topic gives you another opportunity to practice the scientific process. Before going to lab, review scientific investigation and carefully read this lab. Be prepared to use this information to design an experiment with protists or fungi.

## Laboratory Objectives

After completing this lab topic, you should be able to:

1. Discuss the diversity of protists and fungi, and the current interest in their phylogenetic relationships.
2. Describe the diversity of protists, explaining the means of obtaining nutrition and method of locomotion for each group.
3. Identify representative organisms in several major protistan clades.
4. Discuss the ecological role and economic importance of protists.
5. Describe the characteristics and representative organisms of the green algae and their relationship to land plants.
6. Describe the phyla of the kingdom Fungi, recognizing and identifying representative organisms in each.
7. Describe differences in reproduction in fungal phyla.
8. Discuss the ecological role and economic importance of fungi.
9. Design and perform an independent investigation of a protist or an organism in the kingdom Fungi.

## Introduction

Unicellular eukaryotic organisms originated over 2 billion years ago, and today they are found in every habitable region of Earth. The enormous diversity of organisms, their numerous adaptations, and their cellular complexity reflect the long evolutionary history of eukaryotes. For almost 30 years, scientists placed these diverse groups of unicellular organisms into the kingdom Protista. The Protista usually included all organisms not placed in the other eukaryotic kingdoms of Plants, Animals, and Fungi.

From *Investigating Biology Laboratory Manual,* Sixth Edition, Judith G. Morgan and M. Eloise Brown Carter. Copyright © 2008 by Pearson Education, Inc. Published by Benjamin Cummings, Inc. All rights reserved.

This catchall kingdom included not only the unicellular eukaryotes, but also their multicellular relatives, like the giant kelps and seaweeds. However, scientists now agree that the designation kingdom Protista should be abandoned and these eukaryotic organisms that are neither fungi, plants, nor animals, be placed in the domain Eukarya. In this lab topic we will refer to this diverse group as protists meaning a general term, not a taxonomic category.

The most familiar protists, commonly called algae and protozoans, have been well studied since the earliest development of the microscope. Therefore, one might assume that the taxonomic relationships among these groups are well understood. However, their phylogeny (evolutionary history) has been difficult to determine from comparisons of cell structure and function, nutrition, and reproduction. Recent molecular and biochemical research, particularly the ability to sequence ribosomal and transfer RNA genes, has provided strong new evidence for reconstructing the relationships of the protists.

Most recently scientists have suggested that studies of protists using **clades** can be meaningful for indicating evolutionary relationships. A clade is a group of species, all of which are descended from one ancestral species, representing one phylogenetic group. Many characteristics, including molecular and biochemical evidence, are used when organizing clades. As more information from a variety of sources becomes available, major groupings or clades will surely be modified. These investigations into the nature of eukaryotic diversity demonstrate the process of scientific inquiry. New technologies, new ideas, and novel experiments are used to test hypotheses, and the resulting evidence must be consistent with the existing body of knowledge and classification scheme. The results lead to modification of our hypotheses and further research. No matter how many groups or clades are proposed, remember that this is a reflection of the evolution of eukaryotes over the rich history of the earth. It is not surprising that the diversity of life does not easily fit into our constructed categories.

In this lab topic, we will study diverse examples of protists. These protists represent some of the most common clades. In addition to evolutionary relationships, you will give particular attention to nutrition, locomotion, and cellular complexity of each example.

If you complete all of the lab topics in this laboratory manual, you will have studied examples of all the major groups of organisms with the exception of those in domain Archaea. Fungi, one of the kingdoms of the five-kingdom scheme, are studied in this lab topic, and you will investigate plant evolution and animal evolution in subsequent lab topics.

At the end of this lab topic, you will be asked to design a simple experiment to further your investigation of the behavior, ecology, or physiology of one of the organisms studied. As you proceed through the exercises, ask questions about your observations and consider an experiment that you might design to answer one of your questions.

# EXERCISE 1
# The Protists

In this exercise you will study examples of seven major groups (clades) of protists. (See Table 1 below.)

**Table 1**
Groups of Protists Investigated in this Exercise

| Group | Lab Study | Examples |
|---|---|---|
| Euglenozoans | A | *Trypanosoma levisi* |
| Alveolates | B | Paramecia<br>Dinoflagellates |
| Stramenopiles | C | Diatoms<br>Brown algae |
| Foraminiferans and Radiolarians | D | Foraminiferans<br>Radiolarians |
| Amoebozoans | E | *Amoeba*<br>*Physarum* |
| Rhodophyta | F | Red algae |
| Chlorophyta | G | Green algae: *Spirogyra*,<br>*Ulva*, *Chara* |

Protists may be **autotrophic** (photosynthetic) or **heterotrophic** (depending on other organisms for food). Autotrophic organisms are able to convert the sun's energy to organic compounds. The amount of energy stored by autotrophs is called **primary production**. Traditionally, autotrophic protists are called **algae** and heterotrophic protists are called **protozoa**—protists that ingest their food by **phagocytosis** (the uptake of large particles or whole organisms by the pinching inward of the plasma membrane). Some protozoa, euglenoids for example, are **mixotrophic**, capable of photosynthesis and ingestion. As you investigate the diversity of protists and their evolutionary relationships in this exercise, ask questions about the nutritive mode of each. Note morphological characteristics of examples studied. Ask which characteristics are found in organisms in the same clade and those shared with organisms in other clades or groups. Many of these characteristics are examples of evolutionary convergence. Ask questions about the ecology of the organisms. What means of locomotion do they possess, if any? What role do they play in an ecosystem? Do they have any economic value? Where do they live? (Protists live in a diversity of habitats, but most are aquatic. A great variety of protists may be found in **plankton**, the community of organisms found floating in the ocean or in bodies of freshwater.)

## Lab Study A. Euglenozoans—Example: *Trypanosoma levisi*

### Materials

compound microscope

prepared slides of *Trypanosoma levisi*

### Introduction

Organisms in the clade Euglenozoa are grouped together based on the ultrastructure (structure that can be seen only with an electron microscope) of their **flagella** and their mitochondria. Included in this group are some heterotrophs, some autotrophs, and some parasitic species. The many diverse single-celled and colonial flagellates have been a particular challenge to taxonomists. Under the old two-kingdom system of classification, the heterotrophic flagellates were classified as animals, and the autotrophic flagellates (with chloroplasts) were classified as plants. However, euglenozoans include members of each type. The common flagellated, mixotrophic *Euglena* belongs in this clade.

The organism that you will investigate in this exercise, *Trypanosoma levisi,* moves using flagella supported by microtubules. Organisms in the genus *Trypanosoma* are parasites that alternate between a vertebrate and an invertebrate host. *Trypanosoma levisi* lives in the blood of rats and is transmitted by fleas. Its flagellum originates near the posterior end but passes to the front end as a marginal thread of a long undulating membrane. Another organism in this same genus, *T. gambiense,* causes African sleeping sickness in humans. Its invertebrate host is the tsetse fly.

If you did not observe several other examples of flagellates when you studied the organisms living in a termite's gut, turn to that section of the laboratory manual and, following the procedure, observe these organisms. You may see *Trichonympha* and other flagellates, including *Pyrsonympha* with four to eight flagella, *Trichomonas,* and *Calonympha* with numerous flagella originating from the anterior end of the cell.

### Procedure

1. Obtain a prepared slide of *Trypanosoma levisi* (Figure 1) and observe it using low, intermediate, and high powers in the compound microscope.
2. Locate the organisms among the blood cells of the parasite's host.
3. Identify the **flagellum,** the **undulating membrane,** and the **nucleus** in several organisms.

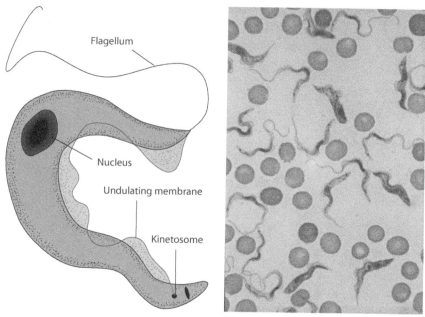

Figure 1.
*Trypanosoma,* **a euglenozoan,** is a flagellated parasite that lives in the blood of its mammalian host. The flagellum originates near the posterior end, but passes along an undulating membrane to the anterior end.

©Biophoto Associates/Science Source/
Photo Researchers, Inc.

## Results

1. In the margin of your lab manual, draw several representative examples of *T. levisi* and several blood cells to show relative cell sizes.
2. Turn to Table 5 and list the characteristics, ecological roles, and economic importance of *T. levisi.*

## Lab Study B. Alveolates—Examples: Paramecia and Dinoflagellates

### Materials

compound microscope
slides and coverslips
cultures of living *Paramecium caudata*
Protoslo or other quieting agent
solution of yeast stained with Congo red
cultures of *Paramecium caudata* that have been fed yeast stained with
   Congo red (optional)
dropper bottle of 1% acetic acid
transfer pipettes
living cultures or prepared slides of dinoflagellates

### Introduction

Alveolates are single-celled organisms; some are heterotrophic, others autotrophic. The common characteristic of all alveolates is the presence of membrane-bound sac-like structures (**alveoli**) just under the cell membrane. New groupings of protistans into clades place ciliates and dinoflagellates in the Alveolates.

5

**Figure 2.**
*Paramecium.* (a) Complete the drawing of a *Paramecium*, labeling organelles and structures. (b) An enlarged view of cilia and the region of alveoli just under the cell membrane.

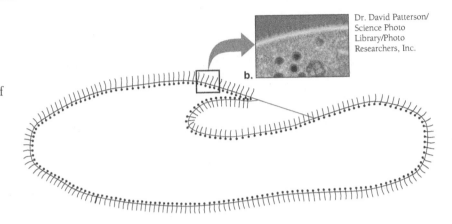

Dr. David Patterson/
Science Photo
Library/Photo
Researchers, Inc.

b.

a.

### Paramecium caudatum

The first example you will investigate in this lab study is *Paramecium caudatum*, a heterotrophic organism that moves about using cilia (short projections from the cell surface). Cilia are generally shorter and more numerous than flagella. Internally both structures are similar in their microtubular arrangement.

### Procedure

1. Using the compound microscope, examine a living *Paramecium* (Figure 2). Place a drop of water from the bottom of the culture on a clean microscope slide. Add a *small* drop of Protoslo or some other quieting solution to the water drop, then add the coverslip.

2. Observe paramecia on the compound microscope using low, then intermediate powers.

3. Describe the movement of a single paramecium. Does movement appear to be directional or is it random? Does the organism reverse direction only when it encounters an object, or does it appear to reverse direction even with no obstruction?

4. Locate a large, slowly moving organism, switch to high power and identify the following organelles:

   **Oral groove:** depression in the side of the cell that runs obliquely back to the mouth that opens into a **gullet.**

   **Food vacuole:** forms at the end of the gullet. Food vacuoles may appear as dark vesicles throughout the cell.

   **Macronucleus:** large, grayish body in the center of the cell. The macronucleus has many copies of the genome and controls most cellular activities, including asexual reproduction.

   **Micronucleus:** often difficult to see in living organisms, this small round body may be lying close to the macronucleus. Micronuclei are involved in sexual reproduction. Many species of paramecia have more than one micronucleus.

   **Contractile vacuole:** used for water balance, two of these form, one at each end of the cell. Each contractile vacuole is made up of a ring of radiating tubules and a central spherical vacuole. Your organism may be under osmotic stress because of the Protoslo, and the contractile vacuoles may be filling and collapsing as they expel water from the cell.

5. Observe feeding in a paramecium. Add a drop of yeast stained with Congo red to the edge of the coverslip and watch as it diffuses around the paramecium. Study the movement of food particles from the oral groove to the gullet to the formation of a food vacuole that will subsequently move through the cell as the food is digested in the vacuole. You may be able to observe the discharge of undigested food from the food vacuole at a specific site on the cell surface.

6. Observe the discharge of **trichocysts,** structures that lie just under the outer surface of the paramecium. When irritated by a chemical or attacked by a predator, the paramecium discharges these long thin threads that may serve as a defense mechanism, as an anchoring device, or to capture prey. Make a new slide of paramecia. Add a drop of 1% acetic acid to the edge of the coverslip and carefully watch a paramecium. Describe the appearance of trichocysts in this species.

## Results

1. Complete the drawing of a paramecium (Figure 2), labeling all the organelles and structures shown in bold in the text.

2. Turn to Table 5 and list the characteristics, ecological roles, and economic importance of paramecia.

Student Media Videos—Ch. 28: Paramecium Vacuole; Paramecium Cilia

## Dinoflagellates

Swirl your hand through tropical ocean waters at night and you may notice a burst of tiny lights. Visit a warm, stagnant inlet and you might notice that the water appears reddish and dead fish are floating on the surface. Both of these phenomena may be due to activities of dinoflagellates—single-celled organisms that are generally photosynthetic. Some dinoflagellates are able to bioluminesce, or produce light. They sometimes can *bloom* (reproduce very rapidly) and cause the water to appear red from pigments in their bodies. If the organisms in this "red tide" are a species of dinoflagellate that releases toxins, fish and other marine animals can be poisoned. Red tides in the Chesapeake Bay are thought to be caused by *Pfiesteria,* a dinoflagellate that produces deadly toxins resulting in invertebrate and fish kills, and that also may be implicated in human illness and death. Dinoflagellates have a cellulose cell wall often in the form of an armor of numerous plates with two perpendicular grooves, each containing a flagellum. Most of these organisms are autotrophic and play an important role in **primary production** in oceans—photosynthesis that ultimately provides food for all marine organisms.

Dinoflagellates have traditionally been considered algae, but they are now thought to share a common ancestor with ciliates, as evidenced by the presence of alveoli.

## Procedure

1. Obtain a prepared slide or make a wet mount of dinoflagellates (Figure 3).

2. Focus the slide on low power and attempt to locate the cells. You may have to switch to intermediate power to see them.

**Figure 3.**
**Dinoflagellates.**
The cell wall is made of cellulose plates with two perpendicular grooves, each containing a flagellum.

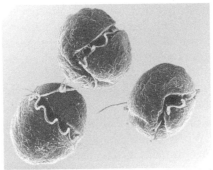

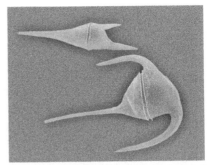

Dr. David M. Phillips/Visuals Unlimited

Dr. Dennis Kunkel/Visuals Unlimited

3. Switch to high power.
4. Identify the perpendicular **grooves** and the **cellulose plates** making up the cell wall. Are the plates in your species elongated into spines? **Flagella** may be visible in living specimens.

### Results

1. Draw several examples of cell shapes in the margin of your lab manual. Note differences between the species on your slide and those in Figure 3.
2. Turn to Table 5 and list the characteristics, ecological roles, and economic importance of dinoflagellates.

 Student Media Video—Ch. 28: Dinoflagellate

## Lab Study C. Stramenopiles— Examples: Diatoms and Brown Algae

### Materials

compound microscope
slides and coverslips
living cultures of diatoms
transfer pipettes
prepared slides of diatomaceous earth (demonstration only)
demonstration materials of brown algae

### Introduction

The clade Stramenopila includes water molds (phylum Oomycetes), diatoms (phylum Bacillariophyta), golden algae (phylum Chrysophyta), and brown algae (phylum Phaeophyta). These organisms are grouped in this clade based on the structure of their flagella (when present). The flagellum has many hair-like lateral projections.

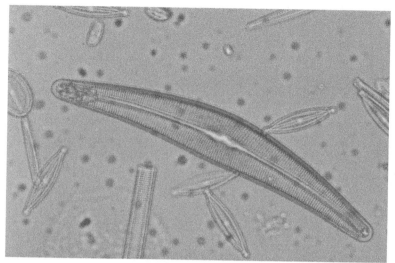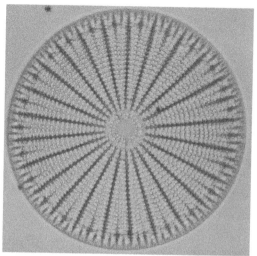

**Figure 4.**                                    Sidney Moulds/Photo Researchers, Inc.                                    John Burbidge/Photo Researchers, Inc.

**Diatoms are important autotrophs found in plankton.** Many different species
and forms exist. All have cell walls made of silica.

In this lab study you will investigate two examples: diatoms and brown algae. Both are autotrophic organisms that play an important role in primary
production in oceans.

## Diatoms (Bacillariophyta)

Diatoms are important autotrophic organisms in plankton. In fact, they are
the most important photosynthesizers in cold marine waters. They can be
unicellular, or they can aggregate into chains or star-like groups. Protoplasts
of these organisms are enclosed by a cell wall made of silica that persists after the death of the cell. These cell wall deposits are mined as **diatomaceous
earth** and have numerous economic uses (for example, in swimming pool
filters and as an abrasive in toothpaste and silver polish). Perhaps the greatest value of diatoms, however, is the carbohydrate and oxygen they produce
that can be utilized by other organisms. Ecologists are concerned about the
effects of acid rain and changing climatic conditions on populations of diatoms and their rate of primary productivity.

Diatom cells are either elongated, boat-shaped, bilaterally symmetrical
**pennate** forms or radially symmetrical **centric** forms. The cell wall consists
of two valves, one fitting inside the other, in the manner of the lid and bottom of a petri dish.

## Procedure

1.  Prepare a wet mount of diatoms (Figure 4) from marine plankton sam-
    ples or other living cultures.
2.  Observe the organisms on low, intermediate, and high powers.
3.  Describe the form of the diatoms in your sample. Are they centric, pen-
    nate, or both?

4. If you are studying living cells, you may be able to detect locomotion. The method of movement is uncertain, but it is thought that contractile fibers just inside the cell membrane produce waves of motion on the cytoplasmic surface that extends through a groove in the cell wall. What is the body form of motile diatoms?

5. Observe a single centric form on high power and note the intricate geometric pattern of the cell wall. Can you detect the two valves?

6. Look for chloroplasts in living forms.

7. Observe diatomaceous earth on demonstration and identify pennate and centric forms.

### Results

1. Sketch several different shapes of diatoms in the margin of your lab manual.

2. Turn to Table 5 and list the characteristics, ecological roles, and economic importance of diatoms.

 **Student Media Videos—Ch. 28: Diatoms Moving; Various Diatoms**

### Brown Algae (Phaeophyta)

Some of the largest algae, the **kelps,** are brown algae. The Sargasso Sea is named after the large, free-floating brown algae *Sargassum*. These algae appear brown because of the presence of the brown pigment **fucoxanthin** in addition to chlorophyll *a*. Brown algae are perhaps best known for their commercial value. Have you ever wondered why commercial ice cream is smoother in texture than homemade ice cream? Extracts of **algin**, a polysaccharide in the cell wall of some brown algae, are used commercially as thickening or emulsifying agents in paint, toothpaste, ice cream, pudding, and in many other commercial food products. *Laminaria,* known as *kombu* in Japan, is added to soups, used to brew a beverage, and covered with icing as a dessert.

### Procedure

Observe examples of brown algae on demonstration (Figure 5).

### Results

1. In Table 2, list the names and distinguishing characteristics of each brown algal species on demonstration. Compare the examples with those illustrated in Figure 5.

2. Turn to Table 5 and list the key characteristics, ecological roles, and economic importance of brown algae.

Blade

Stipe

Holdfast

**a.**

**b.**    Flip Nicklin/Minden Pictures

**c.**    Mark Spencer/Auscape/Minden Pictures

**Figure 5.**

**Examples of multicellular brown algae (phylum Phaeophyta).** The body of a brown alga consists of broad blades, a stemlike stipe, and a holdfast for attachment. These body parts are found in the kelps (a) Sea palm (*Postelsia*) and (b) *Nereocystis*. Rounded air bladders for flotation are seen in (c) *Sargassum* and other species of brown algae.

**Table 2**
Representative Brown Algae

| Name | Body Form (single-celled, filamentous, colonial, leaf-like; broad or linear blades) | Characteristics (pigments, reproductive structures, structures for attachment and flotation) |
|---|---|---|
|  |  |  |
|  |  |  |
|  |  |  |
|  |  |  |

# Lab Study D. Foraminiferans and Radiolarians

## Materials

compound microscope
prepared slides of foraminiferans
prepared slides of radiolarian skeletons (demonstration only)

**Figure 6.**
**Forams** are heterotrophic organisms that move using thread-like pseudopodia. Their shell-like tests are made of calcium carbonate.

Manfred Kage/Peter Arnold, Inc.

## Introduction

Foraminiferans and radiolarians are closely related groups composed of ameboid, heterotrophic organisms with **thread-like pseudopodia** or cellular extensions used in feeding and, in some species, locomotion. You will study examples of foraminiferans and radiolarians.

## Foraminiferans

**Foraminiferans,** commonly called **forams,** are another example of organisms that move and feed using pseudopodia. Forams are marine planktonic (freely floating) or benthic (bottom dwelling) organisms that secrete a calcium carbonate shell-like *test* (a hard outer covering) made up of chambers. In many species, the test consists of chambers secreted in a spiral pattern, and the organism resembles a microscopic snail. Although most forams are microscopic, some species, called *living sands,* may grow to the size of several centimeters, an astounding size for a single-celled protist. Thread-like pseudopodia extend through special pores in the calcium carbonate test. The test can persist after the organism dies, becoming part of marine sand. Remains of tests can form vast limestone deposits.

## Procedure

1. Obtain a prepared slide of representative forams (Figure 6).
2. Observe the organisms first on the lowest power of the compound microscope and then on intermediate and high powers.
3. Note the arrangement and attempt to count the number of chambers in the test. In most species, the number of chambers indicates the relative age of the organisms, with older organisms having more chambers. Which are more abundant on your slide, older or younger organisms?

   Chambers can be arranged in a single row, in multiple rows, or wound into a spiral. Protozoologists determine the foram species based on the appearance of the test. Are different species present?

## Results

1. Sketch several different forams in the margin of your lab manual. Note differences in the organisms on your slide and those depicted in Figure 6.
2. Turn to Table 5 and list the characteristics, ecological roles, and economic importance of forams.

## Radiolarians

The **radiolarians** studied here are common in marine plankton. They secrete skeletons of silicon dioxide that can, as with the forams, collect in vast deposits on the ocean floor. Their thread-like pseudopodia, called **axopodia,** extend outward through pores in the skeleton in all directions from the central spherical cell body.

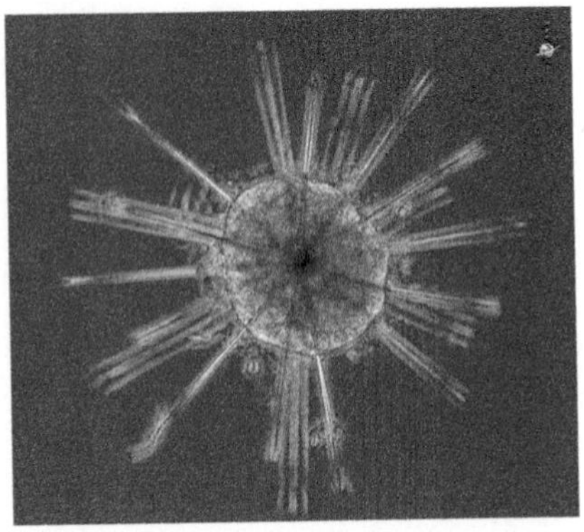

**Figure 7.**
**Radiolarians** are supported by a skeleton of silicon dioxide. They use thread-like pseudopodia to obtain food.

micro*scope

## Procedure

1. Observe slides of radiolarians on demonstration (Figure 7).
2. Observe the size and shape of the skeletons and compare your observations with Figure 7.

## Results

1. Sketch several different radiolarians skeletons in the margin of your lab manual, noting any differences between the organisms on demonstration and those in the figure.

2. Turn to Table 5 and list the characteristics, ecological roles, and economic importance of radiolarians.

# Lab Study E. Amoebozoans—Examples: *Amoeba,* Slime Molds

## Materials

cultures of *Amoeba proteus*
slides and coverslips (for amoeba)
stereoscopic microscopes
*Physarum* growing on agar plates

## Introduction

Amebozoans have pseudopodia as seen in foraminiferia and radiolarians, but the structure is different. Rather than thread-like pseudopodia as seen in these organisms, amebozoans' pseudopodia are *lobe-shaped.* Based on their ameboid characteristics, their phagocytic mode of obtaining nutrition, and molecular systematics, both amoeba and slime molds are included in the clade **Amoebozoa.**

## Amoeba

You have studied **Amoeba proteus,** a protozoan species of organisms that move using lobed-shaped pseudopodia. Amoeba have no fixed body shape and they are naked; that is, they do not have a shell. Different species may be found in a variety of habitats, including freshwater and marine habitats. Recall that pseudopodia are cellular extensions. As the pseudopod extends, endoplasm flows into the extension. By extending several pseudopodia in sequence and flowing into first one and then the next, the amoeba proceeds along in an irregular, slow fashion. Pseudopodia are also used to capture and ingest food. When a suitable food particle such as a bacterium, another protist, or a piece of detritus (fragmented remains of dead organisms) contacts an amoeba, a pseudopod will flow completely around the particle and take it into the cell by phagocytosis.

If you did not observe *Amoeba proteus* or some other naked amoeba, turn to that section of the laboratory manual and, following the procedure, observe these organisms.

 Student Media Videos—Ch. 28: Amoeba; Amoeba Pseudopodia

### Slime Molds (Mycetozoa)

William Crowder, in a classic *National Geographic* article (April 1926) describes his search for strange creatures in a swamp on the north shore of Long Island. This is his description of his findings: "Behold! Seldom ever before had such a gorgeous sight startled my unexpectant gaze. Spreading out over the bark [of a dead tree] was a rich red coverlet . . . consisting of thousands of small, closely crowded, funguslike growths. . . . A colony of these tiny organisms extended in an irregular patch . . . covering an area nearly a yard in length and slightly less in breadth. . . . Each unit, although actually less than a quarter of an inch in height, resembled . . . a small mushroom, though more marvelous than any I have ever seen."

The creatures described by Crowder are heterotrophic organisms called **slime molds.** They have been called plants, fungi, animals, fungus animals, protozoa, Protoctista, Protista, Mycetozoa, and probably many more names. Classifying slime molds as fungi (as in previous classification schemes) causes difficulties because whereas slime molds are phagocytic like protozoa, fungi are never phagocytic but obtain their nutrition by absorption. Characteristics other than feeding mode, including cellular ultrastructure, cell wall chemistry, and other molecular studies, indicate that slime molds fit better with the ameboid protists than with the fungi. These studies suggest that slime molds descended from unicellular amoeba-like organisms.

There are two types of slime molds, plasmodial slime molds and cellular slime molds. In this lab study, you will observe the plasmodial slime mold *Physarum.* The vegetative stage is called a **plasmodium,** and it consists of a multinucleate mass of protoplasm totally devoid of cell walls. This mass feeds on bacteria as it creeps along the surface of moist logs or dead leaves. When conditions are right, it is converted into one or more reproductive structures, called **fruiting bodies,** that produce spores. You may choose to investigate slime molds further in Exercise 3.

### Procedure

1. Obtain a petri dish containing *Physarum* and return to your lab bench to study the organism. Keep the dish closed.

2. With the aid of your stereoscopic microscope, examine the plasmodium (Figure 8). Describe characteristics such as color, size, and shape. Look for a system of branching veins. Do you see any movement? Speculate about the source of the movement. Is the movement unidirectional or bidirectional—that is, flows first in one direction and then in the other? Your instructor may have placed oat flakes or another food source on the agar. How does the appearance of the plasmodium change as it contacts a food source?

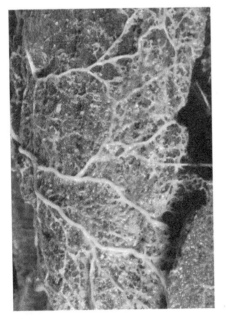

**Figure 8.**

**Slime mold.** Slime molds are protists that share some characteristics with both protozoa and fungi. The vegetative stage of a plasmodial slime mold includes an amoeboid phase consisting of a multinucleate mass known as a plasmodium.

3. Examine the entire culture for evidence of forming or mature fruiting bodies. Are the fruiting bodies stalked or are they sessile, that is, without a stalk? If a stalk is present, describe it.

## Results

1. Sketch the plasmodium and fruiting bodies in the margin of your lab manual. Label structures where appropriate.
2. Turn to Table 5 and list the characteristics, ecological roles, and economic importance of slime molds.

---

Student Media Videos—Ch. 28: Plasmodial Slime Mold Streaming; Plasmodial Slime Mold

---

# Lab Study F: Red Algae (Rhodophyta)

## Materials

examples of red algae on demonstration

## Introduction

The simplest red algae are single celled, but most species have a macroscopic, multicellular body form. The red algae, unlike all the other algae, do not have flagella at any stage in their life cycle. Some scientists suggest that the red algae represent a monophyletic (having a single origin) group and should be placed in their own kingdom. Red algae are autotrophic, containing chlorophyll *a* and the accessory pigments **phycocyanin** and **phycoerythrin** that often mask the chlorophyll, making the algae appear red. These pigments absorb green and blue wavelengths of light that penetrate deep into ocean waters. Many red algae also appear green or black or even blue, depending on the depth at which they are growing. Because of this, color is not always a good characteristic to use when determining the classification of algae. You may have already grown bacteria and fungi on plates of agar. This substance, **agar**, is a polysaccharide extracted from the cell wall of red algae. Another extract of red algae cell walls, **carrageenan**, is used to give the texture of thickness and richness to foods such as dairy drinks and soups. In Asia and elsewhere, the red algae *Porphyra* (known as *nori*) are used as seaweed wrappers for sushi. The cultivation and production of *Porphyra* constitute a billion-dollar industry.

## Procedure

Observe the examples of red algae that are on demonstration (Figure 9).

## Results

1. In Table 3, list the names and distinguishing characteristics of the red algae on demonstration. Compare the demonstration examples with those illustrated in Figure 9.
2. Turn to Table 5 and list the key characteristics, ecological roles, and economic importance of red algae.

a.                                    b.                                    c.

Figure 9.
**Examples of multicellular red algae (phylum Rhodophyta).** (a) Some red algae
have deposits of carbonates of calcium and magnesium in their cell walls and are
important components of coral reefs. (b) Most red algae have delicate, finely
dissected blades. (c) *Porphyra* (or *nori*) is used to make sushi.

Table 3
Representative Red Algae

| Name | Body Form (single-celled, filamentous, colonial, leaf-like) | Characteristics (reproductive structures, structures for attachment or flotation, pigments) |
|---|---|---|
|  |  |  |
|  |  |  |
|  |  |  |
|  |  |  |

## Lab Study G. Green Algae (Chlorophyta)— The Protist-Plant Connection

### Materials

cultures or prepared slides of *Spirogyra* sp.
preserved *Ulva lactuca*
preserved *Chara* sp.

## Introduction

The green algae include unicellular motile and nonmotile, colonial, filamentous, and multicellular species that inhabit primarily freshwater environments. Because green algae share many characteristics with land plants, including storage of amylose (starch) and the presence of chlorophylls *a* and *b*, photosynthetic pathways, and organic compounds called flavonoids, most botanists support the hypothesis that plants evolved from green algae. Results of recent work in sequencing ribosomal and transfer RNA genes confirm the close relationship between green algae and land plants, and have led some scientists to propose that green algae, or at least those known as charophytes, be included in the Plant kingdom. In this exercise you will view several body forms of green algae on demonstration: single-celled, filamentous, colonial, and multicellular. Finally, you will observe the multicellular, branched green algae *Chara* (the stonewort), believed to be most similar to the green algae that gave rise to land plants over 475 million years ago.

If you completed a lab titled Microscopes and Cells, you may remember observing aggregates of single-celled algae, *Protococcus*, and the colonial green algae *Volvox*. In this lab study you will observe the filamentous alga *Spirogyra* and the multicellular algae *Ulva* and *Chara*.

## Procedure

1. Using your compound microscope, observe living materials or prepared slides of the filamentous alga *Spirogyra* (Figure 10a). This organism is common in small, freshwater ponds. The most obvious structure in the cells of the filament is a long chloroplast. Can you determine how the alga got its name? Describe the appearance of the chloroplast.

   Can you see a nucleus in each cell of the filament?

2. Observe the preserved specimen of *Ulva* sp., commonly called sea lettuce (Figure 10b). This multicellular alga is commonly found on rocks or docks in marine and brackish water.

   a. Describe the appearance and body form of *Ulva*.



   b. Are structures present that would serve to attach *Ulva* to its substrate (dock or rock)? If so, describe them.



   c. Compare your specimen of *Ulva* with that shown in the figure.

3. Examine the preserved specimen of the multicellular green alga *Chara* (Figure 10c). This alga grows in muddy or sandy bottoms of clear lakes or ponds. Its body form is so complex that it is often mistaken for a plant, but careful study of its structure and reproduction confirms its classification as a green alga.

   Note the cylindrical branches attached to nodes. Compare your specimen to Figure 10c. Sketch the appearance of your specimen in the margin of your lab manual.

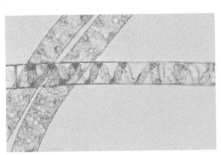

**a.** Brad Mogen/Visuals Unlimited    **b.**    Manfred Kage/Peter Arnold, Inc.    **c.**

**Figure 10.**
**Examples of multicellular green algae (phylum Chlorophyta).** (a) A filamentous green alga, *Spirogyra*. (b) Some green algae are multicellular as in *Ulva,* sea lettuce. (c) A multicellular, branched green alga, *Chara*.

## Results

1. In Table 4, list the names and distinguishing characteristics of each green algal species studied. Compare these examples with those illustrated in Figure 10.
2. Turn to Table 5 and list the key characteristics, ecological roles, and economic importance of green algae.

**Table 4**
Representative Green Algae

| Name | Body Form (single-celled, filamentous, colonial, leaf-like) | Characteristics (pigments, specialized structures, flagella, structures for attachment) |
|---|---|---|
| *Spirogyra* | | |
| *Ulva* | | |
| *Chara* | | |

## Discussion

1. Describe the mechanism for feeding in amoeboid, flagellated, and ciliated protozoans.

2. How do you think amoeboid organisms with skeletons, such as the radiolarians, move food to their cell bodies?

3. Compare the appearance and rate of locomotion in amoeboid, flagellated, and ciliated organisms observed in this exercise.

4. Describe mechanisms for defense in the organisms studied.

5. Compare dinoflagellates and diatoms. What important ecological role is shared by these two groups?

6. What is one characteristic that you could observe under the microscope to distinguish diatoms and dinoflagellates?

7. Slime molds were once placed in the kingdom Fungi. What characteristics suggest that these organisms are protistan?

8. What important ecological role is shared by the macroscopic algae (green, red, and brown)?

9. Based on your observations in the laboratory, what two characteristics might you use to distinguish brown and red algae?

# EXERCISE 2
# The Kingdom Fungi

## Introduction

The kingdom Fungi includes a diverse group of organisms that play important economic and ecological roles. These organisms are unicellular (yeasts) or multicellular, heterotrophic organisms that obtain their nutrients by absorption, digesting their food outside their bodies and absorbing the digestion products into their cells. They often have complex life cycles with alternating sexual and asexual (vegetative) reproduction. They may produce spores either asexually by mitosis or sexually by meiosis.

Fungi are beneficial to humans in many ways. The fungus *Penicillium* is used to produce antibiotics. Yeast, a single-celled fungus, is used in the production of wine, beer, and leavened bread. Fungi are also a source of food in many cultures, with truffles being the most expensive. Black truffles are dark, edible subterranean fungi that sell for $350–$500 per pound. In the United States they grow under specific species of trees in forests in Washington and Oregon. They are located by specially trained truffle-sniffling pigs or dogs. Truffles cannot be grown in a lab or greenhouse.

In ecosystems, fungi share with bacteria the essential role of decomposition, returning to the ecosystem the matter trapped in dead organisms. One extremely important ecological role played by fungi is their mutualistic association with roots of most plants, forming "mycorrhizae." Mycorrhizal fungi increase the plant's ability to capture water and provide the plant with minerals and essential elements. This association greatly enhances plant growth, and may have played a role in plant colonization of land.

Although many fungi are beneficial, others play destructive roles in nature. Some species parasitize animals and plants. Athlete's foot and ringworm are diseases commonly known to humans. Histoplasmosis is a respiratory disease in humans caused by a fungus found in soil and in bat and bird droppings. Wheat rust, potato late blight, and sudden oak death (a potentially devastating disease discovered in the United States in 1995) are plant diseases caused by fungi. The ergot fungus that parasitizes rye causes convulsive ergotism in humans who eat bread made with infested grains. The bizarre behavior of young women who were later convicted of witchcraft in Salem Village, Massachusetts, in 1692 has been attributed to convulsive ergotism.

In this exercise, you will learn about the structure of typical fungi and the characteristics of four important phyla of fungi: Zygomycota, Ascomycota, Basidiomycota, and Deuteromycota. You will see examples of lichens that are associations between fungi and algae. As you observe these examples, consider interesting questions that might be asked about fungi diversity or ecology. You can choose one of these questions to design a simple experiment in Exercise 3.

# Lab Study A. Zygote Fungi—Zygomycota

## Materials

compound microscope
stereoscopic microscope
cultures of *Rhizopus stolonifer*
   with sporangia
cultures of *Pilobolus crystallinus*
   on demonstration

forceps, ethyl alcohol, alcohol lamp
slides and coverslips
dropper bottles of water with

## Introduction

One common organism in the phylum Zygomycota is probably growing in your refrigerator right now. The common bread mold, *Rhizopus stolonifer,* grows on many foods as well as bread. In this lab study, you will observe the structure of this species to see many general fungi characteristics. Fungi are made up of thread-like individual filaments, called **hyphae,** which are organized into the body of the fungus, called the **mycelium.** This filamentous mass secretes enzymes into the substrate and digests food that will then be absorbed into its cells. Cells of fungi have cell walls made of **chitin** combined with other complex carbohydrates, including cellulose. You may recall that chitin is the main component of insect exoskeletons.

### Rhizopus stolonifer

*Rhizopus* reproduces both sexually and asexually. In the zygomycetes (fungi in the phylum Zygomycota), cells of the hyphae are haploid. Hyphae grow over a substrate, for example, a slice of bread, giving the bread a fuzzy appearance. In asexual reproduction, certain hyphae grow upright and develop **sporangia,** round structures, on their tips. Haploid spores develop in the sporangia following mitosis, and when they are mature, they are dispersed through the air. If they fall on a suitable medium, they will absorb water and germinate, growing a new mycelium.

*Rhizopus* also reproduces sexually when compatible mating types designated as (+) and (−) grow side by side. In this case, (+) and (−) hyphae produce extensions called **gametangia** that fuse forming **zygosporangia.** Within the zygosporangia, haploid nuclei fuse (*karyogamy*) producing diploid nuclei. The diploid nuclei then undergo meiosis. Following meiosis, haploid spores are produced in sporangia borne on filaments that emerge from the zygosporangia (Figure 11).

### Pilobolus crystallinus

*Pilobolus crystallinus* (also called the *fungus gun,* or *shotgun fungus*) is another member of the phylum Zygomycota. This fungus is called a **coprophilous** fungus because it grows on dung. It displays many unusual behaviors, one of which is that it is positively phototropic. Perhaps you can investigate this behavior in Exercise 3. Bold et al. (1980) describe asexual reproduction in *Pilobolus.* This species has sporangia as does *Rhizopus,* but rather than similarly dispersing single spores, in *Pilobolus* the sporangium is forcibly discharged as a unit; the dispersion is tied to moisture and diurnal cycles. In nature, in the early evening the sporangia form; shortly after midnight, a swelling appears below the sporangium. Late the following morning, turgor

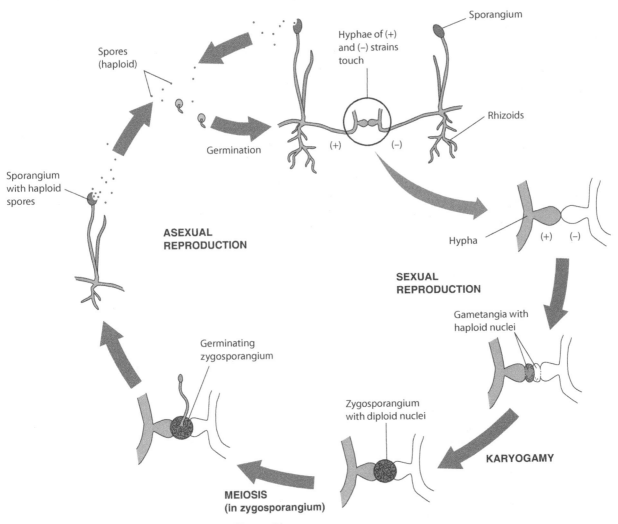

**Figure 11.**
*Rhizopus stolonifer. Rhizopus* reproduces both sexually by zygosporangia and asexually by sporangia producing asexual spores. In sexual reproduction, (+) and (−) mating types fuse and a zygosporangium with diploid nuclei ultimately results.

pressure causes the swelling to explode, propelling the sporangium as far as 2 meters. The sticky sporangium will adhere to grass leaves and subsequently may be eaten by an animal—horse, cow, or rabbit. The intact sporangia pass through the animal's digestive tract and are excreted, and the spores germinate in the fresh dung.

In this lab study you will investigate *Rhizopus* and observe *Pilobolus* on demonstration.

## Procedure

1. Obtain a culture of *Rhizopus* and carry it to your lab station.
2. Examine it using the stereoscopic microscope.
3. Identify the **mycelia, hyphae,** and **sporangia.**
4. Review the life cycle of *Rhizopus* (Figure 11). Locate the structures in this figure that are visible in your culture. Circle the structures involved in asexual reproduction.

5. Using forceps and aseptic technique, remove a small portion of the mycelium with several sporangia and make a wet mount.

6. Examine the hyphae and sporangia using the compound microscope. Are spores visible? How have the spores been produced?

How do the spores compare with the hyphal cells genetically?

How would spores produced by sexual reproduction differ from spores produced asexually?

7. Observe the cultures of *Pilobolus* (Figure 12) growing on rabbit dung agar that are on demonstration.

8. Identify the **sporangia, mycelia,** and **hyphae.** What color are the sporangia and spores?

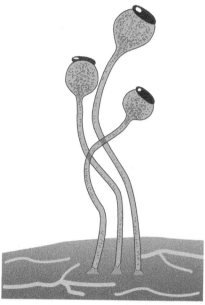

Adapted from illustrations by Miguel Ulloa, Departamento de Botanica, Instituto de Biologia, Universidad Nacional Autonoma de Mexico.

**Figure 12.**
*Pilobolus crystallinus.*

## Results

1. Review the life cycle of *Rhizopus* and the structures observed in the living culture and compare with Figure 11.

2. Review the structures observed in *Pilobolus* and compare with Figure 12.

## Discussion

1. The body form of most fungi, including *Rhizopus,* is a mycelium composed of filamentous hyphae. Using your observations as a basis for your thinking, state why this body form is well adapted to the fungus mode of nutrition.

2. Refer back to the description of *Pilobolus.* Speculate about the adaptive advantage of having a system to propel sporangia, as seen in *Pilobolus.*

## Lab Study B. Sac Fungi—Ascomycota

### Materials

compound microscope

stereoscopic microscope

dried or preserved *Peziza* specimen

prepared slide of *Peziza* ascocarp

preserved or fresh morels

plastic mounts of ergot in rye
 or wheat

### Introduction

Fungi in the phylum Ascomycota are called *sac fungi,* or ascopore-producing fungi. This division includes edible fungi, morels, and truffles, but it also includes several deadly plant and animal parasites. For example, chestnut blight and Dutch elm disease have devastated native populations of chestnut and American elm trees. The fungi causing these diseases were introduced into the United States from Asia and Europe. You may have already examined one example of the phylum Ascomycota when you studied meiosis and crossing over in *Sordaria fimicola.*

Sexual reproduction in the ascomycota fungi produces either four or eight haploid **ascospores** after meiosis in an **ascus.** Recall that spores in *Sordaria* form after meiosis within asci. Asci form within a structure called an **ascocarp.** In *Sordaria* the ascocarp, called a *perithecium,* is a closed, spherical structure that develops a pore at the top for spore dispersal. In some species of sac fungi, the asci are borne on open cup-shaped ascocarps called *apothecia* (sing., *apothecium*). In asexual reproduction, spores are produced, but rather than being enclosed within a sporangium as in zygote fungi, the spores, called **conidia,** are produced on the surface of special reproductive hyphae.

Other features of sac fungi also vary. For example, yeasts are ascomycetes, yet they are single-celled organisms. Yeasts most frequently reproduce asexually by **budding,** a process in which small cells form by pinching off the parent cell. When they reproduce sexually, however, they produce asci, each of which produces four or eight spores.

In this lab study, you will examine a slide of the sac fungi *Peziza* and will observe demonstrations of additional examples of Ascomycota.

### Procedure

1. Obtain a dried or preserved specimen of *Peziza* (Figure 13a). Notice the open, cup-shaped apothecium, the **ascocarp,** that bears asci within the cup (not visible with the naked eye). Fungi with ascocarps shaped in this fashion are called **cup fungi.** The cup may be supported by a stalk.

2. Examine a prepared slide of *Peziza* using low and intermediate magnifications on the compound microscope. This slide is a section through the ascocarp. Identify **asci.** How many spores are present per ascus? Are they diploid or haploid?

3. Complete the sketch of the ascocarp section that follows, labeling **asci, spores, hyphae,** and **mycelium.**

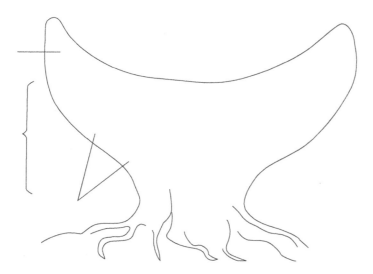

4. Observe the preserved **morels** that are on demonstration (Figure 13b). These fungi resemble mushrooms, but the "cap" is convoluted. Asci are located inside the ridges.

5. Observe demonstrations of the mature inflorescence of wheat or rye grass infected with the ascomycete *Claviceps purpurea,* the **ergot** fungus. The large black structures seen among the grains are the ergot.

## Results

Review the structures observed in *Peziza,* morels, and ergot. Modify Figures 13a and 13b to reflect features of your examples not included in these figures. Sketch ergot examples in the margin of your lab manual.

## Discussion

What characteristics are common to all sac fungi?

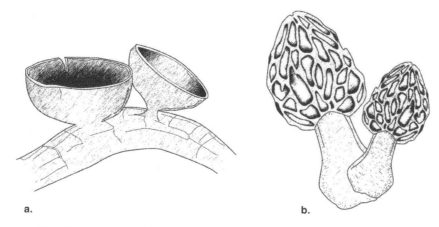

a.                                    b.

Adapted from illustrations by Miguel Ulloa, Departamento de Botanica, Instituto de Biologia, Universidad Nacional Autonoma de Mexico.

**Figure 13.**
**Examples of sac fungi, phylum Ascomycota.** (a) *Peziza* has a cup-shaped ascocarp with asci within the cup. (b) Morels are cup fungi that resemble mushrooms.

# Lab Study C. Club Fungi—Basidiomycota

## Materials

compound microscope
stereoscopic microscope
fresh, ripe mushroom basidiocarps
prepared slides of *Coprinus* pileus sections

## Introduction

The Basidiomycota phylum (club fungi, or basidiospore-producing fungi) includes the fungi that cause the plant diseases wheat rust and corn smut as well as the more familiar puffballs, shelf fungi, and edible and nonedible mushrooms (the latter often called *toadstools*). A mushroom is actually a reproductive structure called a basidiocarp that produces spores by meiosis. Although most mushrooms are relatively small when mature, one basidiocarp in the Royal Botanic Gardens, Kew, England, in 1996 measured 146 cm (57 inches wide) and weighed 284 kg (625 pounds)! Basidiocarps grow upward from an underground mycelial mass. When they form around the rim of the mass, a "fairy ring" of mushrooms appears. In asexual reproduction, conidia form by mitosis. In this lab study, you will study mushrooms and learn some features of their life cycle.

## Procedure

1. Obtain a fresh mushroom, a **basidiocarp,** and identify its parts: The stalk is the **stipe;** the cap is the **pileus.** Look under the cap and identify **gills.** Spores form on the surface of the gills. Examine the gills with the stereoscopic microscope. Do you see spores? Children often make spore prints in scouts or in elementary school by placing a ripe mushroom pileus with the gill side down on a piece of white paper for several hours, allowing the spores to drop to the paper. Scientists use similar spore prints to accurately identify mushrooms.

2. Label the parts of the mushrooms in Figure 14a.

3. Obtain a prepared slide of a section through the pileus of *Coprinus* or another mushroom. Observe it on the compound microscope using low and then intermediate powers. Is your slide a cross section or a longitudinal section through the pileus? Make a sketch in the lab manual margin indicating the plane of your section through the basidiocarp. Compare your section with the fresh mushroom you have just studied and with Figure 14b.

4. Using the prepared slide, observe the surface of several gills using high power. Spores are produced at the tips of small club-shaped structures called **basidia.** Locate a basidium and focus carefully on its end. Here you may see four knoblike protuberances. Each protuberance has a haploid nucleus that formed following meiosis, and each becomes a **basidiospore.** When the spores are mature, they are discharged from the basidium and are dispersed by the wind.

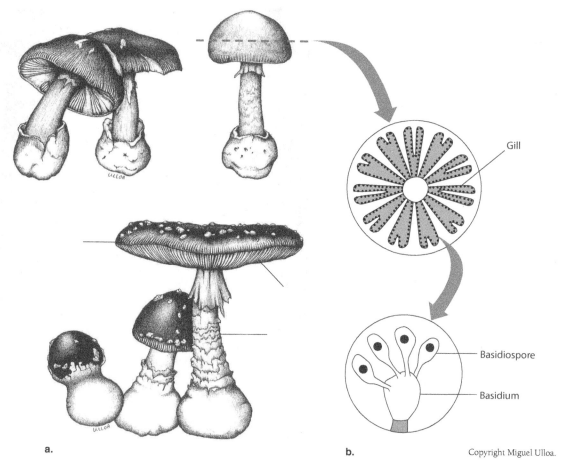

**Figure 14.**
**Club fungi, phylum Basidiomycota.** (a) Mushrooms, or basidiocarps, each consisting of a cap, the pileus; and a stalk, the stipe. (b) A section through the gills on a whole basidiocarp reveals basidia and basidiospores.

### Results

Review the structures observed and label Figure 14a. Modify the figure to include features observed in your materials that differ from the figure.

### Discussion

State the characteristics shared by all Basidiomycota.

## Lab Study D. Imperfect Fungi—Deuteromycota

### Materials

cultures of *Penicillium* on demonstration
Roquefort cheese on demonstration

## Introduction

Most fungi are classified based on their sexual reproductive structures; however, many fungi (as far as is known) reproduce only vegetatively. Because the sexual reproductive stages of these fungi do not exist or have not been found, they are called **asexual,** or **imperfect fungi** (following the botanical use of "imperfect" to indicate a flower lacking one reproductive part). This group is of interest because several human diseases—athlete's foot, ringworm, and candida "yeast" infections—are caused by species of imperfect fungi. Also in this group are several beneficial species—for example, one species of *Penicillium* that produces the antibiotic penicillin and another that is used to make Roquefort and blue cheeses.

## Procedure

1. Observe the *Penicillium* on demonstration. You may have observed something similar growing on oranges or other foods in your refrigerator.
2. Describe the texture and the color of the mycelium.

## Results

Sketch your observations of *Penicillium* in the margin of your lab manual. Note any features that may be important in distinguishing this organism.

## Discussion

Compare the appearance of *Penicillium* with that of *Rhizopus*.

# Lab Study E. Lichens

## Materials

examples of foliose, crustose, and fruticose lichens on demonstration

## Introduction

Lichens are symbiotic associations between fungi and usually algae or cyanobacteria forming a body that can be consistently recognized. The fungal component is usually a sac fungus or a club fungus. The lichen body, called a **thallus,** varies in shape and colors, depending on the species of the components. Reproductive structures can be bright red or pink or green. Photosynthesis in the algae provides nutrients for the fungus, and the fungus provides a moist environment for the algae or cyanobacterium. Because lichens can survive extremely harsh environments, they are often the first organisms to colonize a newly exposed environment such as volcanic flow or rock outcrops, and they play a role in soil formation.

## Procedure

Observe the demonstrations of different lichen types: those with a leafy thallus (**foliose**), a crustlike thallus (**crustose**), or a branching, cylindrical

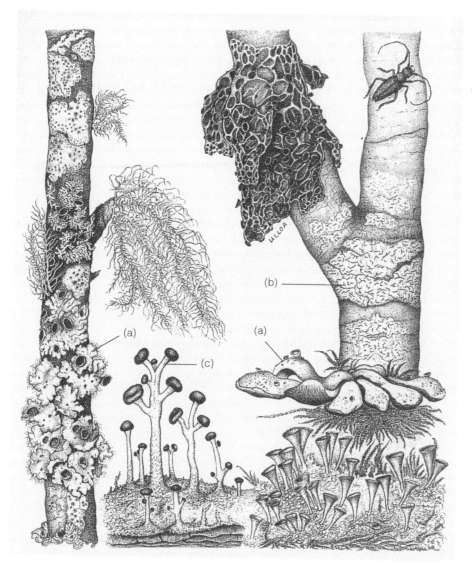

**Figure 15.**
**Lichen types.** Lichens may have (a) a leafy thallus (foliose), (b) a crustlike thallus (crustose), or (c) a cylindrical thallus (fruticose).

thallus (**fruticose**) (Figure 15). Look for cup-shaped or club-like reproductive structures produced by the fungal component of the lichen.

## Results

1. Sketch the lichens on demonstration in the margins of your lab manual.
2. Label any visible reproductive structures, and, if possible, indicate if the fungal component is a sac fungus or a club fungus.
3. Identify and label each according to lichen type.

## Discussion

Imagine that you are the first scientist to observe a lichen microscopically. What observations would lead you to conclude that the lichen is composed of a fungus and an alga?

EXERCISE 3

# Designing and Performing an Open-Inquiry Investigation

## Introduction

In this exercise, you will choose one of the organisms observed in this lab topic and design a simple experiment answering a question about its behavior, growth patterns, or interactions with other species.

Be ready to assign tasks to members of your lab team. Be sure that everyone understands the techniques that will be used. Your experiment will be successful only if you plan carefully, cooperate with your team members, perform lab techniques accurately and systematically, and record and report data accurately.

## Materials

protozoa and algae cultures
cultures of slime molds *Physarum,*
    *Didymium, Dictyostelium*
cultures of *Pilobolus crystallinus,*
    *Rhizopus, Penicillium*
sterile agar plates to grow
    each species
sterile agar with oat flakes
sterile agar with sugar
sterile agar with albumin

sterile agar with pH 6, 7, or 8
aluminum foil
various breads from the health
    food store—wheat, rye, corn,
    potato, rice
bread with preservatives
sterilized dung from various
    animals
mycorrhizae inoculate

## Procedure

1. Choose a question from this list to investigate or choose a question from your own observations. *Write your question in the margin of your lab manual.*

    a. Will varying the molarity of the culture medium change the rate of contractile vacuole formation in paramecia?

    b. Do plasmodia of the same species of slime mold unite when growing on the same agar plate? How about different species of slime mold?

    c. Do slime mold plasmodia demonstrate chemotaxis (response to chemical stimuli such as food molecules) or phototaxis (response to light)?

    d. What happens to slime molds if grown in different temperatures?

    e. Do the same fungi grow on different varieties of bread?

    f. How effective are preservatives in preventing fungal growth on foods?

    g. Is *Pilobolus* phototaxic? What about other fungi?

    h. Does succession take place in dung cultures of fungi? Refer to the milk bacteria succession study and design a similar experiment to investigate this phenomenon in fungi growing on dung.

    i. Is there a difference in the growth of plants growing with and without mycorrhizae?

    j. Can the growth of fungi be altered by supplying different nutrients (e.g., sugar or albumin) in agar culture?

2. Formulate a testable hypothesis.

   **Hypothesis:**

3. Summarize the experiment. (Use separate paper.)

4. Predict the results of your experiment based on your hypothesis.

   **Prediction:** (If/then)

5. Outline the procedures used in the experiment.

   a. On a separate sheet of paper, list in numerical order each exact step of your procedure.

   b. Remember to include the number of replicates (usually a minimum of five), levels of treatment, appropriate time intervals, and controls for each procedure.

   c. If you have an idea for an experiment that requires materials other than those provided, ask your laboratory instructor about availability. If possible, additional supplies will be provided.

   d. When carrying out an experiment, remember to quantify your measurements when possible.

6. Perform the experiment, making observations and collecting data for analysis.

7. **Record observations and data** on a separate sheet of paper. Design tables and graphs, at least one of each. Be thorough when collecting data. Do not just write down numbers, but record what they mean as well. Do not rely on your memory for information that you will need when reporting your results.

8. **Prepare your discussion.** Discuss your results in light of your hypothesis.

   a. Review your hypothesis. Review your results (tables and graphs). Do your results support or falsify your hypothesis? Explain your answer, using data for support.

   b. Review your prediction. Did your results correspond to the prediction you made? If not, explain how your results are different from your predictions, and why this might have occurred.

   c. If you had problems with the procedure or questionable results, explain how they might have influenced your conclusion.

   d. If you had an opportunity to repeat and expand this experiment to make your results more convincing, what would you do?

   e. Summarize the conclusion you have drawn from your results.

9. **Be prepared to report your results to the class.** Prepare to persuade your fellow scientists that your experimental design is sound and that your results support your conclusions.

10. If your instructor requires it, **submit a written laboratory report** in the form of a scientific paper. Keep in mind that although you have performed the experiments as a team, you must turn in a lab report of *your original writing*. Your tables and figures may be similar to those of your team members, but your paper must be the product of your own literature search and creative thinking.

## Questions for Review

1. Complete Table 5 comparing characteristics of all protists investigated in Exercise 1.

2. Complete Table 6 comparing characteristics of fungi (Exercise 2).

3. Compare spore formation in sac fungi and club fungi.

4. Using observations of pigments present, body form, and distinguishing characteristics of the three groups of macroscopic green, brown, and red algae, speculate about where they might be most commonly found in ocean waters.

**Table 5**

Comparison of Protists Studied in Exercise 1

| Group (Clade) | Example(s) | Characteristics | Ecological Role | Economic Importance |
|---|---|---|---|---|
| Euglenozoans | *Trypanosoma levisi* | | | |
| Alveolates | Paramecia | | | |
| | Dinoflagellates | | | |
| Stramenopiles | Diatoms | | | |
| | Brown algae | | | |
| Foraminiferans and Radiolarians | Foraminiferans | | | |
| | Radiolarians | | | |
| Amoebozoans | Amoeba | | | |
| | *Physarum* | | | |
| Rhodophyta | Red algae | | | |
| Chlorophyta | Green algae: *Spirogyra, Ulva Chara* | | | |

**Table 6**
Comparison of Fungi by Major Features

| Phylum | Example(s) | Sexual Reproductive Structures | Asexual Reproductive Structures |
|---|---|---|---|
| Zygomycota (Zygote Fungi) | | | |
| Ascomycota (Sac Fungi) | | | |
| Basidiomycota (Club Fungi) | | | |
| Deuteromycota (Imperfect Fungi) | | | |

# Applying Your Knowledge

1. Scientists are concerned that the depletion of the ozone layer will result in a reduction of populations of marine algae such as diatoms and dinoflagellates. Recall the ecological role of these organisms and comment on the validity of this concern.

2. Imagine an ecosystem with no fungi. How would it be modified?

3. Speculate about a possible evolutionary advantage to the *fungus* for the following:
   a. *Penicillium* makes and secretes an antibiotic.

   b. *Ergot* fungus (parasitizes rye grain) produces a chemical that is toxic to animals.

4. In 1950 the living world was classified simply into two kingdoms: plants and animals. More recently, scientists developed the five-kingdom system of classification: plants, animals, monerans, protists, and fungi. In 2000 there was a general consensus among scientists that three domains with more than five kingdoms was a better system for classifying the diversity of life on Earth. However, there is still no consensus on the number of kingdoms or the clustering of organisms that best represents their evolutionary relationships. Using the protists studied in this lab topic, explain why the classification of this diverse group in particular is problematic. How is solving the problem of organizing protistan diversity a model for understanding the process of science?

# Student Media Activities and Investigations

**Activities**—Ch 28: Tentative Phylogeny of Eukaryotes; Ch. 31: Fungal Reproduction and Nutrition; Fungal Life Cycles.
**Investigation**—Ch. 28: What Kinds of Protists Do Various Habitats Support? Ch. 31: How Does the Fungus *Pilobolus* Succeed as a Decomposer?
www.masteringbio.com

# References

Ahmadjian, V. "Lichens Are More Important Than You Think." *BioScience,* 1995, vol. 45, p. 124.

Alexopoulos, C., C. Mims, and M. Blackwell. *Introductory Mycology,* 4th ed. New York: John Wiley and Sons, Inc., 1996.

Anderson, R. "What to Do with Protists?" *Australian Systematic Botany,* 1998, vol. 11, p. 185.

Bold, H., C. J. Alexopoulos, and T. Delevoryas. *Morphology of Plants and Fungi.* New York: Harper & Row, 1980, p. 654.

Campbell, N., and J. Reece. *Biology,* 8th ed. San Francisco, CA: Benjamin Cummings, 2008.

Crowder, W. "Marvels of Mycetozoa." *National Geographic Magazine,* 1926, vol. 49, pp. 421–443.

Doolittle, W. F. "Uprooting the Tree of Life." *Scientific American,* 2000, vol. 282, pp. 90–95.

Litten, W. "The Most Poisonous Mushrooms." *Scientific American,* 1975, vol. 232.

# Websites

Protist Image Data. Excellent page links:
http://megasun.bch.umontreal.ca/protists/protists.html

Links to pictures of red, brown, and green algae:
http://www.sonoma.edu/biology/algae/algae.html

Seaweeds:
http://www.botany.uwc.ac.za/Envfacts/seaweeds/

The Tree of Life web project—a collaborative effort of biologists from around the world to present information on diversity and phylogeny of organisms:
http://tolweb.org/tree/phylogeny

Mycological Resources on the Internet:
http://mycology.cornell.edu

See an amoeba video and find interesting information on amoebas:
http://www.microscopy.fsu.edu/moviegallery/pondscum/protozoa/amoeba/

Lichens:
www.lichen.com

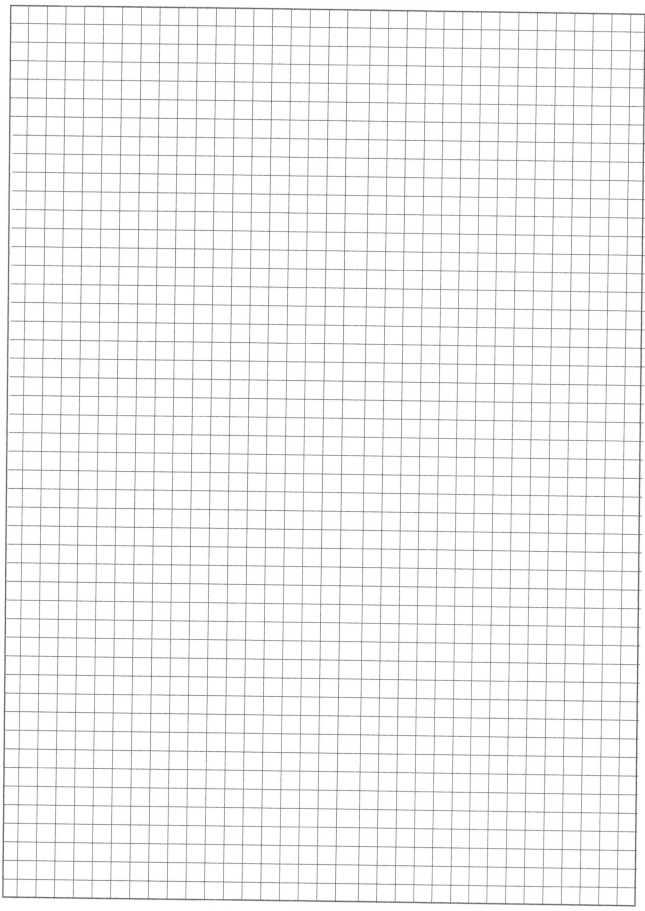

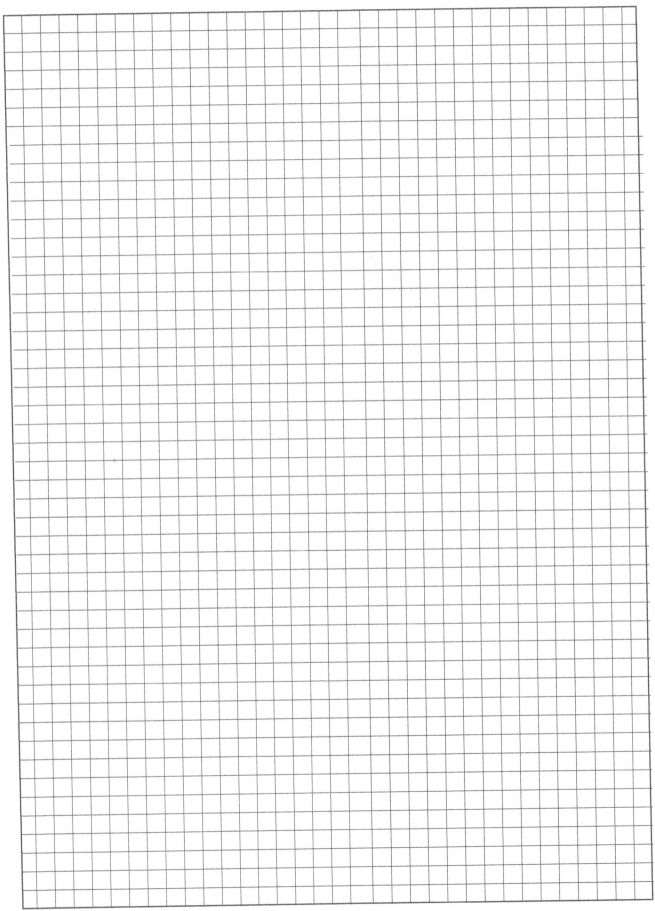

# Plant Diversity: Nonvascular Plants (Bryophytes) and Seedless Vascular Plants

## Laboratory Objectives

After completing this lab topic, you should be able to:

1. Describe the distinguishing characteristics of nonvascular plants and seedless vascular plants.

2. Discuss the ancestral and derived features of nonvascular plants and seedless vascular plants relative to their adaptations to the land environment.

3. Recognize and identify representative members of each phylum of nonvascular plants and seedless vascular plants.

4. Describe the general life cycle and alternation of generations in the nonvascular plants and the seedless vascular plants, and discuss the differences between the life cycles of the two groups of plants using examples.

5. Identify fossil members and their extant counterparts in the seedless vascular plants.

6. Describe homospory and heterospory, including the differences in spores and gametophytes.

7. Discuss the ecological role and economic importance of these groups of plants.

## Introduction

In the history of life on Earth, one of the most revolutionary events was the colonization of land, first by plants, then by animals. Evidence from comparisons of extant land plants and phyla of algae suggests that the first land plants were related to the green algae. These first colonists are thought to be most similar to the living, branched, multicellular green alga *Chara*. Once these simple ancestral plants arrived on land over 475 million years ago, they faced new and extreme challenges in their physical environment. Only individuals that were able to survive the variations in temperature, moisture, gravitational forces, and substrate would thrive. Out of this enormous selective regime would come new and different adaptations and new and different life forms: the land plants.

Land plants generally have complex, multicellular plant bodies that are specialized for a variety of functions. Land plants in the Kingdom **Plantae** produce embryos and have evolved specialized structures for protection of the vulnerable stages of sexual reproduction. The plant body is often covered

From *Investigating Biology Laboratory Manual,* Sixth Edition, Judith G. Morgan and M. Eloise Brown Carter. Copyright © 2008 by Pearson Education, Inc. Published by Benjamin Cummings, Inc. All rights reserved.

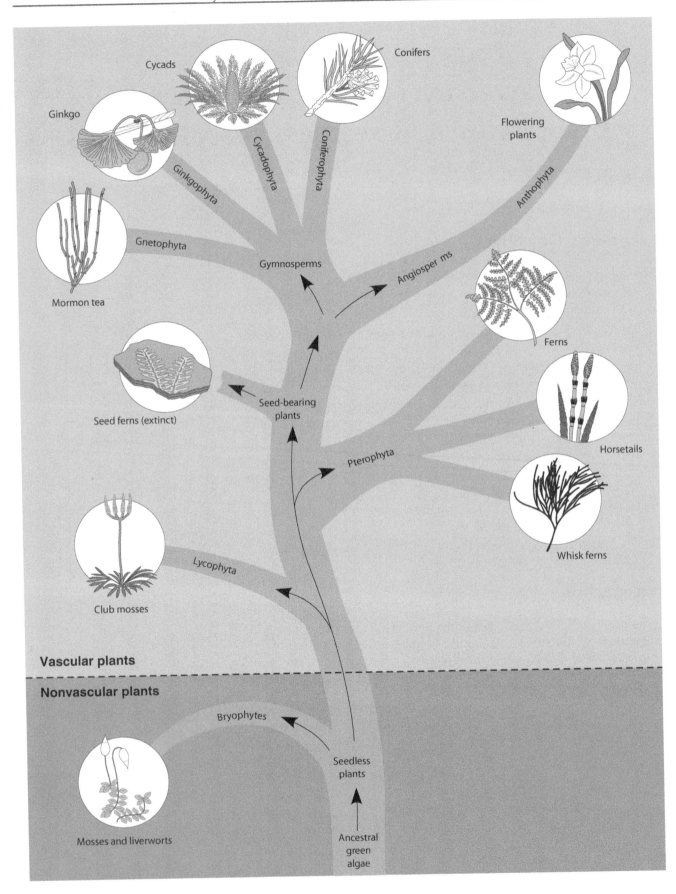

**Table 1**
Classification of Land Plants

| Classification | Common Name | Illustration |
|---|---|---|
| **Nonvascular Plants (Bryophytes)** | | |
| Phylum Bryophyta | Mosses | |
| Phylum Hepatophyta | Liverworts | |
| Phylum Anthocerophyta | Hornworts | |
| **Vascular Plants** | | |
| **Seedless Plants** | | |
| Phylum Lycophyta | Club mosses | |
| Phylum Pterophyta | Ferns, horsetails, whisk ferns | |
| **Seed Plants** | | |
| Gymnosperms | | |
| Phylum Coniferophyta | Conifers | |
| Phylum Cycadophyta | Cycads | |
| Phylum Ginkgophyta | Ginkgo | |
| Phylum Gnetophyta | Mormon tea | |
| Angiosperms | | |
| Phylum Anthophyta | Flowering plants | |

with a waxy cuticle that prevents desiccation. However, the waxy covering also prevents gas exchange, a problem solved by the presence of openings called **stomata** (sing., **stoma**). Some land plants have developed vascular tissue for efficient movement of materials throughout these complex bodies, which are no longer bathed in water. As described in the following section, the reproductive cycles and reproductive structures of these plants are also adapted to the land environment.

You will be investigating the diversity of land plants (Table 1 and Figure 1), some of which will be familiar to you (flowering plants, pine trees, and ferns) and some of which you may never have seen before (whisk ferns, horsetails, and liverworts). *To maintain your perspective in the face of all this*

(☜) **Figure 1.**
**Evolution of land plants.** The nonvascular plants and vascular plants probably evolved from ancestral green algae over 475 million years ago. Seedless vascular plants dominated Earth 300 million years ago, and representatives of two phyla have survived until the present. Seed plants replaced the seedless plants as the dominant land plants, and today flowering plants are the most diverse and successful group in an amazing variety of habitats. The representatives studied in Plant Diversity labs are indicated.

*diversity—and to remember the major themes of these labs—bear in mind the following questions.*

1. What are the special adaptations of these plants to the land environment?
2. How are specialized plant structures related to functions in the land environment?
3. What are the major trends in the plant kingdom as plant life evolved over the past 500 million years?
4. In particular, how has the fundamental reproductive cycle of alternation of generations been modified in successive groups of plants?

## Plant Life Cycles

All land plants have a common sexual reproductive life cycle called **alternation of generations,** in which plants alternate between a haploid **gametophyte** generation and a diploid **sporophyte** generation (Figure 2). In living land plants, these two generations differ in their morphology, but they are still the same species. In all land plants except the bryophytes (mosses and liverworts), the diploid sporophyte generation is the dominant (more conspicuous) generation.

The essential features in the alternation of generations life cycle beginning with the sporophyte are:

- The diploid sporophyte undergoes meiosis to produce haploid **spores** in a protective, nonreproductive jacket of cells called the **sporangium**.
- Dividing by mitosis the spores germinate to produce the haploid gametophyte.

**Figure 2.**
**Alternation of generations.** In this life cycle, a diploid sporophyte plant alternates with a haploid gametophyte plant. Note that haploid spores are produced on the sporophyte by meiosis, and haploid gametes are produced in the gametophyte by mitosis. *Using a colored pencil, indicate the structures that are haploid, and with another color, note the structures that are diploid.*

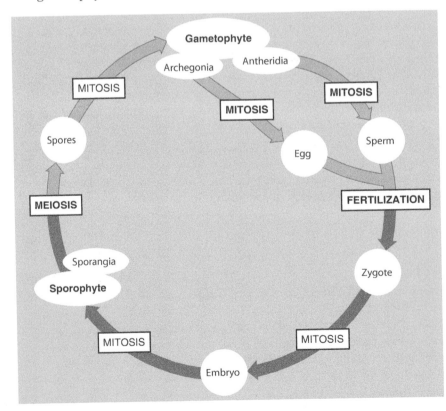

- The gametophyte produces **gametes** inside a jacket of cells forming **gametangia** (sing., **gamtangium**).

- **Eggs** are produced by mitosis in **archegonia** (sing., **archegonium**), and **sperm** are produced in **antheridia** (sing., **anteridium**).

- The gametes fuse (**fertilization**) usually by entrance of the sperm into the archegonium, forming a diploid **zygote**, the first stage of the diploid sporophyte generation.

Note that both gametes and spores are haploid in this life cycle. Unlike the animal life cycle, *the plant life cycle produces gametes by mitosis; spores are produced by meiosis.* The difference between these two cells is that gametes fuse with other gametes to form the zygote and restore the diploid number, while spores germinate to form a new haploid gametophyte plant.

Review the generalized diagram of this life cycle in Figure 2. *Using colored pencils, note the structures that are diploid and those that are haploid.* As you become familiar with variations of this life cycle through specific examples, you will want to continue referring to this general model for review.

Major trends in the evolution of this life cycle include the increased importance of the sporophyte as the photosynthetic and persistent plant that dominates the life cycle; the reduction and protection of the gametophyte within the body of the sporophyte; and the evolution of seeds and then flowers.

# Nonvascular Plants (Bryophytes) and Seedless Vascular Plants

In this lab topic, terrestrial plants will be used to illustrate how life has undergone dramatic changes during the past 500 million years. Not long after the transition to land, plants diverged into at least two separate lineages. One gave rise to the bryophytes, a group of nonvascular plants, including the mosses, and the other to the vascular plants (see Figure 1). Nonvascular bryophytes first appear in the fossil record dating over 420 million years ago and remain unchanged, whereas the vascular plants have undergone enormous diversification. As you review the evolution of land plants, refer to the geological time chart for an overview of the history of life on Earth (Figure 3, on the next page).

---

## EXERCISE 1
# Nonvascular Plants (Bryophytes)

---

The nonvascular plants are composed of three phyla of related plants that share some key characteristics and include mosses (Bryophyta) and liverworts (Hepatophyta). The third phylum, hornworts (Anthocerophyta), will not be seen in lab. (See again Figure 1 and Table 1.) The term *bryophytes* does not refer to a taxonomic category; rather, bryophytes are an ancient group of nonvascular plants that share a common ancestor, appear to have evolved into several different groups independently, and did not give rise to any other living groups of plants. They are small plants generally lacking vascular tissue (specialized cells for the transport of material), although

| Years Ago (millions) | Era / Period / Epoch | | | Life on Earth |
|---|---|---|---|---|
| | **CENOZOIC** | | | |
| | Quaternary | | | |
| | | | Recent | • Origin of agriculture and artificial selection; H. sapiens |
| | | | Pleistocene | |
| 1.8 | Tertiary | | | |
| | | | Pliocene | • Large carnivores; hominoid apes |
| 5 | | | | |
| | | | Miocene | • Forests dwindle; grassland spreads |
| 23 | | | | |
| | | | Oligocene | • Anthropoid apes |
| 35 | | | | |
| | | | Eocene | • Diversification of mammals and flowering plants |
| 57 | | | | |
| | | | Paleocene | • Specialized flowers; sophisticated pollinators and seed distributors |
| 65 | **MESOZOIC** | | | |
| | | Cretaceous | | • Flowering plants established and diversified; many modern families present; extinction of many dinosaurs |
| 145 | | | | |
| | | Jurassic | | • Origin of birds; reptiles dominant; cycads and ferns abundant; first modern conifers and immediate ancestors of flowering plants |
| 208 | | | | |
| | | Triassic | | • First dinosaurs and mammals; forests of gymnosperms and ferns; cycads |
| 245 | **PALEOZOIC** | | | |
| | | Permian | | • Diversification of gymnosperms; origin of reptiles; amphibians dominant |
| 290 | | | | |
| | | Carboniferous | | • First treelike plants; giant woody lycopods and sphenopsids form extensive forests in swampy areas; evolution of early seeds (seed ferns) and first stages of leaves |
| 363 | | | | |
| | | Devonian | | • Diversification of vascular plants; sharks and fishes dominant in the oceans |
| 409 | | | | |
| | | Silurian | | • First vascular plants |
| 439 | | | | |
| | | Ordovician | | • Diversification of algae and plants colonize land |
| 510 | | | | |
| | | Cambrian | | • Diversification of major animal phyla |
| 570 | **PRECAMBRIAN** | | | |
| | | Precambrian | | • Origin of bacteria, archaea, and eukaryotes |
| | Earth is about 4.6 billion years old | | | |

Adapted from James D. Mauseth, *Botany: An Introduction to Plant Biology*, fig. 23.3, p. 667 (Sudbury, MA: Jones and Bartlett Publishers, 1991), www.jbpub.com. Reprinted with permission.

water-conducting tubes appear to be present in some mosses. (However, these tubes may be unrelated to the vascular tissue in vascular plants.) The life cycle for the bryophytes differs from all other land plants because the gametophyte is the dominant and conspicuous plant. Because bryophytes are nonvascular, they are restricted to moist habitats for their reproductive cycle and have never attained the size and importance of other groups of plants. The gametophyte plants remain close to the ground, enabling the motile sperm to swim from the antheridium to the archegonium and fertilize the egg. They have a cuticle but lack stomata on the surface of the gametophyte **thallus** (plant body), which is not organized into roots, stems, and leaves. Stomata are present on the sporophyte in some mosses and hornworts.

Bryophytes are not important economically, with the exception of sphagnum moss, which in its harvested and dried form is known as *peat moss*. Peat moss is absorbent, has an antibacterial agent, and was reportedly once used as bandages and diapers. Today peat moss is used in the horticultural industry, and dried peat is burned as fuel in some parts of the world. Peat lands cover more than one percent of the Earth's surface and store 400 billion metric tons of organic carbon. Harvesting and burning peat releases $CO_2$ to the atmosphere, thus contributing to changes in the global carbon cycle.

## Lab Study A. Bryophyta: Mosses

### Materials

living examples of mosses
prepared slides of *Mnium* archegonia and antheridia
colored pencils

### Introduction

The mosses are the most common group of nonvascular plants, occurring primarily in moist environments but also found in dry habitats that are periodically wet. Refer to Figure 4 on the next page as you investigate the moss life cycle, which is representative of the bryophytes.

### Procedure

1. Examine living colonies of mosses on demonstration. Usually you will find the two generations, gametophyte and sporophyte, growing together.

2. Identify the leafy **gametophytes** and the dependent **sporophytes**, which appear as elongated structures growing above them. Tug gently at the sporophyte and notice that it is attached to the gametophyte. Recall that the sporophyte develops and matures while attached to the gametophyte and receives its moisture and nutrients from the gametophyte.

(☜) **Figure 3.**
**Geological time chart.** The history of life can be organized into time periods that reflect changes in the physical and biological environment. Refer to this table as you review the evolution of land plants in the Plant Diversity labs.

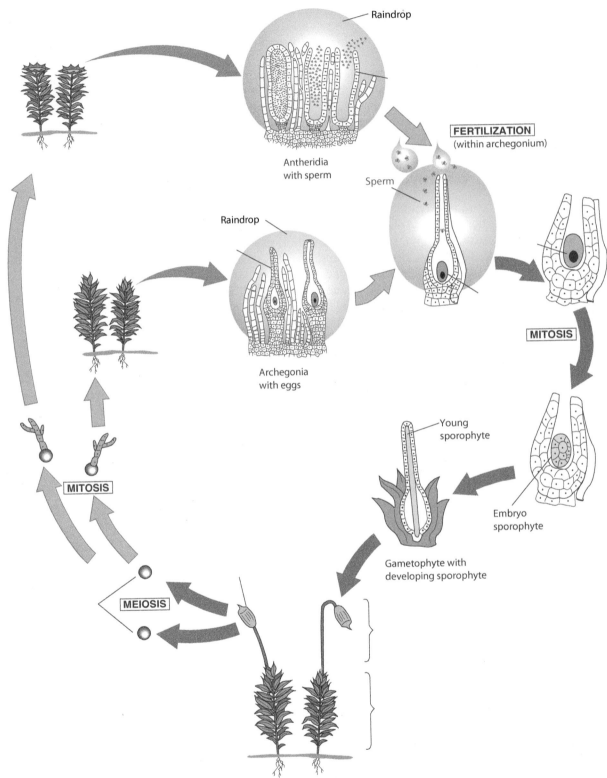

**Figure 4.**
**Moss life cycle.** The leafy moss plant is the gametophyte, and the sporophyte is dependent on it, deriving its water and nutrients from the body of the gametophyte. Review this variation of alternation of generations and label the structures described in Lab Study A. *Using colored pencils, highlight the haploid and diploid structures in different colors. Circle the processes of mitosis and meiosis.*

3. The gametes are produced by the gametophyte in **gametangia** *by mitosis.* Gametangia protect the gametes but are not readily visible without a microscope. Observe under the microscope's low-power lens prepared slides containing long sections of heads of the unisex moss *Mnium*, which contain the gametangia. One slide has been selected to show the **antheridia** (male); the other is a rosette of **archegonia** (female). Sperm-forming tissue will be visible inside the antheridia. On the archegonial slide, look for an archegonium. The moss archegonium has a very long neck and rounded base. It will be difficult to find an entire archegonium in any one section. Search for a single-celled **egg** in the base of the archegonium.

4. Refer to Figure 4 as you follow the steps of fertilization through formation of the gametophyte in the next generation. The sperm swim through a film of water to the archegonium and swim down the neck to the egg, where fertilization takes place. The diploid zygote divides by mitosis and develops into an embryonic sporophyte within the archegonium. As the sporophyte matures, it grows out of the gametophyte but remains attached, deriving water and nutrients from the gametophyte body. **Spores** develop *by meiosis* in the **sporangium** at the end of the sporophyte. The spores are discharged from the sporangium and in a favorable environment develop into new gametophytes.

## Results

1. Review the structures and processes observed and then label the moss life cycle diagram in Figure 4.
2. Using colored pencils, indicate if structures are haploid or diploid and circle the processes of mitosis and meiosis.

## Discussion

Refer to Figure 2, the generalized diagram of the plant life cycle.

1. Are the spores produced by the moss sporophyte formed by meiosis or mitosis? Are they haploid or diploid?

2. Do the spores belong to the gametophyte or sporophyte generation?

3. Are the gametes haploid or diploid? Are they produced by meiosis or mitosis?

4. Is the dominant generation for the mosses the gametophyte or the sporophyte?

5. Can you suggest any ecological role for mosses?

6. What feature of the life cycle differs for bryophytes compared with all other land plants?

## Lab Study B. Hepatophyta: Liverworts

### Materials

living liverworts

### Introduction

Liverworts are so named because their bodies are flattened and lobed. Early herbalists believed that these plants were beneficial in the treatment of liver disorders. Although less common than mosses, liverworts can be found along streams on moist rocks, but because of their small size, you must look closely to locate them.

### Procedure

Examine examples of liverworts on demonstration. Liverworts have a flat **thallus** (plant body). Note the **rhizoids**, rootlike extensions on the lower surface, that primarily anchor plants. Observe the **pores** on the surface of the leaflike thallus. These openings function in gas exchange; however, they are always open since they lack guard cells. On the upper surface of the thallus you should see circular cups called **gemmae cups**, which contain flat disks of green tissue called **gemmae**. The gemmae are washed out of the cups when it rains, and they grow into new, genetically identical liverworts.

### Results

Sketch the overall structure of the liverwort in the margin of your laboratory manual. Label structures where appropriate.

### Discussion

1. Is the plant you observed the gametophyte or sporophyte?

2. Are the gemmae responsible for asexual or sexual reproduction? Explain.

3. Why are these plants, like most bryophytes, restricted to moist habitats, and why are they always small?

4. In this lab topic, you are asked to complete tables that summarize features advantageous to the adaptation of plant groups to the land environment. You may be asked to compare these derived features with others that have changed little (ancestral) in the evolution of land plants. For example, for nonvascular plants, motile sperm might be considered an ancestral feature, while the cuticle would be considered derived.

Complete Table 2, relating the features of nonvascular plants to their success in the land environment. Refer to the lab topic introduction for assistance.

**Table 2**
Ancestral and Derived Features of Nonvascular Plants
as They Relate to Adaptation to Land

| Ancestral Features | Derived Features |
|---|---|
| | |

## EXERCISE 2
# Seedless Vascular Plants

Seedless, terrestrial plants are analogous to the first terrestrial vertebrate animals, the amphibians, in their dependence on water for external fertilization and development of the unprotected, free-living embryo. Both groups were important in the Paleozoic era but have undergone a steady decline in importance since that time. Seedless plants were well suited for life in the vast swampy areas that covered large areas of the Earth in the Carboniferous period but were not suited for the drier areas of the Earth at that time or for later climatic changes that caused the vast swamps to decline and disappear. The fossilized remains of the swamp forests are the coal deposits of today (Figure 3 and Figure 7).

Although living representatives of the seedless vascular plants have survived for millions of years, their limited adaptations to the land environment have restricted their range. All seedless vascular plants have vascular tissue, which is specialized for conducting water, nutrients, and photosynthetic products. Their life cycle is a variation of alternation of generations, in which the sporophyte is the dominant plant; the gametophyte is usually independent of the sporophyte. These plants generally have well developed leaves and roots, stomata and structural support tissue. However, since they still retain the ancestral feature of motile sperm that require water for fertilization, the gametophyte is small and restricted to moist habitats.

Economically, the only important members of this group are the ferns, a significant horticultural resource.

The phyla included in the seedless vascular plants are Lycophyta and Pterophyta (see again Table 1 and Figure 1).

The living examples of lycophytes are small club mosses, spike mosses, and quillworts. (Though named "mosses," these plants have vascular tissue and therefore are not true mosses.) The pterophytes include ferns, horsetails, and whisk ferns, that are remarkably different in overall appearance. Current evidence from molecular biology indicates that these diverse plants share a common ancestor and should all be included in the phylum Pterophyta. This evidence also suggests that pterophytes are more closely related to seed plants than they are to lycophytes.

## Lab Study A. Lycophyta: Club Mosses

### Materials

living *Selaginella* and *Lycopodium*
preserved *Selaginella* with microsporangia and megasporangia
prepared slide of *Selaginella* strobilus, l.s.

### Introduction

Living members of Lycophyta are usually found in moist habitats, including bogs and streamsides. However, one species of *Selaginella*, the resurrection plant, inhabits deserts. It remains dormant throughout periods of low rainfall, but then comes to life—resurrects—when it rains. During the Carboniferous period, lycophytes were not inconspicuous parts of the flora but rather formed the forest canopy; they were the ecological equivalent of today's oaks, hickories, and pines (Figure 7).

Nonvascular plants and most seedless vascular plants produce one type of spore (**homospory**), which gives rise to the gametophyte by mitosis. One advanced feature occasionally seen in seedless vascular plants is the production of two kinds of spores (**heterospory**). Large spores called **megaspores** divide by mitosis to produce the female gametophyte. The numerous small spores, **microspores,** produce the male gametophytes by mitosis. Heterospory and separate male and female gametophytes, as seen in *Selaginella*, are unusual in seedless vascular plants, but characteristic of seed-producing vascular plants.

### Procedure

1. Examine living club mosses, *Selaginella* and *Lycopodium*. Are they dichotomously branched? (The branches would split in two, appearing to form a Y.) Locate sporangia, which may be present either clustered at the end of the leafy stem tips, forming **strobili,** or **cones,** or dispersed along the leafy stems. Note that these plants have small leaves, or bracts, along the stem.

2. Examine preserved strobili of *Selaginella*. Observe the round sporangia clustered in sporophylls (leaflike structures) at the tip of the stem (Figure 5a). These sporangia contain either four megaspores or numerous microspores. Can you observe any differences in the sporangia or spores?

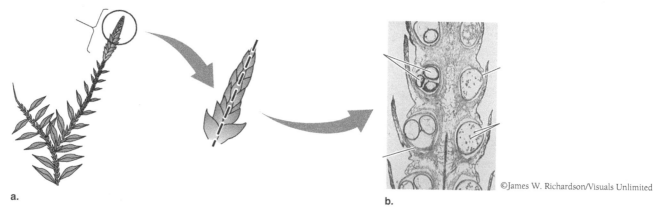

a.                                                                                                    b.

©James W. Richardson/Visuals Unlimited

**Figure 5.**
*Selaginella.* (a) The leafy plant is the sporophyte. The sporangia are clustered at the tips in strobili. (b) Photomicrograph of a longitudinal section through the strobilus of *Selaginella.*

3. Observe the prepared slide of a long section through the strobilus of *Selaginella.* Begin your observations at low power. Are both microspores and megaspores visible on this slide?

   How can you distinguish these spores?

4. Identify the **strobilus, microsporangium, microspores, megasporangium,** and **megaspores** and label Figure 5.

## Results

1. Sketch the overall structure of the club mosses in the margin of your lab manual. Label structures where appropriate.
2. Review Figure 5 of *Selaginella.* Using a colored pencil, highlight the structures that are haploid and part of the gametophyte generation.

## Discussion

1. Are these leafy plants part of the sporophyte or the gametophyte generation? Do you have any evidence to support your answer?

2. What features would you look for to determine if this were a seedless vascular plant?

3. Are microspores and megaspores produced by mitosis or meiosis? (Review the life cycle in Figure 2.)

4. Will megaspores divide to form the female gametophyte or the sporophyte?

 Having trouble with life cycles? Return to the introduction and review the generalized life cycle in Figure 2. Reread the introduction to the study of seedless vascular plants. The key to success is to determine where meiosis occurs and to remember the ploidal level for the gametophyte and the sporophyte.

## Lab Study B. Pterophyta: Ferns, Horsetails, and Whisk Ferns

### Materials

living and/or preserved horsetails (*Equisetum*)
living and/or preserved whisk ferns (*Psilotum*)
living ferns

### Introduction

If a time machine could take us back 400 million years to the Silurian period, we would find that vertebrate animals were confined to the seas, and early vascular plants had begun to diversify on land (Figure 3). By the Carboniferous period, ferns, horsetails, and whisk ferns grew alongside the lycophytes. Until recently, these three groups of seedless vascular plants were placed in separate phyla: Pterophyta (ferns), Sphenophyta (horsetails), and Psilophyta (whisk ferns). Strong evidence from molecular biology now reveals a close relationship among these three groups, supporting a common ancestor for the group and their placement in one phylum, Pterophyta.

Psilophytes (**whisk ferns**) are diminutive, dichotomously branched (repeated Y branches), photosynthetic stems that reproduce sexually by aerial spores. Today, whisk ferns can be found in some areas of Florida and in the tropics. Sphenophytes (**horsetails**) have green jointed stems with occasional clusters of leaves or branches. Their cell walls contain silica that give the stem a rough texture. These plants were used by pioneers to scrub dishes—thus their name, scouring rushes. In cooler regions of North America, horsetails grow as weeds along roadsides. **Ferns** are the most successful group of seedless vascular plants, occupying habitats from the desert to tropical rain forests. Most ferns are small plants that lack woody tissue. An exception is the tree ferns found in tropical regions. Many cultivated ferns are available for home gardeners.

In this lab study you will investigate the diversity of pterophytes, including whisk ferns, horsetails, and a variety of ferns. The plants on demonstration are sporophytes, the dominant generation in seedless vascular plants. You will investigate the life cycle of a fern in Lab Study C, Fern Life Cycle.

## Procedure

1. Examine a living **whisk fern** (*Psilotum nudum*) on demonstration. This is one of only two extant genera of psilophytes.

2. Observe the spherical structures on the stem. If possible, cut one open and determine the function of these structures. Note the dichotomous branching, typical of the earliest land plants.

3. Examine the **horsetails** (*Equisetum* sp.) on demonstration. Note the ribs and ridges in the stem. Also examine the nodes or joints along the stem where branches and leaves may occur in some species. Locate the **strobili** in the living or preserved specimens on demonstration. These are clusters of **sporangia**, which produce **spores.**

4. Examine the living **ferns** on demonstration. Note the deeply dissected leaves, which arise from an underground stem called a **rhizome,** which functions like a root to anchor the plant. Roots arise from the rhizome. Observe the dark spots, or **sori** (sing. **sorus**), which are clusters of sporangia, on the underside of some leaves, called **sporophylls**.

## Results

1. Sketch the overall structure of the whisk fern, horsetail, and fern in the margin of your lab manual. Label structures where appropriate.

2. Are there any leaves on the whisk fern? On the horsetails?

3. Are sporangia present on the whisk fern? On the horsetails? On the ferns?

## Discussion

1. Are the spores in the sporangia produced by mitosis or meiosis?

2. Are the sporangia haploid or diploid? Think about which generation produces them.

3. Once dispersed, will these spores produce the gametophyte or sporophyte generation?

# Lab Study C. Fern Life Cycle

## Materials

living ferns
living fern gametophytes
   with archegonia and
   antheridia
living fern gametophytes
with young sporophytes
   attached
stereoscopic microscope

compound microscope
prepared slide of fern
   gametophytes with
   archegonia, c.s.
colored pencils
Protoslo®
glycerol in dropping bottle

## Introduction

In the previous Lab Study you examined the features of the fern sporophyte. In this lab study you will examine the fern life cycle in more detail, beginning with the diploid sporophyte.

## Procedure

1. Examine the sporophyte leaf with sori (sporophyll) at your lab bench. Make a wet mount of a sorus, using a drop of glycerol, and do not add a cover slip. Examine the sporangia using a dissecting microscope. You will find the stalked **sporangia** in various stages of development. Find a sporangium still filled with **spores** and observe carefully for a few minutes, watching for movement. The sporangia will open and fling the spores into the glycerol.

2. Refer to Figure 6 as you observe the events and important structures in the life cycle of the fern. The haploid spores of ferns fall to the ground and grow into heart-shaped, **gametophyte** plants. All seedless terrestrial plants depend on an external source of water for a sperm to swim to an egg to effect fertilization and for growth of the resulting sporophyte plant. The sexual organs, which bear male and female gametes, are borne on the underside of the gametophyte. Egg cells are produced by mitosis in urnlike structures called **archegonia,** and sperm cells are produced by mitosis in globular structures called **antheridia.** Archegonia are usually found around the notch of the heart-shaped gametophyte, while antheridia occur over most of the undersurface.

3. To study whole gametophytes, make a slide of living gametophytes. View them using the stereoscopic microscope or the scanning lens on the compound microscope. Note their shape and color and the presence of **rhizoids,** rootlike multicellular structures. Locate archegonia and antheridia. Which surface will you need to examine? Sketch in the margin of your lab manual any details not included in Figure 6.

4. If you have seen antheridia on a gametophyte, remove the slide from the microscope. Gently but firmly press on the coverslip with a pencil eraser. View using the compound microscope first on intermediate and then on high power. Look for motile **sperm** swimming with a spiral motion. Each sperm has two flagella. Add a drop of Protoslo to slow down movement of sperm.

5. Observe the cross section of a fern gametophyte with archegonia. Each archegonium encloses an **egg,** which may be visible on your slide.

6. Make a wet mount of a fern gametophyte with a **young sporophyte** attached. Look for a young **leaf** and **root** on each sporophyte.

7. Share slides of living gametophytes with archegonia, antheridia and sperm, and sporophytes until everyone has observed each structure.

## Results

1. Review the structures and processes observed, and then label the stages of fern sexual reproduction outlined in Figure 6.

2. Using colored pencils, circle those parts of the life cycle that are sporophytic (diploid). Use another color to encircle the gametophytic (haploid) stages of the life cycle. Highlight the processes of meiosis and mitosis.

## Discussion

Refer to Figure 2, the generalized diagram of the plant life cycle, and Figure 6, a representation of the fern life cycle.

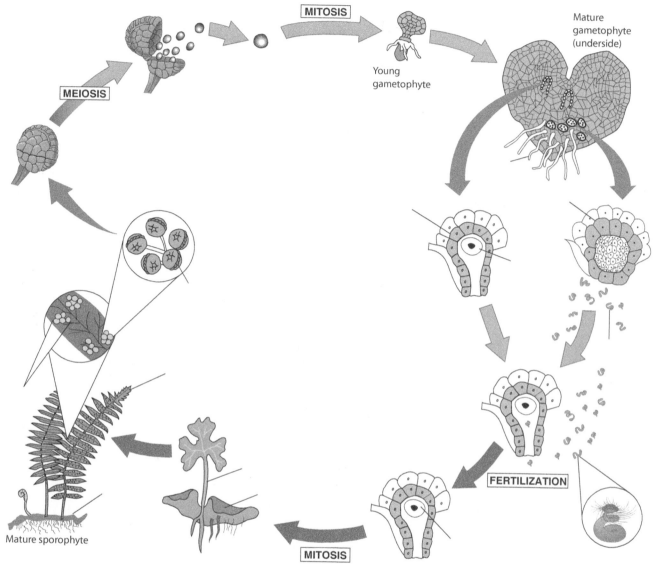

**Figure 6.**
**Fern life cycle.** The familiar leafy fern plant is the sporophyte, which alternates with a small, heart-shaped gametophyte. Review this life cycle, a variation of alternation of generations, and label the structures and processes described in Lab Study C. *Using colored pencils, highlight the haploid and diploid structures in different colors.*

1. Are the spores produced by the fern sporophyte formed by meiosis or mitosis?

2. Do the spores belong to the gametophyte or the sporophyte generation?

3. Are the gametes produced by mitosis or meiosis?

4. Are the archegonia and antheridia haploid or diploid? Think about which generation produces them.

5. Is the dominant generation for the fern the gametophyte or the sporophyte?

6. Can you suggest any ecological role for ferns?

## Lab Study D. Fossils of Seedless Vascular Plants

### Materials

fossils of extinct lycophytes (*Lepidodendron, Sigillaria*)
fossils of extinct sphenophytes (*Calamites*)
fossils of extinct ferns

### Introduction

If we went back in time 300 million years to the Carboniferous period, we would encounter a wide variety of vertebrate amphibians moving about vast swamps dominated by spore-bearing forest trees. Imagine a forest of horsetails and lycophytes the size of trees, amphibians as large as alligators, and enormous dragonflies and roaches! Seedless plants were at their peak during this period and were so prolific that their carbonized remains form the bulk of Earth's coal deposits. Among the most spectacular components of the coal-swamp forest were 100-foot-tall lycophyte trees belonging to the fossil genera *Lepidodendron* and *Sigillaria*, tree ferns, and 60-foot-tall horsetails assigned to the fossil genus *Calamites* (Figures 3 and 7).

### Procedure

Examine flattened fossil stems of *Lepidodendron, Sigillaria, Calamites,* and fossil fern foliage, all of which were recovered from coal mine tailings. Compare these with their living relatives, the lycophytes (club mosses), sphenophytes (horsetails), and ferns, which today are diminutive plants found in restricted habitats.

### Results

1. For each phylum of seedless vascular plants, describe those characteristics that are similar for both living specimens and fossils. For example, do you observe dichotomous branching and similar shape and form of leaves, stems, or sporangia? Refer to the living specimens or your sketches.

©The Field Museum

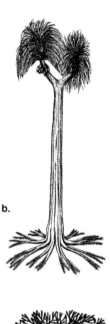

b.

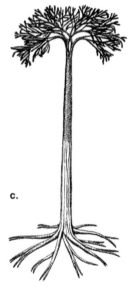

c.

d.

**Figure 7.**
**Seedless vascular plants of the Carboniferous period.** (a) Reconstruction of a swamp forest dominated by lycophytes (b) *Lepidodendron* and (c) *Sigillaria*. (d) *Calamites* was a relative of horsetails. (*No. Geo. 7500c, Field Museum of Natural History, Chicago*)

Lycophytes:

Sphenophytes:

Ferns:

2. Sketch below the overall structure of the fossils. How would you recognize these fossils at a later date? Label structures where appropriate.

b, c, d: Adapted from James D. Mauseth, *Botany: An Introduction to Plant Biology*, fig. 23.3, p. 667 (Sudbury, MA: Jones and Bartlett Publishers, 1991), www.jbpub.com. Reprinted with permission.

## Discussion

The lycophytes, sphenophytes, and ferns were once the giants of the plant kingdom and dominated the landscape. Explain why they are presently restricted to certain habitats and are relatively small in stature.

# Questions for Review

1. Complete Table 3, indicating the ancestral and derived features of seedless vascular plants relative to success in land environments. Recall that in this context the term *ancestral* means a shared trait, while the term *derived* indicates an adaptation to land. For example, traits shared with the nonvascular plants (such as sperm requiring water for fertilization) are ancestral, while the presence of vascular tissue is derived.

**Table 3**
Ancestral and Derived Features of Seedless Vascular
Plants as They Relate to Adaptation to Land

| Ancestral Features | Derived Features |
|---|---|
|  |  |

2. For each of the listed features, describe its contribution, if any, to the success of land plants.

gametangium


cuticle


rhizoid

motile sperm


vascular tissue


gemma


3. Complete Table 4. Identify the function of the structures listed. Indicate whether they are part of the gametophyte or sporophyte generation, and provide an example of a plant that has this structure.
4. What is the major difference between the alternation of generations in the life cycles of nonvascular plants and seedless vascular plants?


**Table 4**
Structures and Functions of the Nonvascular Plants and Seedless Vascular Plants

| Structure | Function | Sporophyte/ Gametophyte | Example |
|---|---|---|---|
| Antheridium | | | |
| Archegonium | | | |
| Spore | | | |
| Gamete | | | |
| Rhizome | | | |
| Gemma | | | |
| Sporangium | | | |
| Strobilus | | | |
| Sorus | | | |

# Applying Your Knowledge

1. The fossil record provides little information about ancient mosses. Do you think that nonvascular plants could ever have been large tree-sized plants? Provide evidence from your investigations to support your answer.

2. On a walk through a botanical garden, you notice a small leafy plant that is growing along the edge of a small stream in a shady nook. You hypothesize that this plant is a lycophyte. What information can you gather to test your hypothesis?

3. Fern antheridia release sperm that then swim toward archegonia in a watery film. The archegonia release a fluid containing chemicals that attract the sperm. This is an example of chemotaxis, the movement of cells or organisms in response to a chemical. What is the significance of chemotaxis to fern (and moss) reproduction?

4. Scientists investigating the evolutionary history (phylogeny) of land plants represent their hypotheses as phylogenetic trees or branching diagrams. Groups of plants that share a common ancestor are called clades, which are represented as lines connected at a branching point (the common ancestor). See the example below.

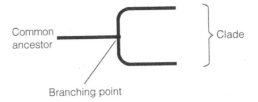

Which two of the phylogenetic trees below best represents the evolutionary history of land plants? Explain your choice of tree using your results from this laboratory topic.

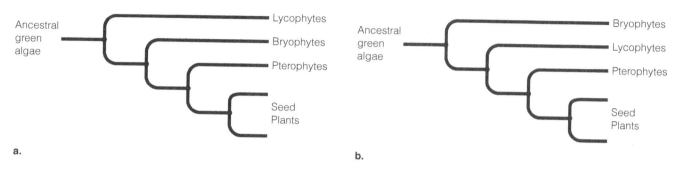

a.

b.

5. Heterospory occasionally occurs in lycophytes and ferns, and in all seed plants. Botanists are convinced that heterospory must have originated more than once in the evolution of plants. Can you suggest one or more advantages that heterospory might provide to plants?

## Investigative Extensions

*C-Ferns, Ceratopteris,* are excellent experimental organisms for investigating the alternation of generations life cycle, comparisons of seedless vascular plants with seed plants, and the physiology of ferns. These small ferns have a short life cycle of 12 days from spore to spore, and they can be grown successfully in small laboratory spaces. Amazingly, the motile sperm, easily visible under the microscope, can swim for two hours in buffer! The following are questions that you might investigate.

1. Fern archegonia secrete phermones to attract swimming sperm for fertilization, an example of chemotaxis (see question 3 in Applying Your Knowledge). Are sperm attracted to other compounds as well, including organic acids that might be present in the fluid secreted by the archegonia? Are there other compounds that might also be attractants? What are the common characteristics of the compounds that are attractants, for example, type of compound or chemical structure?

2. *C-Ferns* produce two types of gametophytes, hermaphrodites (both archegonia and antheridia present) and males (antheridia only). What factors affect the proportion of hermaphrodite and male gametophytes in the population, for example, temperature, light, or population density?

3. Are sperm from male gametophytes more or less attracted by pheromones compared with sperm from the hermaphrodites? Do sperm from both types of gametophytes respond to the same concentration of pheromones or other organic attractants?

Resources, laboratory procedures and preparation instructions are provided at the *C-Fern* web site http://cfern.bio.utk.edu/index.html. Growing materials are available at Carolina Biological Supply, including *C-Fern* Chemotaxis Kit and *C-Fern* Culture Kit.

 # Student Media Activities and Investigations

**Activities**—Ch. 29: Highlights of Plant Phylogeny; Moss Life Cycle; Fern Life Cycle
**Investigations**—Ch. 29: What Are the Different Stages of a Fern Life Cycle?
www.masteringbio.com

## References

Berg, L. R. *Introductory Botany: Plants, People and the Environment*, 2nd ed. Belmont, CA: Thomson Brooks/Cole, 2007.

Hickock, L. G., and T. R. Warne. *C-Fern Manual.* Burlington, NC: Carolina Biological Supply, 2000.

Mauseth, J. D. *Botany: An Introduction to Plant Biology*, 3rd ed. Sudbury, MA: Jones and Bartlett Publishers, 2003.

Raven, P. H., R. F. Evert, and S. E. Eichhorn. *Biology of Plants*, 7th ed. New York: W. H. Freeman Publishers, 2004.

## Websites

The Tree of Life Web Project is a collaborative project of biologists worldwide. Information is provided on all major groups of living organisms including land plants: http://tolweb.org/Embryophytes

An introduction to land plants, including morphology, evolution, and fossils. Images and resources provided: http://www.ucmp.berkeley.edu/plants/plantae.html

Fern basics (click on Learn More about Ferns), images and current research:
http://amerfernsoc.org/

Links to images of plants:
http://botit.botany.wisc.edu/images/130/

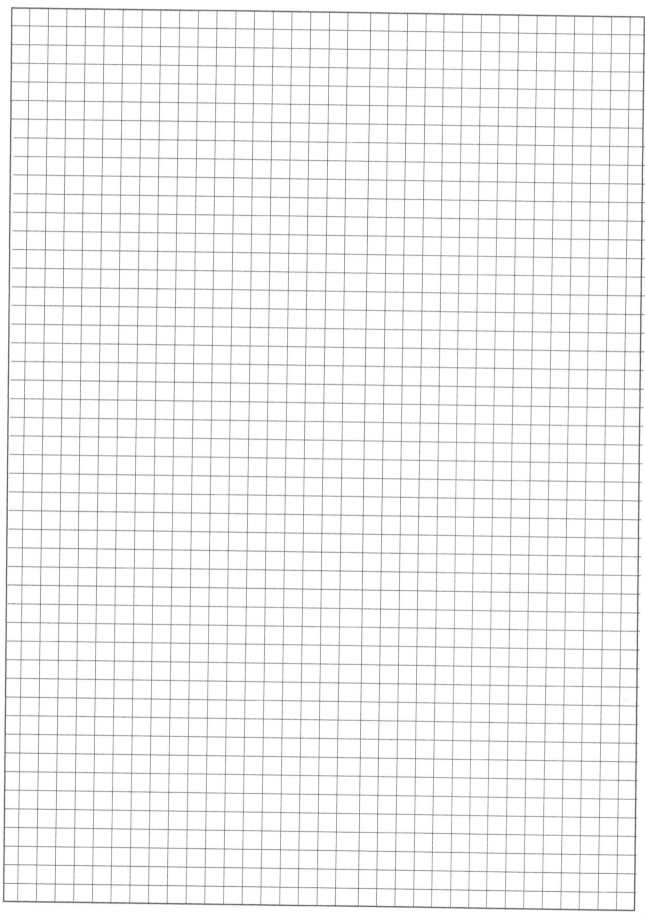

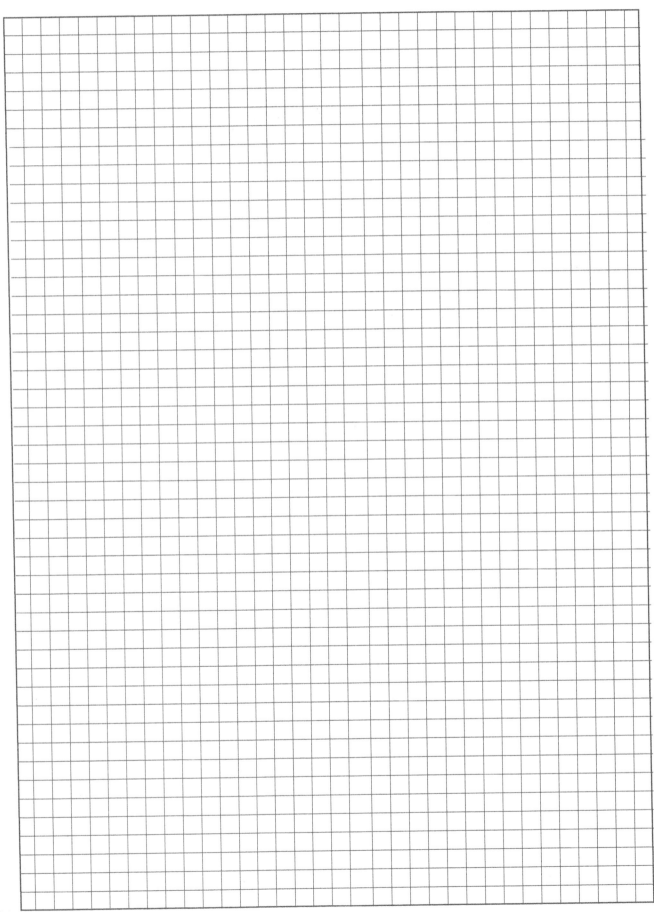

# Plant Diversity: Seed Plants

 Before lab, read the following material on gymnosperms and angiosperms and complete Table 1 by listing (and comparing) the traits of each.

## Laboratory Objectives

After completing this lab topic, you should be able to:

1. Identify examples of the phyla of seed plants.
2. Describe the life cycle of a gymnosperm (pine tree) and an angiosperm.
3. Describe features of flowers that ensure pollination by insects, birds, bats, and wind.
4. Describe factors influencing pollen germination.
5. Identify types of fruits, recognize examples, and describe dispersal mechanisms.
6. Relate the structures of seed plants to their functions in the land environment.
7. Compare the significant features of life cycles for various land plants and state their evolutionary importance.
8. Summarize major trends in the evolution of land plants and provide evidence from your laboratory investigations.

## Gymnosperms

For over 500 million years, plants have been adapting to the rigors of the land environment. The nonvascular bryophytes with their small and simple bodies survived in moist habitats, habitats moist at least for part of their life cycle. During the cool Carboniferous period, vascular seedless plants dominated the landscape of the swamp forests that covered much of the earth. Although these plants were more complex and better adapted to the challenges of the land environment, they still were dependent on water for sperm to swim to the egg. During the Mesozoic era, 150 million years ago, Earth became warmer and drier and the swamp forests declined, presenting another challenge to terrestrial plants and animals. Earth at that time was a world dominated by reptilian vertebrates, including the flying,

From *Investigating Biology Laboratory Manual,* Sixth Edition, Judith G. Morgan and M. Eloise Brown Carter. Copyright © 2008 by Pearson Education, Inc. Published by Benjamin Cummings, Inc. All rights reserved.

running, and climbing dinosaurs. The landscape was dominated by a great variety of seed-bearing plants called **gymnosperms** (literally, "naked seeds"), which in the Carboniferous period had been restricted to dry sites. During the Mesozoic, a number of distinct gymnosperm groups diversified, and a few of the spore-bearing plants survived.

Vertebrate animals became fully terrestrial during the Mesozoic with the emergence of reptiles, which were free from a dependence on water for sexual reproduction and development. The development of the amniotic egg along with an internal method of fertilization made this major transition possible. The amniotic egg carries its own water supply and nutrients, permitting early embryonic development to occur on dry land, a great distance from external water. In an analogous manner, the gymnosperms became free from dependence on water through the development of a process of internal fertilization via the pollen grain and development of a seed, which contains a dormant embryo with a protective cover and special nutrient tissue.

Several features of the gymnosperms have been responsible for their success. They have reduced (smaller-sized) gametophytes; the male gametophyte is a multinucleated pollen grain, and the female gametophyte is small and retained within the sporangium in the ovule of the sporophyte generation. The pollen grain is desiccation resistant and adapted for wind pollination, removing the necessity for fertilization in a watery medium. The pollen tube conveys the sperm nucleus to an egg cell, and the embryonic sporophyte develops within the gametophyte tissues, which are protected by the previous sporophyte generation. The resulting seed is not only protected from environmental extremes, but also is packed with nutritive materials and can be dispersed away from the parent plant. In addition, gymnosperms have advanced vascular tissues: xylem for transporting water and nutrients and phloem for transporting photosynthetic products. The xylem cells are called *tracheids* and are more efficient for transport than those of the seedless vascular plants.

## Angiosperms

A visit to Earth 60 million years ago, during the late Cretaceous period, would reveal a great diversity of mammals and birds and a landscape dominated by **flowering plants,** or **angiosperms** (phylum **Anthophyta**). Ultimately, these plants would diversify and become the most numerous, widespread, and important plants on Earth. Angiosperms now occupy well over 90% of the vegetated surface of Earth and contribute virtually 100% of our agricultural food plants.

The evolution of the flower resulted in enormous advances in the efficient transfer and reception of pollen. Whereas gymnosperms are all wind-pollinated, producing enormous amounts of pollen that reach the appropriate species by chance, the process of flower pollination is mediated by specific agents—insects, birds, and bats—in addition to water and wind. Pollination agents such as the insect are attracted to the flower with its rewards of nectar and pollen. Animal movements provide precise placement of pollen on the receptive portion of the female structures, increasing the probability of fertilization. The process also enhances the opportunity for cross-fertilization among distant plants and therefore the possibility of increased genetic variation.

Angiosperm reproduction follows the trend for reduction in the size of the gametophyte. The pollen grain is the male gametophyte, and the eight-nucleated **embryo sac** is all that remains of the female gametophyte. This generation continues to be protected and dependent on the adult sporophyte plant. The female gametophyte provides nutrients for the developing sporophyte embryo through a unique triploid **endosperm** tissue. Another unique feature of angiosperms is the **fruit.** The seeds of the angiosperm develop within the flower ovary, which matures into the fruit. This structure provides protection and enhances dispersal of the young sporophyte into new habitats.

In addition to advances in reproductive biology, the angiosperms evolved other advantageous traits. All gymnosperms are trees or shrubs, with a large investment in woody, persistent tissue; and their life cycles are long (5 or more years before they begin to reproduce and 2 to 3 years to produce a seed). Flowering plants, on the other hand, can be woody, but many are herbaceous, with soft tissues that survive from one to a few years. It is possible for angiosperms to go from seed to seed in less than one year. As you perform the exercises in this lab, think about the significance of this fact in terms of the evolution of this group. How might generation length affect the rate of evolution? Angiosperms also have superior conducting tissues. Xylem tissue is composed of *tracheids* (as in gymnosperms), but also contains large-diameter, open-ended *vessels.* The phloem cells, called *sieve-tube members,* provide more efficient transport of the products of photosynthesis.

Review the characteristics of gymnosperms and angiosperms described in this introduction, and summarize in Table 1 the advantages of these groups relative to their success on land. You should be able to list several characteristics for each. At the end of the lab, you will be asked to modify and complete the table, based on your investigations.

You will want to return to this table after the laboratory to be sure that the table is complete and that you are familiar with all these important features.

# EXERCISE 1

# Gymnosperms

The term *gymnosperms* refers to a diverse group of seed plants that do not produce flowers. Although they share many characteristics, including the production of pollen, they represent four distinct groups, or phyla. In this exercise, you will observe members of these phyla and investigate the life cycle of a pine, one of the most common gymnosperms.

**Table 1**
Traits for Gymnosperms and Angiosperms
Relative to Their Success on Land

| | Adaptation to the Land Environment |
|---|---|
| Gymnosperms | |
| Angiosperms | |

# Lab Study A. Phyla of Gymnosperms

## Materials

living or pressed examples of conifers, ginkgos, cycads, and Mormon tea

## Introduction

Gymnosperms are composed of several phyla. The largest and best known is Coniferophyta, which includes pines and other cone-bearing trees and shrubs. Cycads (Cycadophyta), which have a palmlike appearance, are found primarily in tropical regions scattered around the world. Ginkgos (Ginkgophyta), with their flat fan-shaped leaves, are native to Asia and are prized as urban trees. An extract of Ginkgo is used as an herbal medicine purported to improve memory. Gnetophyta is composed of three distinct and unusual groups of plants: gnetums, which are primarily vines of Asia, Africa, and South America; *Welwitschia*, a rare desert plant with two leathery leaves; and Mormon tea (*Ephedra*), desert shrubs of North and Central America. Compounds from *Ephedra*, ephedrines, used in diet aids and decongestants, have raised serious concerns due to side effects including cardiac arrest.

## Procedure

1. Observe demonstration examples of all phyla of gymnosperms and be able to recognize their representatives. Note any significant ecological and economic role for these plants.
2. Record your observations in Table 2.

### Table 2
Phyla of Gymnosperms

| Phyla | Examples | Characteristics/Comments |
|---|---|---|
| Coniferophyta | | |
| Ginkgophyta | | |
| Cycadophyta | | |
| Gnetophyta | | |

## Results

1. In the margin of your manual, sketch the overall structure of the plants. Label structures where appropriate.
2. Are there any reproductive structures present for these plants? If so, make notes in the margin of your lab manual.

## Discussion

1. What are the key characteristics shared by all gymnosperms?

2. What is the ecological role of conifers in forest systems?

3. What economically important products are provided by conifers?

## Lab Study B. Pine Life Cycle

### Materials

living or preserved pine branch,
    male and female cones
    (1, 2, and 3 years old)
fresh or dried pine pollen or
    prepared slide of pine pollen

coverslips
prepared slides of male and female
    pine cones
colored pencils
slides

 Review the pine life cycle (Figure 1) before you begin. Follow along as you complete the exercise.

### Introduction

All gymnosperms are **wind-pollinated** trees or shrubs, most bearing unisexual, male, and female reproductive structures on different parts of the same plant. Gymnosperms are **heterosporous**, producing two kinds of spores: male **microspores**, which develop into **pollen**, and female **megaspores.** The megaspore develops into the female gametophyte, which is not free-living as with ferns but retained within the **megasporangium** and nourished by the sporophyte parent plant. Numerous pollen grains (the male gametophytes) are produced in each **microsporangium,** and when they are mature they are released into the air and conveyed by wind currents to the female cone. **Pollen tubes** grow through the tissue of the megasporangium, and the **sperm nucleus** is released to fertilize the egg. After fertilization, development results in the formation of an **embryo.** A **seed** is a dormant embryo embedded in nutrient tissue of the female gametophyte and surrounded by the hardened sporangium wall, or **seed coat.**

 Having trouble with life cycles? The key to success is to determine where meiosis occurs and to remember the ploidal level for the gametophyte and sporophyte.

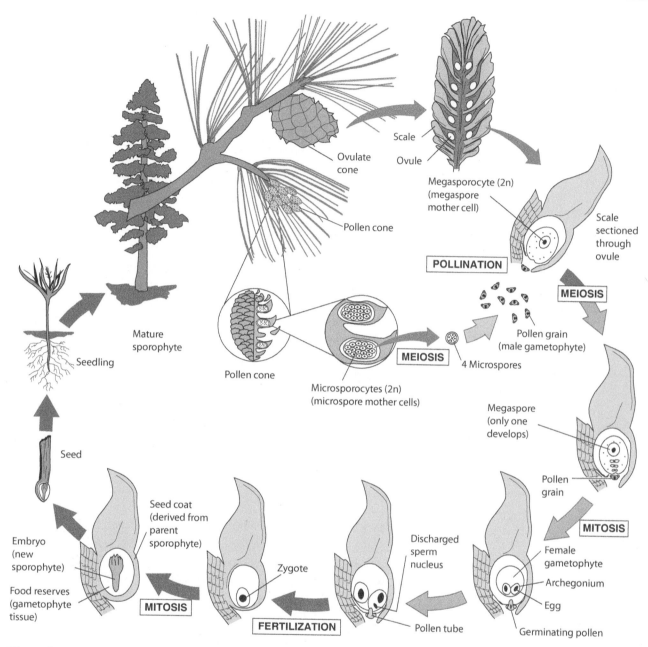

**Figure 1.**

**Pine life cycle.** Observe the structures and processes as described in Exercise 1. *Using colored pencils, indicate the structures that are haploid or diploid. Circle the terms* mitosis, meiosis, *and* fertilization.

## Procedure

1. Pine sporophyte.

   a. Examine the pine branch and notice the arrangement of leaves in a bundle. A new twig at the end of the branch is in the process of producing new clusters of leaves. Is this plant haploid or diploid?

b. Examine the small **cones** produced at the end of the pine branch on this specimen or others in lab. Recall that cones contain clusters of sporangia. What important process occurs in the sporangia?

c. Locate an ovulate cone and a pollen cone. Elongated male **pollen cones** are present only in the spring, producing pollen within overlapping bracts, or scales. The small, more rounded female cones (which look like miniature pine cones) are produced on stem tips in the spring and are called **ovulate cones.** Female cones persist for several years. Observe the overlapping scales, which contain the sporangia.

d. In the margin of your lab manual, sketch observations for future reference.

2. Male gametophyte—development in pollen cones.

a. Examine a longitudinal section of the pollen cone on a prepared slide and identify its parts. Observe that pollen cones are composed of radiating scales, each of which carries two elongated sacs on its lower surface. The sacs are the **microsporangia. Microsporocytes** (microspore mother cells) within microsporangia divide by meiosis. Each produces four haploid **microspores,** which develop into **pollen grains.**

b. Observe a slide of pine pollen. If pollen is available, you can make a wet mount. Note the wings on either side of the grain. The pollen grain is the greatly reduced male gametophyte. The outer covering of the pollen is desiccation resistant. Once mature, pollen will be wind dispersed, sifting down into the scales of the female cones.

c. Sketch, in the margin of your lab manual, observations for future reference.

3. Female gametophyte—development in ovulate cones.

a. Examine a longitudinal section of a young ovulate cone on a prepared slide. Note the **ovule** (containing the megasporangium) on the upper surface of the scales. Diploid **megasporocytes** (megaspore mother cells) contained inside will produce haploid **megaspores,** the first cells of the gametophyte generation. In the first year of ovulate cone development, pollen sifts into the soft bracts (pollination) and the pollen tube begins to grow, digesting the tissues of the ovule.

b. Observe a second-year cone at your lab bench. During the second year, the ovule develops a multicellular female gametophyte with two archegonia in which an egg will form. Fertilization will not occur until the second year, when the pollen tube releases a sperm nucleus into the archegonium, where it unites with the egg to form the **zygote.** In each ovule only one of the archegonia and its zygote develops into a seed.

c. Observe a mature cone at your lab bench. The development of the embryo sporophyte usually takes another year. The female gametophyte will provide nutritive materials stored in the seed for the early stages of growth. The outer tissues of the ovule will harden to form the **seed coat.**

d. In the margin of your lab manual, sketch observations for future reference.

## Results

1. Review the structures and processes observed.
2. Using colored pencils, indicate the structures of the pine life cycle in Figure 1 that are haploid or diploid, and circle the processes of mitosis, meiosis, and fertilization.

## Discussion

1. What is the function of the wings on the pollen grain?

2. Why is wind-dispersed pollen an important phenomenon in the evolution of plants?

3. Are microspores and megaspores produced by mitosis or meiosis?

4. Can you think of at least two ways in which pine seeds are dispersed?

5. One of the major trends in plant evolution is the reduction in size of the gametophytes. Describe the male and female gametophyte in terms of size and location.

---

# EXERCISE 2
# Angiosperms

---

All flowering plants (angiosperms) are classified in the phylum **Anthophyta** (Gk. *anthos,* "flower"). A unique characteristic of angiosperms is the **carpel,** a vessel in which ovules are enclosed. After fertilization, the ovule develops into a seed (as in the gymnosperms), while the carpel matures into a fruit (unique to angiosperms). Other important aspects of angiosperm reproduction include additional reduction of the gametophyte, double fertilization, and an increase in the rapidity of the reproduction process.

The **flowers** of angiosperms are composed of male and female reproductive structures, which are frequently surrounded by attractive or protective leaflike structures collectively known as the **perianth**. The flower functions both to protect the developing gametes and to ensure pollination and fertilization. Although many angiosperm plants are self-fertile, cross-fertilization is important in maintaining genetic diversity. Plants, rooted and stationary, often require transfer agents to complete fertilization. A variety of insects, birds, and mammals transfer pollen from flower to flower. The pollen then germinates into a pollen tube and grows through the female carpel to deliver the sperm to the egg.

Plants must attract pollinators to the flower. What are some features of flowers that attract pollinators? Color and scent are important, as is the shape of the flower. Nectar and pollen provide nutritive rewards for the pollinators as well. The shape and form of some of the flowers are structured to accommodate pollinators of specific size and structure, providing landing platforms, guidelines, and even special mechanisms for the placement of pollen on body parts. While the flower is encouraging the visitation by one type of pollinator, it also may be excluding visitation by others. The more specific the relationship between flower and pollinator, the more probable that the pollen of that species will be successfully transferred. But many successful flowers have no specific adaptations for particular pollinators and are visited by a wide variety of pollinators.

Some plants do not have colorful, showy flowers and are rather inconspicuous, often dull in color, and lacking a perianth. These plants are usually wind-pollinated, producing enormous quantities of pollen and adapted to catch pollen in the wind.

The origin and diversification of angiosperms cannot be understood apart from the coevolutionary role of animals in the reproductive process. Colorful petals, strong scents, nectars, food bodies, and unusual perianth shapes all relate to pollinator visitation. Major trends in the evolution of angiosperms involve the development of mechanisms to exploit a wide variety of pollinators.

In Lab Study A, you will investigate a variety of flowers, observing their shape, structure, and traits that might attract pollinators of various kinds. Following this, in Lab Study B, you will use a key to identify the probable pollinators for some of these flowers. You will follow the life cycle of the lily in Lab Study C and complete the lab by using another key to identify types of fruits and their dispersal mechanisms.

## Lab Study A. Flower Morphology

### Materials

living flowers provided by the instructor and/or students
stereoscopic microscope

### Introduction

Working in teams of two students, you will investigate the structure of the flower (Figure 2). The instructor will provide a variety of flowers, and you may have brought some with you to lab. You will need to take apart each flower carefully to determine its structure, since it is unlikely that all your flowers will follow the simple diagram used to illustrate the structures. Your observations will be the basis for predicting probable pollinators in Lab Study B.

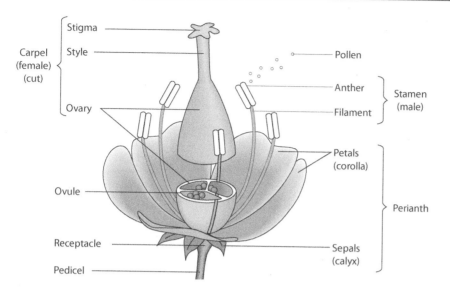

**Figure 2.**
**Flower structures.** Determine the structures of flowers in the laboratory by reviewing this general diagram.

## Procedure

1. Examine fresh flowers of four different species, preferably with different floral characteristics.

2. Identify the parts of each flower using Figure 2 and the list provided following the heading Floral Parts. You may be able to determine the floral traits for large, open flowers by simply observing. However, most flowers will require that you remove the floral structures from the outside toward the center of the flower. Some flowers or structures may require the use of the stereoscopic microscope. For example, the ovary is positively identified by the presence of tiny crystal-like ovules, and these are best seen with the stereoscopic scope.

3. In the margin of your lab manual, sketch any flower shapes or structures that you might need to refer to in the future.

4. Record the results of your observations in Table 3. You will determine pollinators in Lab Study B.

### Floral Parts

**Pedicel:** stalk that supports the flower.

**Receptacle:** tip of the pedicel where the flower parts attach.

**Sepal:** outer whorl of bracts, which may be green, brown, or colored like the petals; may appear as small scales or be petal-like.

**Calyx:** all the sepals, collectively.

**Petal:** colored, white, or even greenish whorl of bracts located just inside the sepals.

**Corolla:** all the petals, collectively.

**Stamen:** pollen-bearing structure, composed of filament and anther.

**Filament:** thin stalk that supports the anther.

**Anther:** pollen-producing structure.

**Carpel:** female reproductive structure, composed of the stigma, style, and ovary, often pear-shaped and located in the center of the flower.

**Stigma:** receptive tip of the carpel, often sticky or hairy, where pollen is placed; important to pollen germination.

**Style:** tissue connecting stigma to ovary, often long and narrow, but may be short or absent; pollen must grow through this tissue to fertilize the egg.

**Ovary:** base of carpel; protects ovules inside, matures to form the fruit.

### Results

Summarize your observations of flower structure in Table 3.

**Table 3**
Flower Morphology and Pollinators

| Features | Plant Names | | | |
|---|---|---|---|---|
| | 1 | 2 | 3 | 4 |
| Number of petals | | | | |
| Number of sepals | | | | |
| Parts absent (petals, stamens, etc.) | | | | |
| Color | | | | |
| Scent (+/-) | | | | |
| Nectar (+/-) | | | | |
| Shape (including corolla shape: tubular, star, etc.) | | | | |
| Special features (landing platform, guidelines, nectar spur, etc.) | | | | |
| Predicted pollinator (see Lab Study B) | | | | |

## Discussion

What structures or characteristics did you observe in your (or other teams')
investigations that you predict are important to pollination?

---

 **Student Media Videos—Ch.30: Flower Blooming
(Time Lapse); Flowering Plant Life Cycle**

---

# Lab Study B. Pollinators

## Materials

living flowers provided by the instructor and/or students
stereoscopic microscope

## Introduction

Flowers with inconspicuous sepals and petals are usually pollinated by
wind. Most showy flowers are pollinated by animals. Some pollinators tend
to be attracted to particular floral traits, and, in turn, some groups of plants
have coevolved with a particular pollination agent that ensures successful
reproduction. Other flowers are generalists, pollinated by a variety of organisms, and still others may be visited by only one specific pollinator.
Based on the floral traits that attract common pollinators (bees, flies, but-
terflies, and hummingbirds), you will predict the probable pollinator for
some of your flowers using a dichotomous key. (Remember, *dichotomous*
refers to the branching pattern and means "divided into two parts.")

In biology, we use a key to systematically separate groups of organisms
based on sets of characteristics. Most keys are based on couplets, or pairs
of characteristics, from which you must choose one or the other, thus, the
term *dichotomous*. For example, the first choice of characteristics in a couplet might be *plants with showy flowers and a scent*, and the other choice in
the pair might be *plants with tiny, inconspicuous flowers with no scent*. You
must choose one or the other statement. In the next step, you would
choose from a second pair of statements listed directly below your first
choice. With each choice, you would narrow the group more and more until, as in this case, the pollinator is identified. *Each couplet or pair of statements from which you must choose will be identified by the same letter or
number.*

## Key to Pollination

I. Sepals and petals reduced or inconspicuous; feathery or relatively large stigma; flower with no odor **wind**

II. Sepals and/or petals large, easily identified; stigma not feathery; flower with or without odor

  A. Sepals and petals white or subdued (greenish or burgundy); distinct odor

    1. Odor strong, heavy, sweet **moth**

    2. Odor strong, fermenting or fruitlike; flower parts and pedicel strong **bat**

    3. Odor of sweat, feces, or decaying meat **fly**

  B. Sepals and/or petals colored; odor may or may not be present

    1. Flower shape regular or irregular,* but not tubular

      a. Flower shape irregular; sepals or petals blue, yellow, or orange; petal adapted to serve as a "landing platform"; may have dark lines on petals; sweet, fragrant odor **bee**

      b. Flower shape regular; odor often fruity, spicy, sweet, or carrionlike **beetle**

    2. Flower shape tubular

      a. Strong, sweet odor **butterfly**

      b. Little or no odor; flower usually red **hummingbird**

*A regular flower shape is one that has radial symmetry (like a daisy or carnation), with similar parts (such as petals) having similar size and shape. Irregular flowers have bilateral symmetry.

## Procedure

Using the key above, classify the flowers used in Lab Study A based on their floral traits and method of pollination.

## Results

1. Record your results in Table 3.
2. If you made sketches of any of your flowers, you may want to indicate the pollinator associated with that flower.

## Discussion

1. Review the Key to Pollination and describe the characteristics of flowers that are adapted for pollination by each of the following agents:

  a. wind


  b. hummingbird


  c. bat

2. Discuss with your lab partner other ways in which keys are used in biology. Record your answers in the space provided.

**Student Media Videos—Ch.30: Bee Pollinating; Bat Pollinating Agave Plant**

# Lab Study C. Angiosperm Life Cycle

## Materials

pollen tube growth medium in
  dropper bottles
dropper bottle of water
petri dish with filter paper to
  fit inside
prepared slides of lily anthers
  and ovary

dissecting probe
brush bristles
compound microscope
flowers for pollen

## Introduction

In this lab study, you will study the life cycle of flowering plants, including the formation of pollen, pollination, fertilization of the egg, and formation of the seed and fruit. You will also investigate the germination of the pollen grain as it grows toward the egg cell.

**Refer to Figures 2 (flower structures) and 3 (angiosperm life cycle) as you complete the exercise.**

## Procedure

1. Pollen grain—the male gametophyte.
   a. Examine a prepared slide of a cross section through the **stamens** of *Lilium*. The slide shows six anthers and may include a centrally located ovary that contains ovules.
   b. Observe a single **anther**, which is composed of four **anther sacs** (microsporangia). Note the formation of **microspores** (with a single nucleus) from diploid **microsporocytes** (microspore mother cells). You may also see mature **pollen grains** with two nuclei.
2. Development of the female gametophyte.
   a. Examine a prepared slide of the *Lilium* ovary and locate the developing ovules. Each **ovule**, composed of the megasporangium and other tissues, contains a diploid **megasporocyte** (megaspore mother cell), which produces **megaspores** (haploid), only one of which survives. The megaspore will divide three times by mitosis to produce the eight nuclei in the **embryo sac**, which is the greatly reduced female gametophyte. Note that angiosperms do not even produce an archegonium.

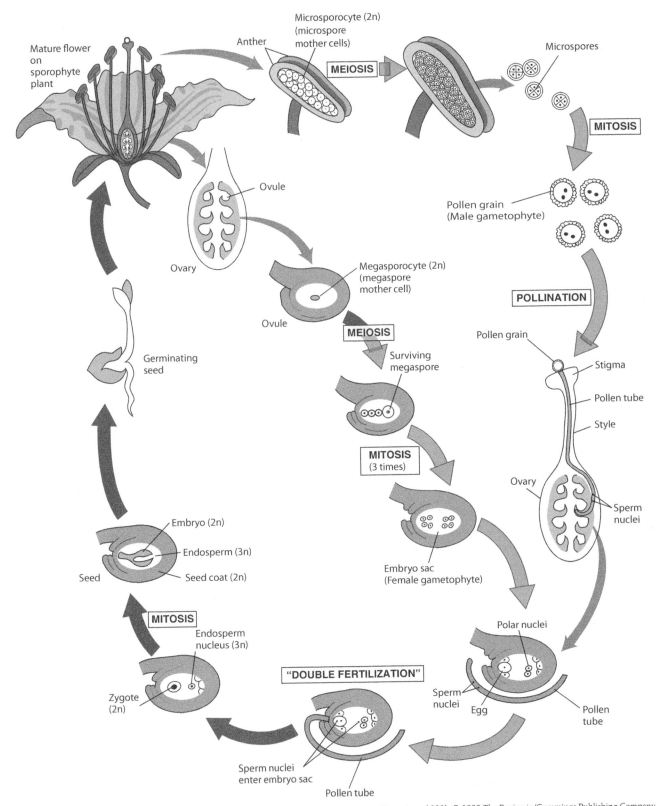

Adapted from N. Campbell, J. Reece, and L. Mitchell, *Biology,* 5th ed. (Menlo Park, CA: Benjamin/Cummings, 1999), © 1999 The Benjamin/Cummings Publishing Company.

**Figure 3.**
**Angiosperm life cycle.** Observe the structures and processes as described in Exercise 2. *Using colored pencils, indicate the structures that are haploid or diploid. Circle the terms* mitosis, meiosis, *and* double fertilization.

b. Your slide will not contain all stages of development, and it is almost impossible to find a section that includes all eight nuclei. Locate the three nuclei near the opening to the ovule. One of these is called the **egg cell**. The two nuclei in the center are the **polar nuclei** (or central cell).

3. Pollination and fertilization.

When pollen grains are mature, the anthers split and the pollen is released. When pollen reaches the stigma, it germinates to produce a **pollen tube,** which grows down the style and eventually comes into contact with the opening to the ovule. During this growth, one pollen nucleus divides into two **sperm nuclei.** One sperm nucleus fuses with the egg to form the **zygote,** and the second fuses with the two polar nuclei to form the triploid **endosperm,** which will develop into a rich nutritive material for the support and development of the embryo. The fusion of the two sperm nuclei with nuclei of the embryo sac is referred to as **double fertilization.** Formation of triploid endosperm and double fertilization are unique to angiosperms.

Once the pollen grain is deposited on the stigma of the flower, it must grow through the stylar tissue to reach the ovule. You will examine pollen tube growth by placing pollen in pollen growth medium to stimulate germination. Pollen from some plants germinates easily; for others a very specific chemical environment is required. Work with a partner, following the next steps.

a. Using a dissecting probe, transfer some pollen from the anthers of one of the plants available in the lab to a slide on which there are 2 to 3 drops of pollen tube growth medium and a few brush bristles or grains of sand (to avoid crushing the pollen). Add a coverslip. Alternatively, touch an anther to the drop of medium, then add brush bristles and a coverslip.

b. Examine the pollen under the compound microscope. Observe the shape and surface features of the pollen.

c. Prepare a humidity chamber by placing moistened filter paper in a petri dish. Place the slide in the petri dish, and place it in a warm environment.

d. Examine the pollen after 30 minutes and again after 60 minutes to observe pollen tube growth. The pollen tubes should appear as long, thin tubes extending from the surface or pores in the pollen grain.

e. Record your results in Table 4 in the Results section. Indicate the plant name and the times when pollen tube germination was observed.

4. Seed and fruit development.

The zygote formed at fertilization undergoes rapid mitotic phyla, forming the embryo. The endosperm also divides; the mature ovule forms a seed. At the same time, the surrounding ovary and other floral tissues are forming the fruit. In Lab Study D, you will investigate the types of fruits and their function in dispersal.

## Results

1. Review the structures and processes observed in the angiosperm life cycle, Figure 3. Indicate the haploid and diploid structures in the life cycle, using two different colored pencils.

Having trouble with life cycles? The key to success is to determine where meiosis occurs and to remember the ploidal level for the gametophyte and sporophyte.

2. Sketch observations of slides in the margin of your lab manual for later reference.
3. Record the results of pollen germination studies in Table 4. Compare your results with those of other teams who used different plants. This is particularly important if your pollen did not germinate.

**Table 4**
Results of Pollen Germination Studies

| Plant Name | 30 min(+/-) | 60 min(+/-) |
|---|---|---|
|  |  |  |

**Discussion**

1. What part of the life cycle is represented by the mature pollen grain?

2. How does the female gametophyte in angiosperms differ from the female gametophyte in gymnosperms?

3. Do you think that all pollen germinates indiscriminately on all stigmas? How might pollen germination and growth be controlled?

# Lab Study D. Fruits and Dispersal

## Materials

variety of fruits provided by the instructor and/or students

## Introduction

The seed develops from the ovule, and inside is the embryo and its nutritive tissues. The fruit develops from the ovary or from other tissues in the flower. It provides protection for the seeds, and both the seed and the fruit may be involved in dispersal of the sporophyte embryo.

## Procedure

1. Examine the fruits and seeds on demonstration.
2. Use the Key to Fruits on the next page to help you complete Table 5. Remember to include the dispersal mechanisms for fruits and their seeds in the table.

## Results

1. Record in Table 5 the fruit type for each of the fruits keyed. Share results with other teams so that you have information for all fruits in the lab.

## Table 5
Fruit Types and Dispersal Mechanisms

| Plant Name | Fruit Type | Dispersal Method |
|---|---|---|
|  |  |  |

2. For each fruit, indicate the probable method of dispersal—for example, wind, water, gravity, ingestion by birds, mammals, or insects, or adhesion to fur and socks.
3. For some fruits, the seeds rather than the fruit are adapted for dispersal. In the milkweed, for example, the winged seeds are contained in a dry ovary. Indicate in Table 5 if the seeds have structures to enhance dispersal. Recall that seeds are inside fruits. The dandelion "seed" is really a fruit with a fused ovary and seed coat.

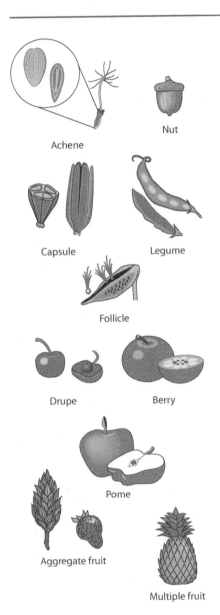

Achene

Nut

Capsule

Legume

Follicle

Drupe

Berry

Pome

Aggregate fruit

Multiple fruit

## Key to Fruits

I.  Simple fruits (one ovary)
   A.  Dry fruits (at maturity)
      1.  Fruits with one seed
         a.  Ovary wall and seed coat are fused    **achene***
         b.  Ovary wall hard or woody but can be separated from the seed    **nut**
      2.  Fruits with two to many seeds
         a.  Ovary with several cavities (seen when cut in cross section) and several too many seeds    **capsule**
         b.  Ovary with one cavity
         c.  Mature ovary opens along both sides    **legume**
         d.  Mature ovary opens along one side    **follicle**
   B.  Fleshy fruits
      1.  Ovary with one seed, which is surrounded by a very hard stone (outer covering of the seed is formed from the inner ovary wall)    **drupe**
      2.  Ovary with many seeds; does not have a "stone"
         a.  All of mature ovary tissue is soft and fleshy; surrounding flower tissue does not develop into fruit    **berry**†
         b.  Fleshy fruit develops in part from surrounding tissue of the flower (base of sepals and petals); therefore, ovary wall seen as "core" around seeds    **pome**
II.  Compound fruits (more than one ovary)
   A.  Fruit formed from ovaries of many flowers    **multiple fruit**
   B.  Fruit formed from several ovaries in one flower    **aggregate fruit**

*In the grass family, an achene is called a **grain**.
†Berries of some families have special names: citrus family = **hesperidium**; squash family = **pepo**.

## Discussion

1.  How might dry fruits be dispersed? Fleshy fruits?

2.  Describe the characteristics of an achene, drupe, and berry.

## Questions for Review

1. Complete Table 6. Compare mosses, ferns, conifers, and flowering plants relative to sexual life cycles and adaptations to the land environment. Return to Table 1 and modify your entries.

2. Identify the function of each of the following structures found in seed plants. Consider their function in the land environment.

   pollen grain:


   microsporangium:

   flower:


   carpel:


**Table 6**
Comparison of Important Characteristics of Land Plants

| Features |  Moss |  Fern |  Conifer |  Flowering Plant |
|---|---|---|---|---|
| Gametophyte or sporophyte dominant | | | | |
| Water required for fertilization | | | | |
| Vascular tissue (+/-) | | | | |
| Homosporous or heterosporous | | | | |
| Seed (+/−) | | | | |
| Pollen grain (+/−) | | | | |
| Fruit (+/−) | | | | |
| Examples | | | | |

seed:

fruit:

endosperm:

3. Plants have evolved a number of characteristics that attract animals and ensure pollination, but what are the benefits to animals in this relationship?

4. Why is internal fertilization essential for true terrestrial living?

## Applying Your Knowledge

1. Explain how the rise in prominence of one major group (angiosperms, for example) does not necessarily result in the total replacement of a previously dominant group (gymnosperms, for example).

2. In 1994 naturalists in Australia discovered a new genus and species of conifer, *Wollemia nobilis*, growing in a remote area not far from the city of Sydney. This was the first new conifer discovered since 1948. Wollemi pine (not really a pine) is in a family that had a global distribution 90 million years ago in the Cretaceous period. Scientists used a variety of different evidence to decide where this rare tree should be placed in the "Tree of Life." What evidence would be necessary to determine that this is in the phylum Coniferophyta?

To support the conservation of this ecosystem and three groups of trees (less than 100 individuals), botanical gardens are propagating these trees for sale. Although seeds have been collected, the commercially available plants are from cuttings and tissue culture. Based on your understanding of the life cycle of conifers, why is it not practical to reproduce Wollemi pines from seed or even to sell the seeds?

3. Your neighbor's rose garden is being attacked by Japanese beetles, so she dusts her roses with an insecticide. Now, to her dismay, she realizes that the beans and squash plants in her vegetable garden are flowering, but are no longer producing vegetables. She knows beetles feed on leaves of roses and squash plants. What is the problem? Explain to your neighbor the relationship among flowers, fruits (vegetables, in the gardening language), and insects.

4. Seed plants provide food, medicine, fibers, beverages, building materials, dyes, and psychoactive drugs. Using web resources, your textbook, and library references, describe examples of human uses of plants in Table 7. Indicate whether your example is a gymnosperm or angiosperm. Based on your research, what is the relative economic importance of angiosperms and gymnosperms?

**Table 7**
Uses of Seed Plants: Angiosperms and Gymnosperms

| Uses of Plants | Example | Angiosperm/ Gymnosperm |
|---|---|---|
| Food | | |
| Beverage | | |
| Medicine | | |
| Fibers | | |
| Materials | | |
| Dyes | | |
| Drugs | | |

5. Describe the major trends in the evolution of land plants.

## Investigative Extensions

Pollen germinates easily in the laboratory for some species and not at all for others. In some species, a biochemical signal is required from the stigma to initiate germination. Think about the advantages to the species if pollen germinates easily or if it requires a biochemical signal. You can investigate the factors that affect pollen germination and pollen tube growth using flowers available in the laboratory that did not germinate using a general growth medium. Develop an investigation based on questions generated by your observations in this lab topic or consider one of the following suggestions.

1. Are factors present in the stigma necessary for pollen germination? Mince a small piece of the stigma in sucrose and then add it to a slide with pollen in pollen growth medium. (The sucrose concentration in the growth medium can also be varied, since this may affect pollen germination). Compare pollen germination using the stigma material from closely related species and then from those distantly related. For example, try different species of the Mustard Family or even different varieties of one species of *Brassica*. Remember that Fast Plants (*B. rapa*) are mustards as is *Arabadopsis*, another plant used in genetic studies.

2. What essential micronutrients are needed for pollen germination? Some species are sensitive to micronutrients in the growth medium, including boron and calcium. Research various growth media and test these with flowers that failed to germinate. Which of the micronutrients in the growth medium is necessary for pollen germination in your plants? Prepare growth medium omitting one of each of the components and observe pollen germination.

3. How do environmental factors, such as temperature and light, affect the rate of pollen tube growth?

## Student Media Activities and Investigations

**Activities**—Ch.29: Terrestrial Adaptations of Plants; Highlights of Plant Phylogeny; Ch.30: Pine Life Cycle; Angiosperm Life Cycle; Ch.38: Seed and Fruit Development
**Investigations**—Ch.30: How Are Trees Identified by Their Leaves? Ch.38: What Tells Desert Seeds When to Germinate?
www.masteringbio.com

## References

Berg, L. R. *Introductory Botany: Plants, People and the Environment,* 2nd ed. Belmont, CA: Thomson Brooks/ Cole, 2007.

Levetin, E. and K. McMahon. *Plants and Society,* 4th ed. New York: McGraw Hill Co., 2006.

Mauseth, J. D. *Botany: An Introduction to Plant Biology,* 3rd ed. Sudbury, MA: Jones and Bartlett Publishers, 2003.

McLoughlin, S. and V. Vajda. "Ancient Wollemi Pines Resurgent." *American Scientist,* 2005. Vol. 93, pp. 540–547.

Raven, P. H., R. F. Evert, and S. E. Eichhorn. *Biology of Plants,* 7th ed. New York: W. H. Freeman Publishers, 2004.

Rui, M. *The Pollen Tube: A Cellular and Molecular Perspective,* New York: Springer, 2006.

# Websites

Interesting and informative sites describing human uses of plants. *Wayne's Word: A Newsletter of Natural History Trivia:*
http://daphne.palomar.edu/wayne/wayne.htm

Tree of Life Project includes phylogeny of living organisms, movies, references, current research, and ideas for independent investigations:
http://tolweb.org/tree?group=Spermatopsida& contgroup=Embryophytes

University of California Berkeley Museum of Palentology site with images and resources for both living and fossil seed plants:
http://www.ucmp.berkeley.edu/plants/plantae.html

Images, maps and additional links for plants of North America:
http://npdc.usda.gov/

University of Michigan Dearborn site for the uses of plants by Native Americans:
http://herb.umd.umich.edu/

Society for Economic Botany:
http://www.econbot.org/_welcome_/to_seb.php

Plant Conservation Alliance site with projects, medicinal and other plant uses:
http://www.nps.gov/plants/

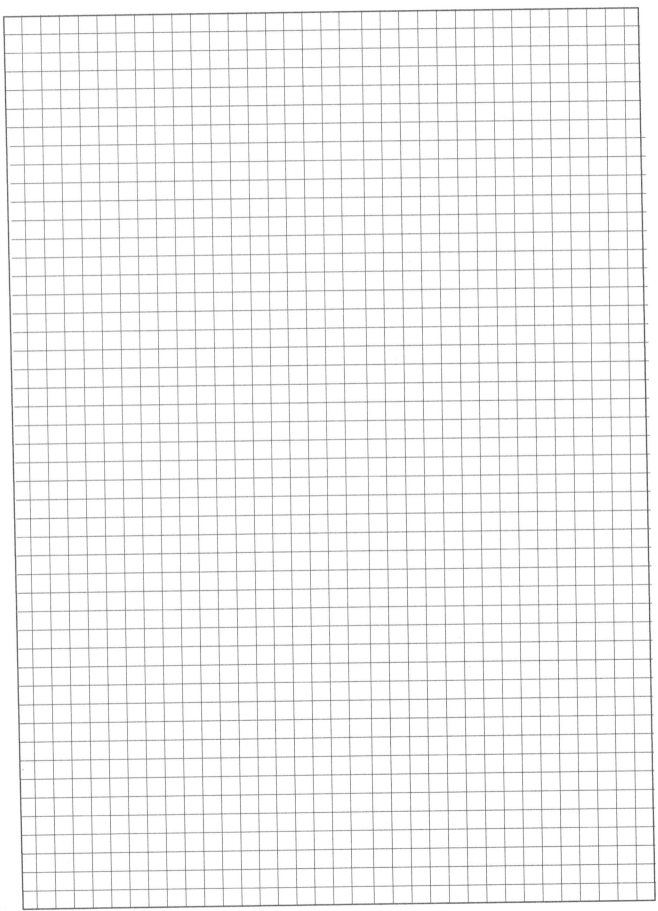

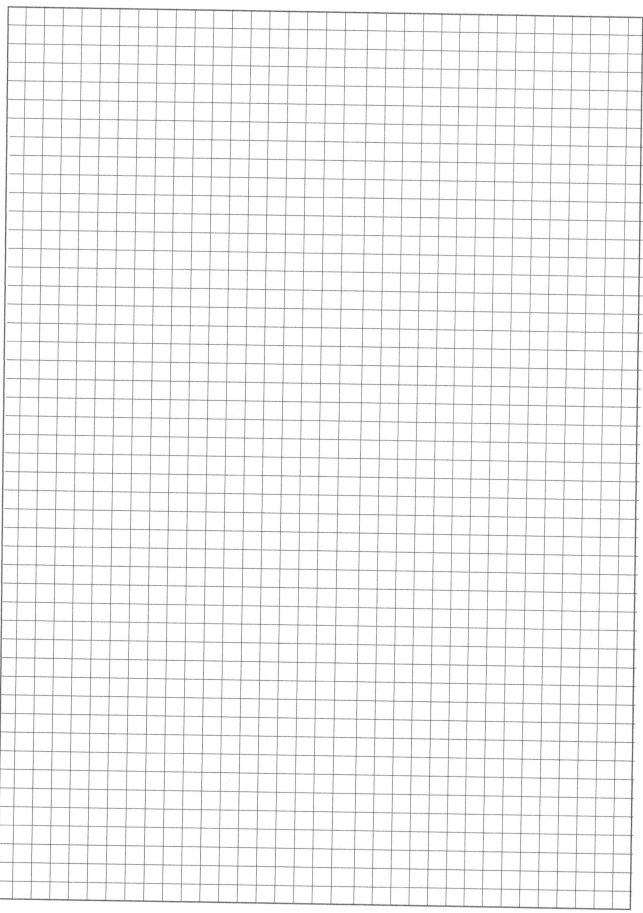

# Animal Diversity: Porifera, Cnidaria, Platyhelminthes, Annelida, and Mollusca

## Laboratory Objectives

After completing this lab topic, you should be able to:

1. Compare the anatomy of the representative animals, describing similarities and differences in organs and body form that allow the animal to carry out body functions.
2. Discuss the impact of molecular studies on traditional phylogenetic trees.
3. Discuss the relationship between body form and the lifestyle or niche of the organism.

## Introduction

Animals are classified in the domain **Eukarya**, kingdom **Animalia** (clade Metazoa). They are multicellular organisms and are **heterotrophic,** meaning that they obtain food by ingesting other organisms or their by-products. Careful study of comparative anatomy, embryology, and most recently, genetic and molecular data, reveals many similarities in structure and development. Collectively, this evidence implies an ancestral evolutionary relationship among all animals. Animals are thought to have arisen about 575 million years ago, with most body forms appearing by the end of the Cambrian period. Scientists recognize over 35 major groups of present-day animals based on differences in body architecture. In this lab topic you will investigate body form and function in examples of nine major groups of animals. You will use these investigations to ask and answer questions comparing general features of morphology and relating these features to the lifestyle of each animal.

Since the beginning of the scientific study of animals, scientists have attempted to sort and group closely related organisms. Taxonomists have divided the metazoa into two major groups: **Parazoa,** which includes the sponges, and **Eumetazoa,** which includes all other animals. This division is made because the body form of sponges is so different from that of other animals that most biologists think that sponges are not closely related to any other animal groups.

Animals in Eumetazoa differ in physical characteristics, such as symmetry which may be **radial** (parts arranged around a central axis), or **bilateral** (right and left halves are mirror images). Other differences include the type of body cavity (coelom) and such basic embryological differences as the number of germ

From *Investigating Biology Laboratory Manual,* Sixth Edition, Judith G. Morgan and M. Eloise Brown Carter. Copyright © 2008 by Pearson Education, Inc. Published by Benjamin Cummings, Inc. All rights reserved.

layers present in the embryo and the embryonic development of the digestive tract. Some animals have a saclike body form with only one opening into a digestive cavity. Others have two outer openings, a mouth and an anus, and the digestive tract forms essentially a "tube within a tube." Those animals that are bilaterally symmetrical (clade Bilateria) are divided into two major groups, depending on differences in early development and the origin of the mouth and the anus. An embryonic structure, the blastopore, develops into a mouth in the **protostomes** and into an anus in the **deuterostomes.**

"Traditional" phylogenetic trees have been challenged by the results of molecular studies, particularly evidence from analysis of the gene coding for ribosomal RNA (rRNA). This is true not only for protists, but also for animals. Particularly in the protostomes, molecular studies have led to a regrouping of many traditionally established phylogenetic relationships. For example, for over 200 years zoology publications have assumed that annelids (segmented worms in the phylum Annelida) and arthropods (e.g., insects) are closely related based on their segmented bodies. Zoologists also noted, however, that annelids have developmental patterns similar to several groups that are not segmented. For example, annelids are like molluscs (e.g., clams) in having a developmental stage called the "trochophore larva." Recent molecular evidence helps to clarify this puzzle as it supports the hypothesis that annelids and molluscs are closely related, and separate from arthropods.

Molecular studies have led taxonomists to create two large groups within the protostomes, **Lophotrochozoa** and **Ecdysozoa.** Annelids, molluscs, and several more phyla not studied here are placed in the clade Lophotrochozoa. The name reflects the trochophore larvae found in annelids and molluscs. Also included in this clade are flatworms (phylum Platyhelminthes). Although flatworms lack such characteristics as a body cavity, the "tube-within-a-tube" body plan with mouth and anus, and elaborate internal organs, recent molecular evidence indicates that they should be grouped with annelids and molluscs in the Lophotrochozoa clade. Evidence from ribosomal DNA sequences indicates that roundworms or nematodes (phylum Nematoda), arthropods (phylum Arthropoda), and several other phyla belong in the clade Ecdysozoa. Animals in this clade undergo molting (ecdysis) or the shedding of an outer body cover. In nematodes this covering is called the **cuticle.** In arthropods the covering is the **exoskeleton.**

Another surprising result of rRNA and other molecular evidence is that the nature of the body cavity may not be a characteristic that indicates major phylogenetic branching. In traditional phylogenetic groupings, flatworms and nematodes were considered primitive, neither group having a true coelom. Ribosomal evidence has now moved nematodes to a different position with arthropods in the metazoan tree.

Figure 1a is a diagram showing organisms classified in the *traditional* organization of animal phylogeny. This phylogeny is based on *morphology* and *development*. Figure 1b is a diagram showing the *new molecular-based* phylogeny. The order of animals studied in this lab is based on Figure 1b, the molecular-based phylogeny. However, as you study the animals, note those morphological characteristics that were the basis of the traditional system of classification. These characteristics may give evidence of the influence of ecological events in the development of different morphologies. Be ready to discuss how these similarities or differences may have arisen secondarily or through secondary simplifications.

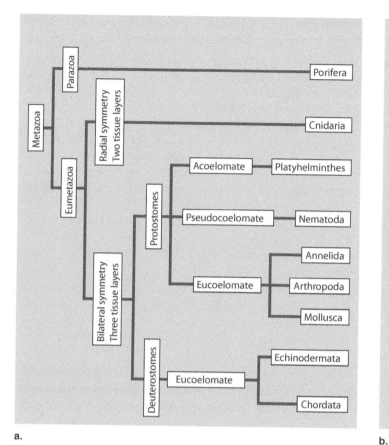

a.

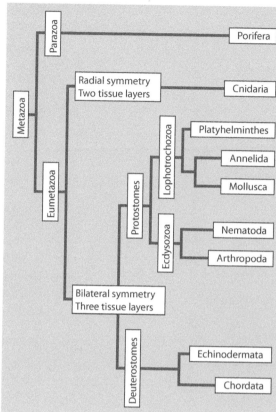

b.

**Figure 1.**

**Phylogenetic organization of animals.**

(a) A traditional phylogeny based on morphology and embryology. (b) Proposed phylogeny based on new molecular evidence. Protostomes are grouped in Lophotrochozoa or Ecdysozoa.

Much work remains to resolve the branching order within the lophotrochozoan and ecdysozoan clades. Scientists are collecting evidence from studies based on mitochondrial DNA sequencing, ribosomal genes, *Hox* genes, and genes coding for various proteins.

The animals you will study in this lab are the sponge, hydra, planarian, clamworm, earthworm, and clam (mussel). As you study each animal, relate your observations to the unifying themes of this lab: *phylogenetic relationships* and criteria that are the basis for animal classification, the *relationship between form and function,* and the *relationship of the environment and lifestyle to form and function.* The questions at the end of the lab topics will help you do this.

In your comparative study of these organisms, you will investigate 13 characteristics. Before you begin the dissections, become familiar with the following characteristics and their descriptions:

1. *Symmetry.* Is the animal (a) radially symmetrical (parts arranged around a central axis), (b) bilaterally symmetrical (right and left halves are mirror images), or (c) asymmetrical (no apparent symmetry)?

2. *Tissue organization.* Are cells organized into well-defined tissue layers (structural and functional units)? How many distinctive layers are present?

3. *Body cavity.* Is a body cavity present? A body cavity—the space between the gut and body wall—is present only in three-layered organisms, that is, in organisms with the embryonic germ layers ectoderm, mesoderm, and endoderm. There are three types of body forms related to the presence of a body cavity and its type (Figure 2).
   a. Acoelomate, three-layered bodies without a body cavity. Tissue from the mesoderm fills the space where a cavity might be; therefore, the tissue layers closely pack on one another.
   b. Pseudocoelomate, three-layered bodies with a cavity between the endoderm (gut) and mesoderm (muscle).
   c. Eucoelomate (coelomate), three-layered bodies with the coelom, or cavity, *within* the mesoderm (completely surrounded by mesoderm). In coelomate organisms, mesodermal membranes suspend the gut within the body cavity.

4. *Openings into the digestive tract.* Can you detect where food enters the body and digestive waste exits the body? Some animals have only one opening, which serves as both a mouth and an anus. Others have a body called a "tube within a tube," with an anterior mouth and a posterior anus.

5. *Circulatory system.* Does this animal have open circulation (the blood flows through coelomic spaces in the tissue as well as in blood vessels), or does it have closed circulation (the blood flows entirely through vessels)?

6. *Habitat.* Is the animal terrestrial (lives on land) or aquatic (lives in water)? Aquatic animals may live in marine (sea) or fresh water.

7. *Organs for respiration (gas exchange).* Can you detect the surface where oxygen enters the body and carbon dioxide leaves the body? Many animals use their skin for respiration. Others have special organs, including gills in aquatic organisms and lungs in terrestrial organisms. Insects have a unique system for respiration, using structures called *spiracles* and *tracheae*.

8. *Organs for excretion.* How does the animal rid its body of nitrogenous waste? In many animals, these wastes pass out of the body through the skin by diffusion. In others, there are specialized structures, such as Malpighian tubules, lateral excretory canals, lateral canals with flame cells, structures called *nephridia*, and kidneys.

9. *Type of locomotion.* Does the organism swim, crawl on its belly, walk on legs, burrow in the substrate, or fly? Does it use cellular structures, such as cilia, to glide its body over the substrate?

10. *Support systems.* Is there a skeleton present? Is it an endoskeleton (inside the epidermis or skin of the animal), or is it an exoskeleton (outside the body wall)? Animals with no true skeleton can be supported by water: Fluid within and between cells and in body chambers such as a gastrovascular cavity or coelom provides a "hydrostatic skeleton."

11. *Segmentation.* Can you observe linear repetition of similar body parts? The repetition of similar units, or segments, is called *segmentation*. Segments can be more similar (as in the earthworm) or less similar (as in a lobster). Can you observe any degree of segmentation? Have various segments become modified for different functions?

12. *Appendages.* Are there appendages (organs or parts attached to a trunk or outer body wall)? Are these appendages all along the length of the

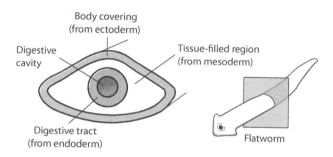

Body covering
(from ectoderm)

Digestive
cavity

Tissue-filled region
(from mesoderm)

Digestive tract
(from endoderm)

Flatworm

**a.** Acoelomate

**Figure 2.**

**Three types of body cavities.** (a) In acoelomate animals, the mesoderm fills the space where a cavity might be. (b) In pseudocoelomate animals, the body cavity lies between tissues derived from endoderm and mesoderm. (c) In eucoelomate (coelomate) animals, the body cavity is lined with mesoderm.

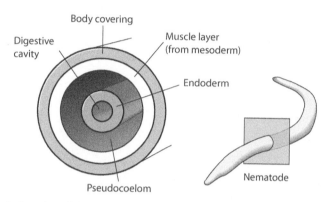

Body covering

Digestive
cavity

Muscle layer
(from mesoderm)

Endoderm

Pseudocoelom

Nematode

**b.** Pseudocoelomate

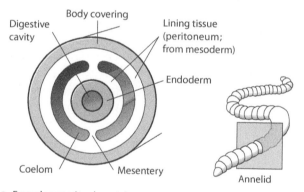

Body covering

Digestive
cavity

Lining tissue
(peritoneum;
from mesoderm)

Endoderm

Coelom

Mesentery

Annelid

**c.** Eucoelomate (coelomate)

Adapted from N. Campbell, *Biology,* 4th ed. (Menlo Park, CA: Benjamin/Cummings, 1996), © 1996 The Benjamin/Cummings Publishing Company.

body, or are they restricted to one area? Are they all similar, or are they modified for different functions?

13. *Type of nervous system.* Do you see a brain and nerve cord? Is there more than one nerve cord? What is the location of the nerve cord(s)? Are sensory organs or structures present? Where and how many? What purpose do such structures serve (for example, eyes for light detection)?

As you carefully study or dissect each organism, refer to these thirteen characteristics, observe the animal, and record your observations in the summary table. You may find it helpful to make sketches of difficult structures or dissections in the margin of your lab manual for future reference.

*Before you begin this study, become thoroughly familiar with dissection techniques, orientation terms, and planes and sections of the body. Be able to use the terms associated with bilateral symmetry—anterior, posterior, dorsal, ventral, proximal, and distal—as you dissect and describe your animals.*

 **Wear gloves while dissecting preserved animals.**

# EXERCISE 1
# Phylum Porifera—Sponges (*Scypha*)

## Materials

dissecting needle
compound microscope
stereoscopic microscope
preserved and dry bath sponges

prepared slide of *Scypha* in
longitudinal section
preserved *Scypha* in watch glass

## Introduction

Sponges are classified in a separate group, Parazoa, because of their unique body form. You will observe the unique sponge structure by observing first a preserved specimen and then a prepared slide of a section taken through the longitudinal axis of the marine sponge *Scypha*. You will observe other more complex and diverse sponges on demonstration.

## Procedure

1. Obtain the preserved sponge *Scypha* and observe its external characteristics using the stereoscopic microscope, comparing your observations with Figure 3a.

   a. Note the vaselike shape of the sponge and the **osculum,** a large opening to the body at one end. The end opposite the osculum attaches the animal to the substrate.

   b. Note the invaginations in the body wall, which form numerous folds and channels. You may be able to observe needlelike **spicules** around the osculum and protruding from the surface of the body. These spicules are made of calcium carbonate: They give support and protection to the sponge body and prevent small animals from entering the sponge's internal cavity.

2. Using the compound microscope, examine a prepared slide of a sponge body in longitudinal section and compare it with Figure 3b.

   a. Again, locate the osculum. This structure is not a mouth, as its name implies, but an opening used as an outlet for the current of water passing through the body wall and the **central cavity,** or **spongocoel.** The water enters the central cavity from channels and pores in the body. The central cavity is not a digestive tube or body cavity, but is only a channel for water.

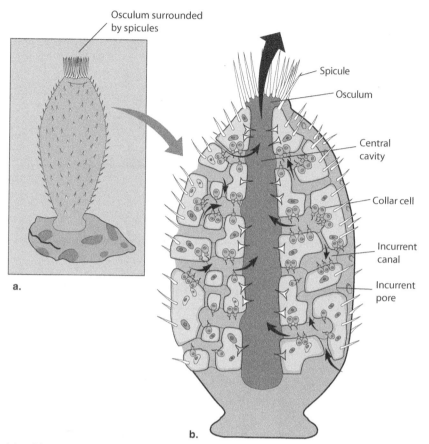

Osculum surrounded by spicules

a.

b.

Spicule

Osculum

Central cavity

Collar cell

Incurrent canal

Incurrent pore

**Figure 3.**

**The sponge *Scypha.*** (a) The entire sponge; (b) a longitudinal section through the sponge.

Adapted from L. Mitchell, J. Mutchmor, and W. Dolphin, *Zoology* (Menlo Park, CA: Benjamin/Cummings, 1988), © 1988 The Benjamin/Cummings Publishing Company.

b. Note the structure of the body wall. Are cells organized into definite tissue layers, or are they best described as a loose organization of various cell types? Various cells in the body wall carry out the functions of digestion, contractility, secretion of the spicules, and reproduction (some cells develop into sperm and eggs). One cell type unique to sponges is the **choanocyte,** or **collar cell.** These cells line the central cavity and the channels leading into it. Each collar cell has a flagellum extending from its surface. The collective beating of all flagella moves water through the sponge body. Small food particles taken up and digested by collar cells are one major source of nutrition for the sponge. How would you hypothesize about the movement of oxygen and waste throughout the sponge body and into and out of cells?

3. Observe examples of more complex sponges on demonstration. The body of these sponges, sometimes called "bath sponges," contains a complex series of large and small canals and chambers. The same cells that were described in *Scypha* are present in bath sponges, but, in addition to spicules, there is supportive material that consists of a soft proteinaceous substance called **spongin.** These sponges often grow to fit the

shape of the space where they live, and observing them gives you a good clue about the symmetry of the sponge body. How would you describe it?

## Results

Complete the summary table, filling in all information for sponge characteristics in the appropriate row.

---

EXERCISE 2

# Phylum Cnidaria—Hydras (*Hydra*)

## Materials

stereoscopic microscope
compound microscope
living *Hydra* culture
water flea culture
dropper bottles of water, 1% acetic acid, and methylene blue

prepared slide of *Hydra* sections
watch glass
depression slide
pipettes and bulbs
microscope slide and coverslip

## Introduction

Cnidarians are a diverse group of organisms, all of which have a **tissue grade** of organization, meaning that tissues, but no complex organs, are present. Included in this group are corals, jellies, sea anemones, and Portuguese men-of-war. Most species are marine; however, there are a few freshwater species. Two body forms are present in the life cycle of many of these animals—an umbrella-like, free-swimming stage, and a cylindrical, attached or stationary form. The stationary forms often grow into colonies of individuals. In this exercise you will observe some of the unique features of this group by observing the solitary, freshwater organism *Hydra*.

## Procedure

1. Place several drops of freshwater pond or culture water in a watch glass or depression slide. Use a dropper to obtain a living hydra from the class culture, and place the hydra in the drop of water. Using a stereoscopic microscope, observe the hydra structure and compare it with Figure 4a. Note any movement, the symmetry, and any body structures present. Note the **tentacles** that surround the "mouth," the only opening into the central cavity. Tentacles are used in capturing food and in performing a certain type of locomotion, much like a "handspring." To accomplish this

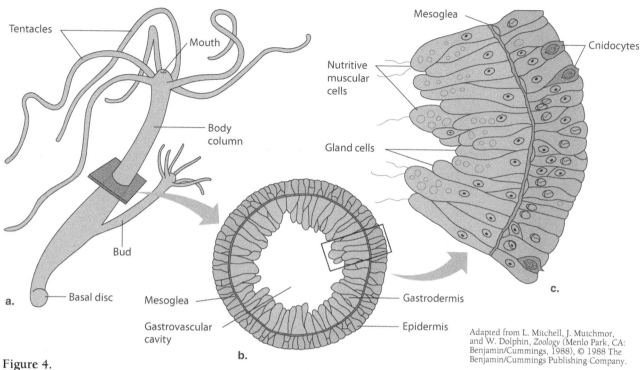

**Figure 4.**

*Hydra.* (a) A whole mount of *Hydra;* (b) enlargement showing a cross section through the body wall, revealing two tissue layers; and (c) further enlargement showing details of specialized cells in the body wall, including cnidocytes.

Adapted from L. Mitchell, J. Mutchmor, and W. Dolphin, *Zoology* (Menlo Park, CA: Benjamin/Cummings, 1988), © 1988 The Benjamin/Cummings Publishing Company.

motion, the hydra attaches its tentacles to the substrate and flips the basal portion of its body completely over, reattaching the base to a new position. If water fleas (*Daphnia*) are available, place one or two near the tentacles of the hydra and note the hydra's behavior. Set aside the hydra in the depression slide and return to it in a few moments.

2. Study a prepared slide of *Hydra* sections using the compound microscope and compare your observations with Figure 4b and 4c.

   Are definite tissue layers present? If so, how many?

   Given what you know of embryology, what embryonic layers would you guess give rise to the tissue layers of this animal's body?

3. Not visible with the microscope is a network of nerve cells in the body wall, which serves as the nervous system. There is no concentration of nerve cells into any kind of brain or nerve cord.

4. Observe the central cavity, called a **gastrovascular cavity.** Digestion begins in this water-filled cavity (**extracellular digestion**), but many food particles are drawn into cells in the **gastrodermis** lining the cavity, where **intracellular digestion** occurs.

5. Do you see signs of a skeleton or supportive system? How do you think the body is supported? Are appendages present?

6. Recalling the whole organism and observing this cross section, are organs for gas exchange present? How is gas exchange accomplished?

7. Do you see any organs for excretion?

8. Are specialized cell types seen in the layers of tissues?

Cnidarians have a unique cell type called **cnidocytes,** which contain a stinging organelle called a **nematocyst.** When stimulated, the nematocyst will evert from the cnidocyte with explosive force, trapping food or stinging predators. Look for these cells.

9. To better observe cnidocytes and nematocysts, turn your attention again to your living hydra and follow this procedure:

   a. Using a pipette, transfer the hydra to a drop of water on a microscope slide and carefully add a coverslip.

   b. Use your microscope to examine the hydra, first on low, then intermediate, and finally on high powers, focusing primarily on the tentacles. The cnidocytes will appear as swellings. If your microscope is equipped with phase contrast, switch to phase. Alternatively, add a drop of methylene blue to the edge of the coverslip. Locate several cnidocytes with nematocysts coiled inside.

   c. Add a drop of 1% acetic acid to the edge of the coverslip and, watching carefully using intermediate power, observe the rapid discharge of the nematocyst from the cnidocyte.

   d. Using high power, study the discharged nematocysts that will appear as long threads, often with large spines, or barbs, at the base of the thread.

## Results

Complete the summary table, recording all information for *Hydra* characteristics in the appropriate row.

## Discussion

What major differences have you detected between *Scypha* and *Hydra* body forms? List and describe them.

 Student Media Videos—Ch. 33: *Hydra* Building; *Hydra* Eating *Daphnia*; Jelly Swimming; Thimble Jellies

EXERCISE 3

# Phylum Platyhelminthes— Planarians (*Dugesia*)

## Materials

stereoscopic microscope
compound microscope
living planarian
watch glass

prepared slide of whole mount of
   planarian
prepared slide of planarian cross
   sections

## Introduction

The phylum Platyhelminthes (clade Lophotrochozoa) includes planarians, free-living flatworms; that is, they are not parasitic and their body is dorsoventrally flattened. They are found under rocks, leaves, and debris in freshwater ponds and creeks. They move over these surfaces using a combination of muscles in their body wall and cilia on their ventral sides.

## Procedure

1. Add a dropperful of pond or culture water to a watch glass. Use a dropper to obtain a living planarian from the class culture. Using your stereoscopic microscope, observe the planarian. Describe its locomotion. Is it directional? What is the position of its head? Does its body appear to contract?

As you observe the living planarian, you will see two striking new features with regard to symmetry that you did not see in the two phyla previously studied. What are they?

2. Add a *small* piece of fresh liver to the water near the planarian. The planarian may approach the liver and begin to feed by extending a long tubular **pharynx** out of the **mouth**, a circular opening on the ventral side of the body. If the planarian feeds, it will curve its body over the liver and extend the pharynx, which may be visible in the stereoscopic microscope.

   After observing the planarian's feeding behavior, return it to the culture dish, if possible, without the liver.

3. Using the lowest power on the compound microscope, observe the prepared slide of a whole planarian and compare it with Figure 5.

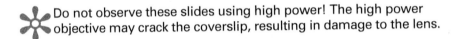

Do not observe these slides using high power! The high power objective may crack the coverslip, resulting in damage to the lens.

Examine the body for possible digestive tract openings. How many openings to the digestive tract are present?

Observe again the pharynx and the mouth. The pharynx lies in a **pharyngeal chamber** inside the mouth. The proximal end of the pharynx opens into a dark-colored, branched intestine. If the intestine has been stained on your slide, you will see the branching more easily.

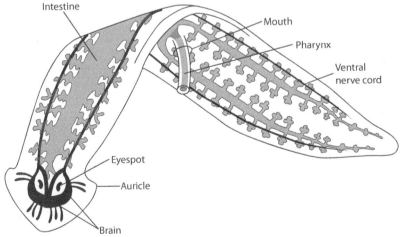

**Figure 5.**
**A planarian.** The digestive system consists of a mouth, a pharynx, and a branched intestine. A brain and two ventral nerve cords (plus transverse nerves connecting them, not shown) make up the nervous system.

Adapted from N. Campbell, J. Reece, and L. Mitchell, *Biology*, 5th ed. (Menlo Park, CA: Benjamin/Cummings, 1999), © 1999 The Benjamin/Cummings Publishing Company.

4. Continue your study of the whole planarian. The anterior blunt end of the animal is the head end. At each side of the head is a projecting **auricle.** It contains a variety of sensory cells, chiefly of touch and chemical sense. Between the two auricles on the dorsal surface are two pigmented **eyespots.** These are pigment cups into which retinal cells extend from the brain, with the photosensitive end of the cells inside the cup. Eyespots are sensitive to light intensities and the direction of a light source but can form no images. Beneath the eyespots are two cerebral ganglia that serve as the **brain.** Two ventral nerve cords extend posteriorly from the brain. These are connected by transverse nerves to form a ladderlike **nervous system.**

5. Study the prepared slide of cross sections of a planarian. You will have several sections on one slide. One section should have been taken at the level of the pharynx and pharyngeal chamber. Do you see a body cavity in any of the sections? (The pharyngeal chamber and spaces in the gut are not a body cavity.) What word describes this body cavity condition (see Figure 2a)?

    a. How many tissue layers can be detected? Speculate about their embryonic origin.

       Flatworms are the first group of animals to have three well-defined embryonic tissue layers, enabling them to have a variety of tissues and organs. Reproductive organs and excretory organs consisting of two lateral excretory canals and "flame cells" that move fluid through the canals are derived from the embryonic mesoderm. Respiratory, circulatory, and skeletal systems are lacking.

    b. How do you think the body is supported?

    c. How does gas exchange take place?

## Results

1. Diagram the flatworm as seen in a cross section at the level of the pharynx. Label the **epidermis, muscle** derived from **mesoderm,** the lining of the digestive tract derived from **endoderm,** the **pharynx,** and the **pharyngeal chamber.**

2. Complete the summary table, recording all information for planarian characteristics in the appropriate row.

**Discussion**

One of the major differences between Cnidaria and Platyhelminthes is radial versus bilateral symmetry. Discuss the advantage of radial symmetry for sessile (attached) animals and bilateral symmetry for motile animals.

---

# EXERCISE 4

# Phylum Annelida—Clamworms (*Nereis*) and Earthworms (*Lumbricus terrestris*)

The phylum Annelida (clade Lophotrochozoa) includes a diverse group of organisms inhabiting a variety of environments. Examples range in size from microscopic to several meters in length. Most species are marine, living free in the open ocean or burrowing in ocean bottoms. Others live in fresh water or in soils. One group of annelids, the leeches, are parasitic and live on the blood or tissues of their hosts. In this exercise, you will study the clamworm, a marine annelid, and the earthworm, a terrestrial species. Keep in mind features that are adaptations to marine and terrestrial habitats as you study these organisms.

## Lab Study A. Clamworms (*Nereis*)

### Materials

dissecting tools
dissecting pan
preserved clamworm

disposable gloves
dissecting pins

### Introduction

Species of *Nereis* (clamworms) are commonly found in mud flats and on the ocean floor. These animals burrow in sediments during the day and emerge to feed at night. As you observe the clamworm, note features that are characteristic of all annelids, as well as features that are special adaptations to the marine environment.

### Procedure

1. Observe the preserved, undissected clamworm and compare it with Figure 6. How would you describe the symmetry of this organism?

2. Determine the anterior and posterior ends. At the anterior end, the well-differentiated head bears **sensory appendages.** Locate the mouth, which leads into the digestive tract.

3. A conspicuous new feature of these organisms is the presence of **segmentation,** the division of the body along its length into segments. Posterior to the head region, the segments bear fleshy outgrowths called **parapodia.** Each parapodium contains several terminal bristles called **setae.** In Lab Study B, you will see that the earthworm has setae but does not have parapodia. Suggest functions for parapodia and setae in the marine clamworm.

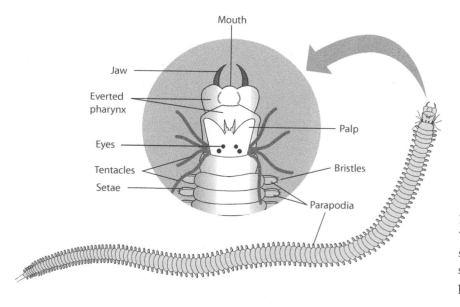

**Figure 6.**
**The clamworm, *Nereis*.** The head has sensory appendages, and each segment of the body bears two parapodia with setae.

4. Holding the animal in your hand and using sharp-pointed scissors, make a middorsal incision the full length of the body. Carefully insert the tip of the scissors and lift up with the tips as you cut. Pin the opened body in the dissecting pan but do not put pins through the head region.

5. Locate the **intestine.** Do you see the "tube-within-a-tube" body plan?

6. Two **muscle layers,** one inside the skin and a second lying on the surface of the intestine, may be visible with the stereoscopic microscope. With muscle in these two positions, what kind of coelom does this animal have (see Figure 2c)?

7. Continuing your observations with the unaided eye and the stereoscopic microscope, look for **blood vessels,** particularly a large vessel lying on the dorsal wall of the digestive tract. This vessel is contractile and propels the blood throughout the body. You should be able to observe smaller lateral blood vessels connecting the dorsal blood vessel with another on the ventral side of the intestine. As you will see, in the earthworm these connecting vessels are slightly enlarged as "hearts" around the anterior portion of the digestive tract (around the esophagus). This is not as obvious in *Nereis*. What is this type of circulatory system, with blood circulating through continuous closed vessels?

8. Gas exchange must take place across wet, thin surfaces. Do you see any organs for gas exchange (gills or lungs, for example)? How do you suspect that gas exchange takes place?

9. Do you see any signs of a skeleton? What would serve as support for the body?

10. Clamworms and earthworms have a small bilobed brain (a pair of ganglia) lying on the surface of the digestive tract at the anterior end of the worm. You can see this more easily in an earthworm.

## Lab Study B. Earthworms (*Lumbricus terrestris*)

### Materials

dissecting instruments
compound microscope
stereoscopic microscope

preserved earthworm
prepared slide of cross section
   of earthworm

## Introduction

*Lumbricus* species, commonly called *earthworms,* burrow through soils rich in organic matter. As you observe these animals, note features that are adaptations to the burrowing, terrestrial lifestyle.

## Procedure

1. Obtain a preserved earthworm and identify its anterior end by locating the mouth, which is overhung by a fleshy dorsal protuberance called the **prostomium.** The anus at the posterior end has no such protuberance. Also, a swollen glandular band, the **clitellum** (a structure that secretes a cocoon that holds eggs), is located closer to the mouth than to the anus (Figure 7).

   a. Using scissors, make a middorsal incision along the anterior third of the animal, as you did for *Nereis.* You can identify the dorsal surface in a couple of ways. The prostomium is dorsal, and the ventral surface of the worm is usually flattened, especially in the region of the clitellum. Cut to the prostomium. Pin the body open in a dissecting pan near the edge. You may need to cut through the septa that divide the body cavity into segments.

   b. Using a stereoscopic microscope or hand lens, look for the small **brain** just behind the prostomium on the surface of the digestive tract. Note the two nerves that pass from the brain around the pharynx and meet ventrally. These nerve tracts continue posteriorly as a **ventral nerve cord** lying in the floor of the coelom.

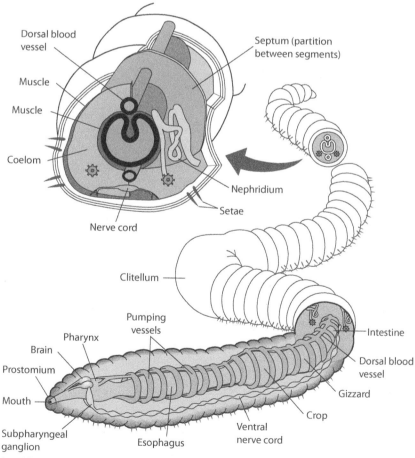

**Figure 7.**

**The earthworm.** The small brain leads to a ventral nerve cord. A pair of nephridia lie in each segment.

Adapted from N. Campbell, J. Reece, and L. Mitchell, *Biology,* 5th ed. (Menlo Park, CA: Benjamin/Cummings, 1999), © 1999 The Benjamin/Cummings Publishing Company.

c. Look for the large **blood vessel** on the dorsal wall of the digestive tract. You may be able to see the enlarged lateral blood vessels (**hearts**) around the anterior portion of the digestive tract.

d. Identify (from anterior to posterior) the **pharynx, esophagus, crop** (a soft, swollen region of the digestive tract), **gizzard** (smaller and more rigid than the crop), and **intestine.**

e. Excretion in the clamworm and earthworm is carried out by organs called **nephridia.** A pair of these minute, white, coiled tubes is located in each segment of the worm body. Nephridia are more easily observed in the earthworm than in *Nereis* and should be studied here. To view these organs, cut out an approximately 2-cm-long piece of the worm posterior to the clitellum and cut it open along its dorsal surface. Cut through the septa and pin the piece to the dissecting pan near the edge to facilitate observation with the stereoscopic microscope. The coiled tubules of the nephridia are located in the coelomic cavity, where waste is collected and discharged to the outside through a small pore.

2. Using the compound microscope, observe the prepared slide of a cross section of the earthworm.

   a. Locate the **thin cuticle** lying outside of and secreted by the **epidermis.** Recall the habitat of this organism and speculate about the function of the cuticle.

   b. Confirm your decision about the type of coelom by locating **muscle layers** inside the epidermis and also lying on the surface of the **intestine** near the body cavity.

   c. Locate the **ventral nerve cord,** lying in the floor of the coelom, just inside the muscle layer.

## Results

Complete the summary table, recording all information for clamworm and earthworm characteristics in the appropriate row.

 Student Media Video—Ch. 33: Earthworm Locomotion

## Discussion

A major new feature observed in the phylum Annelida is the segmented body. Speculate about possible adaptive advantages provided by segmentation.

# EXERCISE 5
# Phylum Mollusca—Clams

## Materials

dissecting instruments
dissecting pan

preserved clam or mussel
disposable gloves

## Introduction

Second only to the phylum Arthropoda in numbers of species, the phylum Mollusca (clade Lophotrochozoa) includes thousands of species living in many diverse habitats. Most species are marine. Others live in fresh water or on land. Many mollusks are of economic importance, being favorite human foods. Mollusks include such diverse animals as snails, slugs, clams, squids, and octopuses. Although appearing diverse, most of these animals share four characteristic features: (1) a hard external **shell** for protection; (2) a thin structure called the **mantle**, which secretes the shell; (3) a **visceral mass** in which most organs are located; and (4) a muscular **foot** used for locomotion.

In this exercise, you will dissect a clam, a molluscan species with a shell made of two parts called **valves.** Most clams are marine, although many genera live in freshwater lakes and ponds.

 Wear gloves while dissecting preserved animals.

## Procedure

1. Observe the external anatomy of the preserved clam. Certain character-istics will become obvious immediately. Can you determine symmetry, support systems, and the presence or absence of appendages? Are there external signs of segmentation? Record observations.

2. Before you continue making observations, determine the dorsal, ven-tral, anterior, posterior, right, and left regions of the animal. Identify the two valves. The valves are held together by a **hinge** near the **umbo,** a hump on the valves. The hinge and the umbo are located **dorsally,** and the valves open **ventrally.** The umbo is displaced **anteriorly.** Hold the clam vertically with the umbo away from your body, and cup one of your hands over each valve. The valve in your right hand is the right valve; the valve in your left hand is the left valve. The two valves are held together by two strong **adductor** muscles inside the shell. Compare your observations with Figure 8.

 Be cautious as you open the clam! Hold the clam in the dissecting pan in such a way that the scalpel will be directed toward the bottom of the pan.

**Figure 8.**
**Anatomy of a clam.** The soft body parts are protected by the shell valves. Two adductor muscles hold the valves closed. Most major organs are located in the visceral mass. In this diagram, the left mantle, left pair of gills, and half of the visceral mass have been removed.

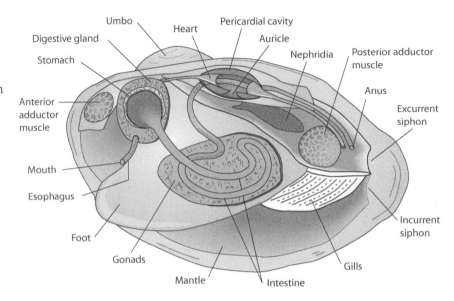

3. To study the internal anatomy of the clam, you must open it by prying open the valves. (A wooden peg may have been inserted between the two valves.) Insert the handle of your forceps or scalpel between the valves and twist it to pry the valves farther open. Carefully insert a scalpel blade, directed toward the dorsal side of the animal, into the space between the left valve and a flap of tissue lining the valve. The blade edge should be just ventral to (that is, below) the anterior adductor muscle (see Figure 8). The flap of tissue is the left **mantle.** Keeping the scalpel blade pressed flat against the left valve, carefully loosen the mantle from the valve and press the blade dorsally. You will feel the tough **anterior adductor muscle.** Cut through this muscle near the valve.

4. Repeat the procedure at the posterior end and cut the posterior adductor muscle. Lay the clam on its right valve and carefully lift the left valve. As you do this, use your scalpel to loosen the mantle from the valve. If you have been successful, you should have the body of the clam lying in the right valve. It should be covered by the mantle. Look for pearls between the mantle and the shell. How do you think pearls are formed?

5. Look at the posterior end of the animal where the left and right mantle come together. Hold the two mantle flaps together and note the two gaps formed. These gaps are called **incurrent** (ventral) and **excurrent** (dorsal) **siphons.** Speculate about the function of these siphons.

6. Lift the mantle and identify the **visceral mass** and the **muscular foot.**

7. Locate the **gills,** which have a pleated appearance. One function of these structures is obvious, but they have a second function as well. As water comes into the body (how would it get in?), it passes through the gills, and food particles are trapped on the gill surface. The food is then moved anteriorly (toward the mouth) by coordinated ciliary movements.

8. Locate the **mouth** between two flaps of tissue just ventral to the anterior adductor muscle. Look just above the posterior adductor muscle and locate the **anus.** How is it oriented in relation to the excurrent siphon?

9. Imagine that this is the first time you have seen a clam. From the observations you have made, what evidence would indicate whether this animal is aquatic or terrestrial?

10. The **heart** of the clam is located in a sinus, or cavity, just inside the hinge, dorsal to the visceral mass (see Figure 8). This cavity, called the *pericardial cavity,* is a reduced **true coelom.** The single ventricle of the heart actually surrounds the **intestine** passing through this cavity. Thin auricles, usually torn away during the dissection, empty into the heart via openings called **ostia.** Blood passes from **sinuses** in the body into the auricles. What type of circulatory system is this?

11. Ventral to the heart and embedded in mantle tissue are a pair of greenish brown tissue masses, the **nephridia,** or kidneys. The kidneys remove waste from the pericardial cavity.

12. Open the visceral mass by making an incision with the scalpel, dividing the mass into right and left halves. Begin this incision just above the foot and cut dorsally. You should be able to open the flap produced by this cut and see organs such as the **gonads, digestive gland, intestine,** and **stomach.** Clam chowder is made by chopping up the visceral mass.

13. It is difficult to observe the nervous system in the clam. It consists of three ganglia, one near the mouth, one in the foot, and one below the posterior adductor muscle. These ganglia are connected by nerves.

Now that you have dissected the clam, you should have concluded that there is no sign of true segmentation. Also, appendages (attached to a trunk or body wall) are absent.

## Results

Complete the Summary Table, recording all information for clam characteristics in the appropriate row.

## Discussion

List several features of clam anatomy that enable it to survive in a marine environment.

By the end of today's laboratory period, you should have completed observations of all animals described.

## Applying Your Knowledge

A hydra (*Chlorophyra viridissima*) is bright green, and yet it does not synthesize chlorophyll. Think about the structure of the hydra and its feeding and digestive habits. What do you think is the origin of the green pigment in this species?

## Investigative Extensions

1. Earthworms are among the most familiar inhabitants of soil. They play an important role in improving the texture and adding organic matter to soil. You may have read Darwin's estimate that over 50,000 earthworms may inhabit one acre of British farmland. Earthworms are readily available from biological supply houses, or you may collect your own to use in experiments. Following are questions that you might investigate.

   a. Why do earthworms come out of their burrows when it rains? Is it because they may drown in the water in their burrows? Does rain stimulate mating behavior and are the worms coming to the surface to mate? Does the pH of the soil change as it rains, and is the burrow becoming too acidic or alkaline? What is the optimum pH range for earthworms? Does rain create conditions more favorable for migration to new habitats?

   b. What effects do chemicals used in agriculture have on earthworm populations? Compare numbers and health of earthworms in containers of soil to which varying amounts of fertilizers, pesticides, or herbicides have been added.

   c. Do earthworms in the soil stimulate plant growth? Compare the biomass of plants grown in containers with and without earthworms present.

2. An amazing diversity of organisms has evolved from the foot-mantle-visceral mass body plan of mollusks. Living terrestrial, freshwater, and marine snails and bivalves are available from biological supply houses, aquarium supply stores, or from ponds or terrestrial sites in your area. Consider the following questions that you might investigate. (A Google search for "snail experiments" yields over 1,140,000 entries, including experiments being performed in the International Space Station.)

a. What effect does sedimentation have on aquatic snail populations? Consider changes in water chemistry and/or substrate.

b. What effect does temperature have on the growth and/or reproduction of aquatic or terrestrial snails or slugs? Why would this question be of interest?

c. Invasive aquatic plants have become a major concern of scientists worldwide. For example, water hyacinth, introduced into ponds in the southern U.S., chokes ponds and waterways, in some cases hindering human and fish navigation. Ponds may become so choked that they dry up, destroying habitat for alligators, turtles, fish, and other native species. Design a greenhouse experiment to test the efficacy of aquatic snails in controlling the growth of invasive aquatic plants.

## Student Media Activities and Investigations

**Activities**—Ch. 32: Animal Phylogenetic Tree; Ch. 33: Characteristics of Invertebrates
**Investigations**—Ch. 32: How Do Molecular Data Fit Traditional Phylogenies?
www.masteringbio.com

## References

Adoutte, A., G. Balavoine, N. Lartillot, O. Lespinet, B. Prud'homme, and R. de Rosa. "The New Animal Phylogeny: Reliability and Implications." *Proc. Natl. Acad. Sci.* USA, 2000, vol. 97, no. 9, pp. 4453–4456.

Balavoine, G. "Are Platyhelminthes Coelomates Without a Coelom? An Argument Based on the Evolution of Hox Genes." *American Zoologist,* 1989, vol. 38, pp. 843–858.

Erwin, D., J. Valentine, and D. Jablonski. "The Origin of Animal Body Plans." *American Scientist,* 1997, vol. 85, pp. 126–137.

Mallatt, J. and C. Winchell. "Testing the New Animal Phylogeny: First Use of Combined Large-Subunit and Small-Subunit rRNA Sequences to Classify Protostomes." *Molecular Biology and Evolution,* 2002, vol. 19, pp. 289–301.

## Websites

Includes descriptions of many invertebrates and vertebrates, links to insect keys, references:
http://animaldiversity.ummz.umich.edu/site/index.html

The Tree of Life web project provides information on all major groups of organisms, including invertrebrates:
http://tolweb.org/Bilateria

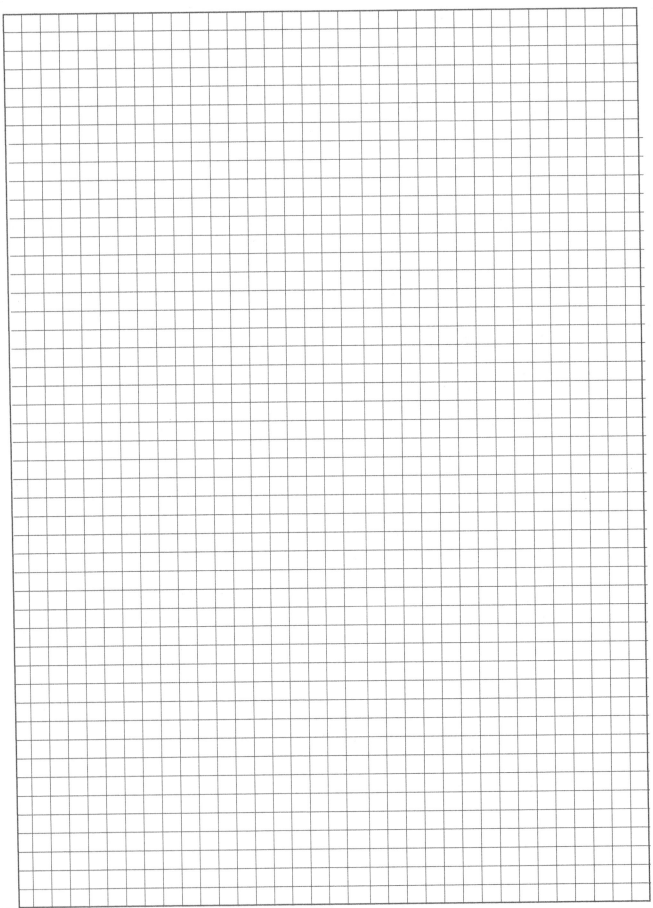

# Animal Diversity: Nematoda, Arthropoda, Echinodermata, and Chordata

In this lab topic you will study examples of two protostome phyla included in the clade **Ecdysozoa**, Nematoda (Exercise 1) and Arthropoda (Exercise 2). Recall that these organisms have coverings on their body surfaces. In Exercises 3 and 4, you will study two deuterostome phyla, Echinodermata and Chordata.

As you continue your study of representative organisms, continue to record your observations in Table 1 at the end of this lab topic. Keep in mind the big themes you are investigating.

1. What clues do similarities and differences among organisms provide about phylogenetic relationships?
2. How is body form related to function?
3. How is body form related to environment and lifestyle?
4. What characteristics can be the criteria for major branching points in producing a phylogenetic tree (representing animal classification)?

---

## EXERCISE 1
## Phylum Nematoda— Roundworms (*Ascaris*)

---

### Materials

dissecting instruments
dissecting pan
dissecting pins
compound microscope
disposable gloves

preserved *Ascaris*
prepared slide of cross section
   of *Ascaris*
hand lens (optional)

From *Investigating Biology Laboratory Manual,* Sixth Edition, Judith G. Morgan and M. Eloise Brown Carter. Copyright © 2008 by Pearson Education, Inc. Published by Benjamin Cummings, Inc. All rights reserved.

## Introduction

**Roundworms,** or nematodes (clade Ecdysozoa), are among the most abundant and resilient organisms on earth. NASA is using the nematode *Caenorhabditis elegans* in experiments to test the way weightlessness and space radiation affect an organism's genes. NASA has additional plans to launch worms into orbit aboard small satellites in the near future. *C. elegans* is a small roundworm—only one millimeter in length. *Ascaris,* the roundworm you will study in this exercise, is considerably larger.

*Ascaris* lives as a parasite in the intestines of mammals such as horses, pigs, and humans. Recall that ecdysozoans secrete exoskeletons that must be shed as the animal grows. Nematodes are covered with a proteinaceous **cuticle** that sheds periodically. Most often these parasites are introduced into the mammalian body when food contaminated with nematode eggs is eaten. Keep in mind the problem of adaptation to a parasitic lifestyle as you study the structure of this animal.

 Wear disposable gloves while dissecting preserved animals.

## Procedure

1. Wearing disposable gloves, obtain a preserved *Ascaris* and determine its sex. Females are generally larger than males. The posterior end of the male is sharply curved.

2. Use a hand lens or a stereoscopic microscope to look at the ends of the worm. A mouth is present at the anterior end. Three "lips" border this opening. A small slitlike **anus** is located ventrally near the posterior end of the animal.

3. Open the animal by making a middorsal incision along the length of the body with a sharp-pointed probe or sharp scissors. Remember that the anus is slightly to the ventral side (Figure 1). Be careful not to go too deep. Once the animal is open, pin the free edges of the body wall to the dissecting pan, spreading open the body. Pinning the animal near the edge of the pan will allow you to view it using the stereoscopic microscope. As you study the internal organs, you will note that there is a **body cavity.** This is not a true coelom, however, as you will see shortly when you study microscopic sections. From your observations, you should readily identify such characteristics as symmetry, tissue organization, and digestive tract openings.

    a. The most obvious organs you will see in the dissected worm are **reproductive organs,** which appear as masses of coiled tubules of varying diameters.

    b. Identify the flattened **digestive tract,** or intestine, extending from mouth to anus. This tract has been described as a "tube within a tube," the outer tube being the body wall.

    c. Locate two pale lines running laterally along the length of the body in the body wall. The excretory system consists of two longitudinal tubes lying in these two **lateral lines.**

    d. There are no organs for gas exchange or circulation. Most parasitic roundworms are essentially anaerobic (require no oxygen).

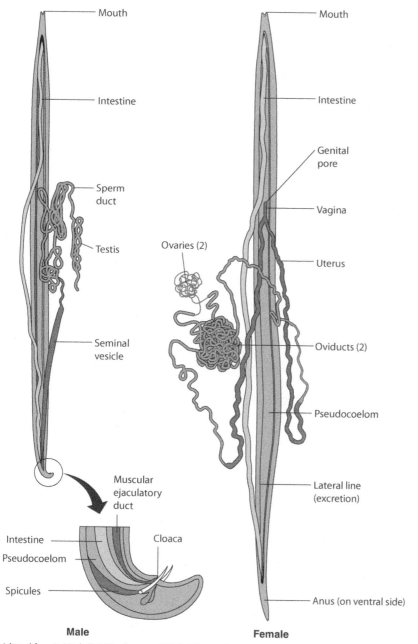

**Figure 1.**
**Male and female *Ascaris*.** The digestive tract originates at the mouth and terminates in the anus. Reproductive structures fill the body cavity.

Adapted from L. Mitchell, J. Mutchmor, and W. Dolphin, *Zoology* (Menlo Park, CA: Benjamin/Cummings, 1988), © 1988 The Benjamin/Cummings Publishing Company.

e. How would nourishment be taken into the body and be circulated?

f. The nervous system consists of a ring of nervous tissue around the anterior end of the worm, with one dorsal and one ventral nerve cord. These structures will be more easily observed in the prepared slide.

g. Do you see signs of segmentation in the body wall or in the digestive, reproductive, or excretory systems?

h. Do you see signs of a support system? What do you think supports the body?

4. Using the compound microscope, observe a prepared slide of a cross section through the body of a female worm. Note that the body wall is made up of (from outside inward) **cuticle** (noncellular), **epidermis** (cellular), and **muscle fibers.** The muscle (derived from mesoderm) lies at the outer boundary of the body cavity. Locate the **intestine** (derived from endoderm). Can you detect muscle tissue adjacent to the endodermal layer?

   What do we call a coelom that is lined by mesoderm (outside) and endoderm (inside)?

5. Most of the body cavity is filled with reproductive organs. You should see cross sections of the two large **uteri,** sections of the coiled **oviducts** with small lumens, and many sections of the **ovaries** with no lumen. What do you see inside the uteri?

6. By carefully observing the cross section, you should be able to locate the **lateral lines** for excretion and the dorsal and ventral **nerve cords.**

## Results

1. Sketch the cross section of a female *Ascaris.* Label the **cuticle, epidermis, muscle fibers, intestine, body cavity** (give specific name), **reproductive organs,** (uterus, oviduct, ovary), **lateral lines,** and **dorsal** and **ventral nerve cords.**

2. List some features of *Ascaris* that are possible adaptations to parasitic life.

3. Complete the summary table, Table 1, recording all information for roundworm characteristics in the appropriate row. You will use this information to complete Table 2 and answer questions in the Applying Your Knowledge section at the end of this lab topic.

 Student Media Video—Ch. 33: *C. elegans* Crawling

## Discussion

1. Discuss the significance of an animal's having two separate openings to the digestive tract, as seen in *Ascaris*.

2. What are the advantages of a body cavity being present in an animal?

EXERCISE 2
# Phylum Arthropoda

Organisms in the phylum Arthropoda (clade Ecdysozoa) have been very successful species. Evidence indicates that arthropods may have lived on Earth half a billion years ago. They can be found in almost every imaginable habitat: marine waters, fresh water, and almost every terrestrial niche. Many species are directly beneficial to humans, serving as a source of food. Others make humans miserable by eating their homes, infesting their domestic animals, eating their food, and biting their bodies. These organisms have an exoskeleton that periodically sheds as they grow. In this exercise, you will observe the morphology of two arthropods: the crayfish (an aquatic arthropod) and the grasshopper (a terrestrial arthropod).

## Lab Study A. Crayfish (*Cambarus*)

### Materials

dissecting instruments
dissecting pan

preserved crayfish
disposable gloves

## Introduction

Crayfish live in streams, ponds, and swamps, usually protected under rocks and vegetation. They may walk slowly over the substrate of their habitat, but they can also swim rapidly using their tails. The segmentation seen in annelids is seen also in crayfish and all arthropods; however, you will see that the segments are grouped into functional units.

## Procedure

1. Obtain a preserved crayfish, study its external anatomy, and compare your observations with Figure 2. Describe the body symmetry, supportive structures, appendages, and segmentation, and state the adaptive advantages of each characteristic.

   a. body symmetry

   b. supportive structures

   c. appendages

   d. segmentation

2. Identify the three regions of the crayfish body: the **head, thorax** (fused with the head), and **abdomen.** Note the appendages associated with each region. Speculate about the functions of each of these groups of appendages.

   a. head appendages

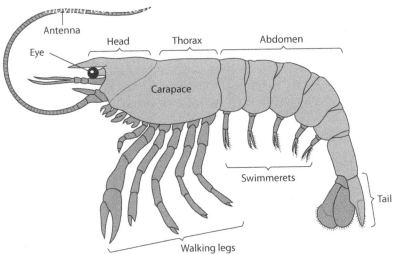

**Figure 2.**
**External anatomy of a crayfish.** The body is divided into head, thorax, and abdominal regions. Appendages grouped in a region perform specific functions.

Adapted from L. Mitchell, J. Mutchmor, and W. Dolphin, *Zoology* (Menlo Park, CA: Benjamin/Cummings, 1988), © 1988 The Benjamin/Cummings Publishing Company.

b. thoracic appendages

c. abdominal appendages

3. Feathery **gills** lie under the lateral extensions of a large, expanded exoskeletal plate called the **carapace** (see Figure 2). To expose the gills, use scissors to cut away a portion of the plate on the left side of the animal. What is the function of the gills? Speculate about how this function is performed.

4. Remove the dorsal portion of the carapace to observe other organs in the head and thorax. Compare your observations with Figure 3.
    a. Start on each side of the body at the posterior lateral edge of the carapace and make two lateral cuts extending along each side of the thorax and forward over the head, meeting just behind the eyes. This should create a dorsal flap in the carapace.
    b. Carefully insert a needle under this flap and separate the underlying tissues as you lift the flap.
    c. Observe the **heart**, a small, angular structure located just under the carapace near the posterior portion of the thorax. (If you were not successful in leaving the tissues behind as you removed the carapace, you may have removed the heart with the carapace.) Thin threads

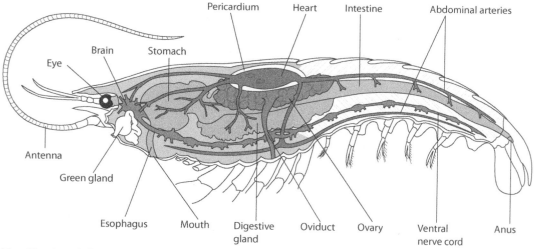

Adapted from L. Mitchell, J. Mutchmor, and W. Dolphin, *Zoology* (Menlo Park, CA: Benjamin/Cummings, 1988), © 1988 The Benjamin/Cummings Publishing Company.

**Figure 3.**

**Internal anatomy of the crayfish.** Large digestive glands fill much of the body cavity. The intestine extends from the stomach through the tail to the anus. The green glands lie near the brain in the head.

leading out from the heart are **arteries.** Look for holes in the heart wall. When blood collects in **sinuses** around the heart, the heart relaxes, and these holes open to allow the heart to fill with blood. The holes then close, and the blood is pumped through the arteries, which distribute it around the body. Blood seeps back to the heart, since no veins are present. What is the name given to this kind of circulation?

d. Locate the **stomach** in the head region. It is a large, saclike structure. It may be obscured by the large, white **digestive glands** that fill the body cavity inside the body wall. Leading posteriorly from the stomach is the **intestine.** Make longitudinal cuts through the exoskeleton on either side of the dorsal midline of the abdomen. Lift the exoskeleton and trace the intestine to the anus. (When shrimp are "deveined" in preparation for eating, the intestine is removed.) Given all of the organs and tissues around the digestive tract and inside the body wall in the body cavity, what kind of coelom do you think this animal has?

e. Turn your attention to the anterior end of the specimen again. Pull the stomach posteriorly (this will tear the esophagus) and look inside the most anterior portion of the head. Two **green glands** (they do not look green), the animal's excretory organs, are located in this region. These are actually long tubular structures that resemble nephridia but are compacted into a glandular mass. Waste and excess water pass from these glands to the outside of the body through pores at the base of the antennae on the head.

f. Observe the **brain** just anterior to the green glands. It lies in the midline with nerves extending posteriorly, fusing to form a **ventral nerve cord.**

 Student Media Video—Ch. 33: Lobster Mouth Parts

## Results

Complete Table 1, recording all information for crayfish characteristics in the appropriate row. Use this information to complete Table 2 and answer questions in the Applying Your Knowledge section at the end of this lab topic.

## Discussion

How does the pattern of segmentation differ in the crayfish and the earthworm?

# Lab Study B. Grasshoppers (*Romalea*)

## Materials

dissecting instruments
dissecting pan

preserved grasshopper
disposable gloves

## Introduction

The grasshopper, an insect, is an example of a terrestrial arthropod. Insects are the most successful and abundant of all land animals. They are the principal invertebrates in dry environments, and they can survive extreme temperatures. They are the only invertebrates that can fly. As you study the grasshopper, compare the anatomy of this terrestrial animal with that of the aquatic crayfish, just studied. This comparison should suggest ways that terrestrial animals have solved the problems of life out of water.

## Procedure

1. Observe the external anatomy of the grasshopper. Compare your observations with Figure 4.

   a. Note the symmetry, supportive structures, appendages, and segmentation of the grasshopper.

   b. Observe the body parts. The body is divided into three regions: the **head,** the **thorax** (to which the legs and wings are attached), and the **abdomen.** Examine the appendages on the head, speculate about their functions, and locate the mouth opening into the digestive tract.

   c. Turning your attention to the abdomen, locate small dots along each side. These dots are **spiracles,** small openings into elastic air tubes, or **tracheae,** that branch to all parts of the body and constitute the respiratory system of the grasshopper. This system of tubes brings oxygen directly to the cells of the body.

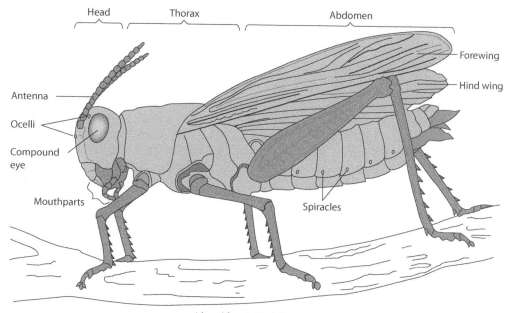

**Figure 4.**
**External anatomy of the grasshopper.** The body is divided into head, thorax, and abdominal regions. Wings and large legs are present. Small openings, called *spiracles,* lead to internal tracheae, allowing air to pass into the body.

Adapted from L. Mitchell, J. Mutchmor, and W. Dolphin, *Zoology* (Menlo Park, CA: Benjamin/Cummings, 1988), © 1988 The Benjamin/Cummings Publishing Company.

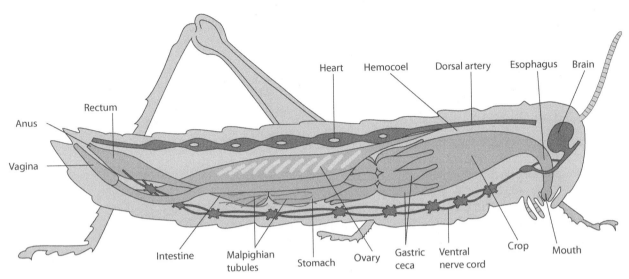

**Figure 5.**
**Internal anatomy of the grasshopper.** The digestive tract, extending from mouth to anus, is divided into specialized regions: the esophagus, crop, stomach, intestine, and rectum. Gastric ceca attach at the junction of the crop and the stomach. Malpighian tubules empty excretory waste into the anterior end of the intestine.

2. Remove the exoskeleton. First take off the wings and, starting at the posterior end, use scissors to make two lateral cuts toward the head. Remove the dorsal wall of the exoskeleton and note the segmented pattern in the muscles inside the body wall. Compare your observations with Figure 5 as you work.

   a. A space between the body wall and the digestive tract, the **hemocoel** (a true coelom), in life is filled with colorless blood. What type of circulation does the grasshopper have?

   The heart of a grasshopper is an elongate, tubular structure lying just inside the middorsal body wall. This probably will not be visible.

   b. Locate the digestive tract and again note the mouth. Along the length of the tract are regions specialized for specific functions. A narrow **esophagus** leading from the mouth expands into a large **crop** used for food storage. The crop empties into the **stomach,** where digestion takes place. Six pairs of fingerlike extensions called **gastric pouches** or **ceca** connect to the digestive tract where the crop and the stomach meet. These pouches secrete digestive enzymes and aid in food absorption. Food passes from the stomach into the **intestine,** then into the **rectum,** and out the **anus.** Distinguish these regions by observing constrictions and swellings along the tube. There is usually a constriction between the stomach and the intestine where the Malpighian tubules (discussed below) attach. The intestine is shorter and usually smaller in diameter than the stomach. *The intestine expands into an enlarged rectum that absorbs excess water from any undigested food, and relatively dry excrement passes out the anus.*

c. The excretory system is made up of numerous tiny tubules, the **Malpighian tubules,** which empty their products into the anterior end of the intestine. These tubules remove wastes and salts from the blood. Locate these tubules.

d. Push aside the digestive tract and locate the **ventral nerve cord** lying medially inside the ventral body wall. Ganglia are expanded regions of the ventral nerve cord found in each body segment. Following the nerve cord anteriorly, note that branches from the nerve cord pass around the digestive tract and meet, forming a brain in the head.

## Results

Complete Table 1, recording all information for grasshopper characteristics in the appropriate row. Use this information to complete Table 2 and answer questions in the Applying Your Knowledge section at the end of this lab topic.

## Discussion

1. Describe how each of the following external structures helps the grasshopper live successfully in terrestrial environments.

   a. Exoskeleton

   b. Wings

   c. Large, jointed legs

   d. Spiracles

2. Describe how each of the following internal structures helps the grasshopper live successfully in terrestrial environments.

   a. Tracheae

   b. Malpighian tubules

   c. Rectum

## EXERCISE 3

# Deuterostome—Phylum Echinodermata—Sea Star

Echinodermata is one of three phyla in the group of animals called deuterostomes. You will study another deuterostome phylum in Exercise 4, phylum Chordata. Examples of echinoderms include the sea star, sea urchin, sea cucumber, and sea lily. Some of the most familiar animals in the animal kingdom are in the phylum Chordata—fish, reptiles, amphibians, and mammals. Take a look at a sea star (starfish) in the salt-water aquarium in your lab or in a tidal pool on a rocky shore. What are the most obvious characteristics of this animal? Then imagine a chordate—a fish, dog, or even yourself. You might question why these two phyla are considered closely related phylogenetically. The most obvious difference is a very basic characteristic—the sea star has radial symmetry and most chordates that you imagine have bilateral symmetry. The sea star has no head or other obvious chordate features and it crawls around using hundreds of small suction cups called tube feet. Most chordates show strong cephalization and move using appendages. Your conclusion from the superficial observations might be that these two phyla are not closely related. Your observations are a good example of the difficulty faced by taxonomists when comparing animals based only on the morphology of adults. Taxonomists must collect data from studies of developmental and—as we discovered with the protostomes—molecular similarities before coming to final conclusions.

In this and the following exercise, you will examine an echinoderm, the adult sea star (demonstration only), and two chordates, asking questions about their morphology and adaptation to their habitats. You may not be convinced of their phylogentic relationships, however, until you study early development in sea urchins and sea stars. At that time, you will see that chordates and echinoderms have similar early embryonic developmental patterns, including the formation of the mouth and anus and the type of cleavage.

## Materials

whole preserved sea stars on demonstration
several dissected sea stars on demonstration showing the internal contents
of the body and the inside surface of oral and aboral halves of the body

## Introduction

The sea star is classified in the phylum Echinodermata. They are marine animals with an endoskeleton of small, spiny calcareous plates bound together by connective tissue. Their symmetry is radial pentamerous (five-parted). They have no head or brain and few sensory structures. All animals in this phylum have a unique **water-vascular system** that develops from mesoderm and consists of a series of canals carrying water that enters the body through an outer opening, the **madreporite.** The canals are located inside the body and include a ring around the central disk of the body and tubes or canals that extend out into each arm. The canals then terminate in many small structures called **tube feet** along the groove on the

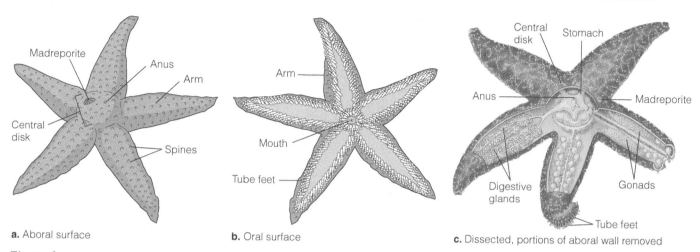

**a.** Aboral surface

**b.** Oral surface

**c.** Dissected, portions of aboral wall removed

**Figure 6.**

(a) Aboral surface of a sea star. (b) Oral surface of a sea star. (c) Dissected sea star with portions of the aboral wall removed.

oral side of each arm. Tube feet extend to the outside of the body and end in a small suction cup in most species. By contracting muscles and forcing fluid into its tube feet, the sea star can extend and attach the feet to hard surfaces such as the surface of a clamshell, or rocks on the ocean shore.

## Procedure

1. Observe the preserved sea star on demonstration. Locate the **aboral** surface—the "upper" surface away from the mouth (Figure 6a). The downside is the **oral** surface where the mouth is located (Figure 6b).

2. Count the number of arms that extend out from the **central disk.** Echinoderms are usually pentamerous, meaning that their arms are in multiples of five. Occasionally a sea star with six arms will be found. Arms that are damaged or lost can be regenerated, and an extra arm may regenerate.

3. Observe the animal's aboral surface (Figure 6a). Locate the **madreporite,** a small porous plate displaced to one side of the central disk that serves to take water into the water vascular system.

   Notice that the surface of the animal's body is spiny. The spines project from calcareous plates of the **endoskeleton.** The endoskeleton is derived from the embryonic germ layer mesoderm. In life, the entire surface of the body is covered with an **epidermis** derived from ectoderm that may not be visible with the naked eye.

4. Observe the dissected sea star on demonstration (Figure 6c). In this dissection the entire aboral surface has been lifted off the body and placed to the side, inside up. This exposes the internal organs. The endoskeleton and its calcareous plates are obvious as viewed from the inside of the body.

5. Inside the body the organs are located in a **true body cavity.** Small delicate projections of the body cavity protrude between the plates of the endoskeleton to the outside of the body. These projections, covered with epidermis, are called **skin gills** or dermal branchiae, and function in the exchange of oxygen and carbon dioxide with the water bathing the animal's body. In addition, nitrogenous waste passes through these

skin gills into the surrounding water; these structures thus have both respiratory and excretory functions.

6. The central disk contains the stomach, a portion of which can be everted through the mouth on the oral side of the animal. A small anus is located on the aboral body surface, although very little fecal material is ejected here. Most digestion takes place in the stomach, which may be everted into the body of a clam. The digested broth is then sucked up into the sea star body. After feeding, the sea star draws in its stomach by contracting its stomach muscles.

7. Conspicuous organs in the arms of the animal are gonads and digestive glands. Other systems cannot be easily observed in this preparation. A reduced circulatory system (hemal system) exists, but its function is not well defined. It consists of tissue strands and unlined sinuses. The nervous system includes a nerve ring around the mouth and radial nerves with epidermal nerve networks. There is no central nervous system.

## Results

Complete Table 1, recording in the appropriate row all information you have been able to observe. Use this information to complete Table 2 and answer questions in the Applying Your Knowledge section at the end of this lab topic.

 **Student Media Video—Ch. 33: Echinoderm Tube Feet**

## Discussion

1. Imagine that you are a zoologist studying sea stars for the first time. What characteristics would you note from the dissection of an adult animal that might give a clue to its phylogenetic relationships—that it belongs with deuterostomes rather than protostomes?

2. What structures have you observed that appear to be unique to echinoderms?

3. How would you continue your study to obtain more information that might help in classifying these animals?

4. Given the fact that other deuterostomes are bilaterally symmetrical, what is one explanation for the radial symmetry of most adult echinoderms?

# EXERCISE 4
# Deuterostome—Phylum Chordata

Up to this point, all the animals you have studied are commonly called **invertebrates,** a somewhat artificial designation based on the absence of a backbone. Those animals with a backbone are called **vertebrates.** The phylum Chordata studied in this exercise includes two subphyla of invertebrates and a third subphylum of vertebrates, animals that have a bony or cartilaginous endoskeleton with a vertebral column. Chordates inhabit terrestrial and aquatic (freshwater and marine) environments. One group has developed the ability to fly. The body plan of chordates is unique in that these animals demonstrate a complex of four important characteristics at some stage in their development. In this exercise, you will discover these characteristics.

You will study two chordate species: the lancelet, an invertebrate in the subphylum Cephalochordata, and the pig, a vertebrate in the subphylum Vertebrata. The third subphylum, Urochordata, will not be studied.

## Lab Study A. Lancelets (*Branchiostoma,* formerly *Amphioxus*)

### Materials

compound microscope
stereoscopic microscope
preserved lancelet in watch glass

prepared slide of whole mount of
  lancelet
prepared slide of cross section of
  lancelet

### Introduction

Lancelets are marine animals that burrow in sand in tidal flats. They feed with their head end extended from their burrow. They resemble fish superficially, but their head is poorly developed, and they have unique features not found in fish or other vertebrates. They retain the four unique characteristics of chordates throughout their life cycle and are excellent animals to use to demonstrate these features. In this lab study, you will observe preserved lancelets, prepared slides of whole mounts, and cross sections through the body of a lancelet.

## Procedure

1. Place a preserved lancelet in water in a watch glass and observe it using the stereoscopic microscope. Handle the specimen with care and *do not dissect it*. Note the fishlike shape of the slender, elongate body. Locate the anterior end by the presence at that end of a noselike **rostrum** extending over the mouth region, surrounded by small tentacles. Notice the lack of a well-defined head. Look for the segmented muscles that surround much of the animal's body. Can you see signs of a tail? If the animal you are studying is mature, you will be able to see two rows of 20 to 25 white gonads on the ventral surface of the body.

2. Return the specimen to the correct container.

3. Observe the whole mount slide of the lancelet and compare your observations with Figure 7.

 **Use only the lowest power on the compound microscope to study this slide.**

a. Scan the entire length of the body wall. Do you see evidence of segmentation in the muscles?

b. Look at the anterior end of the animal. Do you see evidence of a sensory system? Describe what you see.

**Figure 7.**
**The lancelet, whole mount.** The rostrum extends over the mouth region. The pharynx, including the pharyngeal gill slits, leads to the intestine, which exits the body at the anus. Note that a tail extends beyond the anus. Structures positioned from the dorsal surface of the body inward include a dorsal fin, the nerve cord, and the notochord.

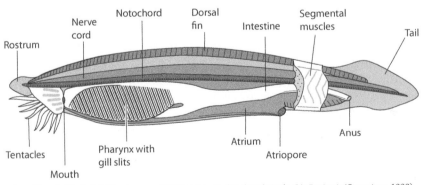

Adapted from L. Mitchell, J. Mutchmor, and W. Dolphin, *Zoology* (Menlo Park, CA: Benjamin/Cummings, 1988), © 1988 The Benjamin/Cummings Publishing Company.

c. Locate the mouth of the animal at the anterior end. See if you can follow a tube from just under the rostrum into a large sac with numerous gill slits. This sac is the **pharynx with gill slits,** a uniquely chordate structure. Water and food pass into the pharynx from the mouth. Food passes posteriorly from the pharynx into the intestine, which ends at the anus on the ventral side of the animal, several millimeters before the end. The extension of the body beyond the anus is called a **post-anal tail.** You may have studied worms in a previous lab. If so, where was the anus located in these animals? Was a post-anal region present? Explain.

d. Water entering the mouth passes through the gill slits and collects in a chamber, the **atrium,** just inside the body wall. The water ultimately passes out of the body at a ventral pore, the **atripore.** Surprisingly, the gill slits are not the major gas exchange surface in the lancelet body. Because of the great activity of ciliated cells in this region, it is even possible that blood leaving the gill region has less oxygen than that entering the region. The function of gill slits is simply to strain food from the water. The major site for gas exchange is the body surface.

e. Now turn your attention to the dorsal side of the animal. Beginning at the surface of the body and moving inward, identify the listed structures and speculate about the function of each one.

**dorsal fin:**

**nerve cord:**

**notochord:**

The nerve cord is in a dorsal position. Have you seen only a dorsal nerve cord in any of the animals previously studied?

The notochord is a cartilage-like rod that lies ventral to the nerve cord and extends the length of the body. Have you seen a notochord in any of the previous animals?

The lancelet circulatory system is not visible in these preparations, but the animal has **closed circulation** with dorsal and ventral aortae, capillaries, and veins. Excretory organs, or nephridia (not visible here), are located near the true coelom, which surrounds the pharynx.

4. Observe the slide of cross sections taken through the lancelet body. There may be several sections on this slide, taken at several positions along the length of the body. Find the section through the pharynx and compare it with Figure 8.

 **Study this slide on the lowest power.**

In cross section, it is much easier to see the structural relationships among the various organs of the lancelet. Identify the following structures and label them on Figure 8.

a. **Segmental muscles.** They are located on each side of the body, under the skin.

b. **Dorsal fin.** This projects upward from the most dorsal surface of the body.

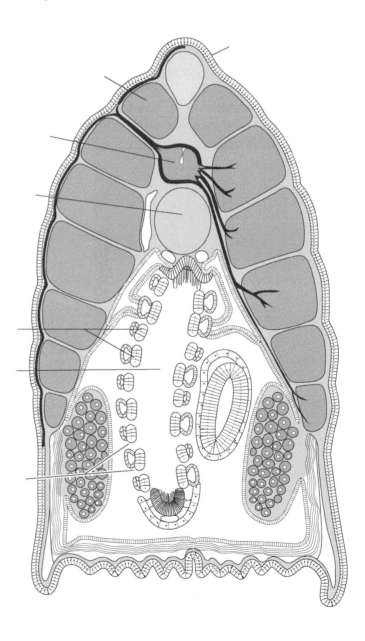

**Figure 8.**
**Cross section through the**
**pharyngeal region of the lancelet.**

c. **Nerve cord.** You may be able to see that the nerve cord contains a small central canal, thus making it hollow. The nerve cord is located in the dorsal region of the body, ventral to the dorsal fin between the lateral bundles of muscle.

d. **Notochord.** This is a large oval structure located just ventral to the nerve cord.

e. **Pharynx with gill slits.** This structure appears as a series of dark triangles arranged in an oval. The triangles are cross sections of **gill bars.** The spaces between the triangles are **gill slits,** through which water passes into the surrounding chamber.

## Results

1. Complete the diagram of the lancelet cross section in Figure 8. Label all the structures listed in step 4 of the Procedure section.

2. Complete Table 1, recording all information for lancelet characteristics in the appropriate row. Use this information to complete Table 2 and answer questions in the Applying Your Knowledge section at the end of this lab topic.

## Discussion

Describe the uniquely chordate features that you have detected in the lancelet that were not present in the animals previously studied.

## Lab Study B. Fetal Pigs (*Sus scrofa*)

### Materials

preserved fetal pig                    disposable gloves
dissecting pan

### Introduction

The pig is a terrestrial vertebrate. In this lab study, working with your lab partner, you will observe external features only, observing those characteristics studied in other animals in previous exercises. Compare the organization of the vertebrate body with the animals previously studied. As you dissect the pig in subsequent labs, come back to these questions and answer the ones that cannot be answered in today's lab study.

### Procedure

1. Obtain a preserved fetal pig from the class supply and carry it to your desk in a dissecting pan.

 **Use disposable gloves to handle preserved animals.**

2. With your lab partner, read each of the following questions. Drawing on observations you have made of other animals in the animal diversity lab studies, predict the answer to each question about the fetal pig. Then examine the fetal pig and determine the answer, if possible. Give evidence for your answer based on your observations of the pig, your knowledge of vertebrate anatomy, or your understanding of animal phylogeny.

a. What type of symmetry does the pig body have?

Prediction:


Evidence:


b. How many layers of embryonic tissue are present?

Prediction:


Evidence:


c. Are cells organized into distinct tissues?

Prediction:


Evidence:


d. How many digestive tract openings are present? Would you describe this as a "tube within a tube"?

Prediction:


Evidence:


e. Is the circulatory system open or closed?

Prediction:


Evidence:

f. What is the habitat of the animal?
   Prediction:


   Evidence:


g. What are the organs for respiration?
   Prediction:


   Evidence:


h. What are the organs for excretion?
   Prediction:


   Evidence:


i. What is the method of locomotion?
   Prediction:


   Evidence:


j. Are support systems internal or external?
   Prediction:


   Evidence:


k. Is the body segmented?
   Prediction:


   Evidence:

l. Are appendages present?

Prediction:


Evidence:


m. What is the position and complexity of the nervous system?

Prediction:


Evidence:


## Results

Complete Table 1, recording all information for pig characteristics in the appropriate row. Use this information to complete Table 2 and answer questions in the Applying Your Knowledge section that follows.


# Questions for Review

1. Complete the summary table, Table 1, recording in the appropriate row information about characteristics of all animals studied.
2. Using Table 1, complete Table 2. Categorize all animals studied based on the 13 basic characteristics. Use this information to answer questions in the Applying Your Knowledge section that follows.


# Applying Your Knowledge

1. Using specific examples from the animals you have studied, describe ways that organisms have adapted to specific environments.
   a. Compare organisms adapted to aquatic environments with those from terrestrial environments.
   b. Compare adaptations of the parasitic *Ascaris* with the earthworm or clamworm, free-living organisms.

2. The phylum Platyhelminthes also includes many examples of parasitic flatworms, for example, tapeworms and trematodes (flukes). Using Web resources, choose an example of a parasitic flatworm and compare morphological differences between this organism and the planarian that reflect specific life-style adaptations.

3. In your studies of animal phyla, you observed segmentation in widely diverse clades, for example, annelids (Lophotrochozoa), arthropods (Ecdysozoa), and chordates (Deuterostomia). How can you explain this in terms of their evolutionary history?

4. Upon superficial examination, the body form of certain present-day animals might be described as simple, yet these animals may have developed specialized structures, perhaps unique to their particular phylum. Illustrate this point using examples from some of the simpler organisms you have dissected.

5. One might conclude that certain trends can be detected, trends from ancestral features (those that arose early in the evolution of animals) to more derived traits (those that arose later). However, animals with ancestral characteristics still successfully exist on Earth today. Why is this so? Why have the animals with derived traits not completely replaced the ones with ancestral traits? Use examples from the lab to illustrate your answer.

6. A major theme in biology is the relationship between form and function in organisms. Select one of the major characteristics from Table 1, and illustrate the relationship of form and function for this characteristic using examples from the organisms studied.

**Table 1**
Summary Table of Animal Characteristics

| Animal | Symmetry | Tissue Organization | Type of Body Cavity | Digestive Openings | Circulatory System | Habitat | Respiratory Organs |
|---|---|---|---|---|---|---|---|
| Sponge | | | | | | | |
| Hydra | | | | | | | |
| Planarian | | | | | | | |
| Clamworm/ earthworm | | | | | | | |
| Clam | | | | | | | |
| Roundworm | | | | | | | |
| Crayfish | | | | | | | |
| Grasshopper | | | | | | | |
| Sea star | | | | | | | |
| Lancelet | | | | | | | |
| Pig | | | | | | | |

**Table 1**
Summary Table of Animal Characterstics (*continued*)

| Animal | Excretory System | Locomotion | Support System | Segmentation | Appendages | Nervous System Organization |
|---|---|---|---|---|---|---|
| Sponge | | | | | | |
| Hydra | | | | | | |
| Planarian | | | | | | |
| Clamworm/ earthworm | | | | | | |
| Clam | | | | | | |
| Roundworm | | | | | | |
| Crayfish | | | | | | |
| Grasshopper | | | | | | |
| Sea star | | | | | | |
| Lancelet | | | | | | |
| Pig | | | | | | |

**Table 2**
Comparison of Organisms by Major Features

| | |
|---|---|
| **1. Tissue Organization**<br><br>   a. distinct tissues absent:<br><br><br><br>   b. distinct tissues present: | **5. Circulatory System**<br><br>   a. none:<br><br><br><br>   b. open:<br><br><br><br>   c. closed: |
| **2. Symmetry**<br>   a. radial:<br><br><br><br>   b. bilateral: | **6. Habitat**<br>   a. aquatic:<br><br><br><br>   b. terrestrial:<br><br><br><br>   c. parasitic: |
| **3. Body Cavity**<br>   a. acoelomate:<br><br><br><br>   b. pseudocoelomate:<br><br><br><br>   c. eucoelomate: | **7. Organs for Gas Exchange**<br>   a. skin:<br><br><br><br>   b. gills:<br><br><br><br>   c. lungs:<br><br><br><br>   d. spiracles/tracheae: |
| **4. Openings to Digestive Tract**<br>   a. one:<br><br><br><br>   b. two: | |

**Table 2**
Comparison of Organisms by Major Features *(continued)*

| | |
|---|---|
| **8. Organs for Excretion**<br>(list organ and animals) | **11. Segmented Body**<br>  a. no:<br><br>  b. yes: |
| | **12. Appendages**<br>  a. yes:<br><br>  b. no: |
| **9. Type of Locomotion**<br>(list type and animals) | |
| | **13. Nervous System**<br>  a. ventral nerve cord:<br><br>  b. dorsal nerve cord:<br><br>  c. other: |
| **10. Support System**<br>  a. external:<br><br>  b. internal:<br><br>  c. hydrostatic: | |

# Student Media Activities and Investigations

**Activities**—Ch. 32: Animal Phylogenetic Tree; Ch. 33: Characteristics of Invertebrates; Ch. 34: Characteristics of Chordates

**Investigations**—Ch. 32: How Do molecular Data Fit Traditional Phylogenies? Ch. 33: How Are Insect Species Identified?

www.masteringbio.com

## Investigative Extensions

1. Scientists worldwide are concerned about reports of global warming. Crayfish are common inhabitants of freshwater streams, ponds, and swamps, all of which may be affected by a warming earth. Design an experiment to test the thermal limits that can be tolerated by crayfish.

   Design similar experiments to test the effects of pesticides, fertilizers, herbicides, petroleum products, or human wastes—all of which may be present in runoff into crayfish habitat from farmlands or urban development.

2. Arthropods are the dominant animals on the earth, both in number of species and number of individuals. Now that you are familiar with the characteristics of insects (terrestrial arthropods), using an entomology (study of insects) text or insect identification key, determine the diversity of arthropods, or specifically insects, found in various habitats. You might sample a given amount of soil taken from several different environments. For example, you might compare arthropod diversity in a deciduous forest with that of a cultivated field with that of a manicured lawn.

   You might also investigate arthropod diversity in habitats that differ in moisture. Compare well-drained soil (along a ridge) with saturated soil (along a creek, in a marsh, or in a bog).

3. N. A. Cobb, famous nematologist, writes: "If all the matter in the universe except the nematodes were swept away, our world would still be dimly recognizable . . . We should find its mountains, hills, vales, rivers, lakes, and oceans represented by a film of nematodes" (1915). Nematodes are everywhere and many are readily available for study.

   Design an experiment to investigate the diversity of nematodes present in several sources; for example, fresh and rotting fruits, soils collected from different sources or treated with different chemicals, roots of plants—trees or vegetables grown for human consumption. (Many nematodes are plant parasites, and many have been imported on foods or nursery stock.)

   Are there nematodes in drinking water? How could you investigate this question? How could you collect the nematodes?

## References

Aguinaldo, A. M., J. M. Turbeville, L. S. Linford, M. C. Rivera, J. R. Garey, R. A. Raff, J. A. Lake. "Evidence for a Clade of Nematodes, Arthropods, and other Moulting Animals." *Nature*, 29 May 1997 (387), pp. 489–493.

Cobb, N. A. "Nematodes and Their Relationships." Year Book Dept. Agric. 1914, pp. 457–490. Washington, DC: Dept. Agric. 1915.

Hickman, C. P., L. S. Roberts, A. Larson, and H. I'Anson. *Integrated Principles of Zoology*, 12th ed. Boston: McGraw Hill, 2004.

## Websites

Includes descriptions of many invertebrates and vertebrates, links to insect keys, references:
http://animaldiversity.ummz.umich.edu/index.html

The Tree of Life web project provides information on all major groups of organisms, including invertebrates:
http://tolweb.org/Bilateria

Report of an experiment testing nematodes for space experiments:
http://news-service.stanford.edu/News/2004/february/worms-24.html.

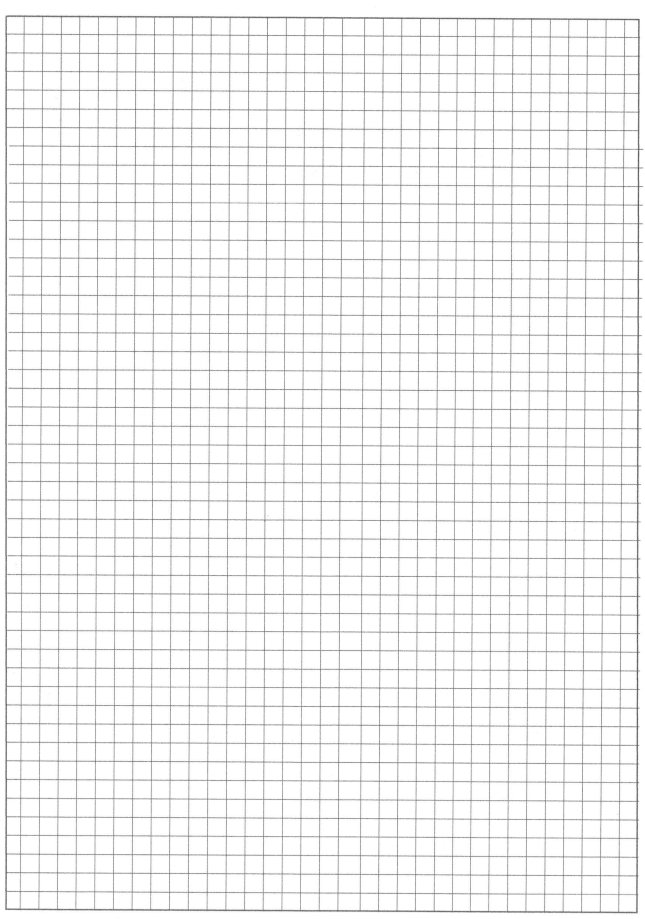

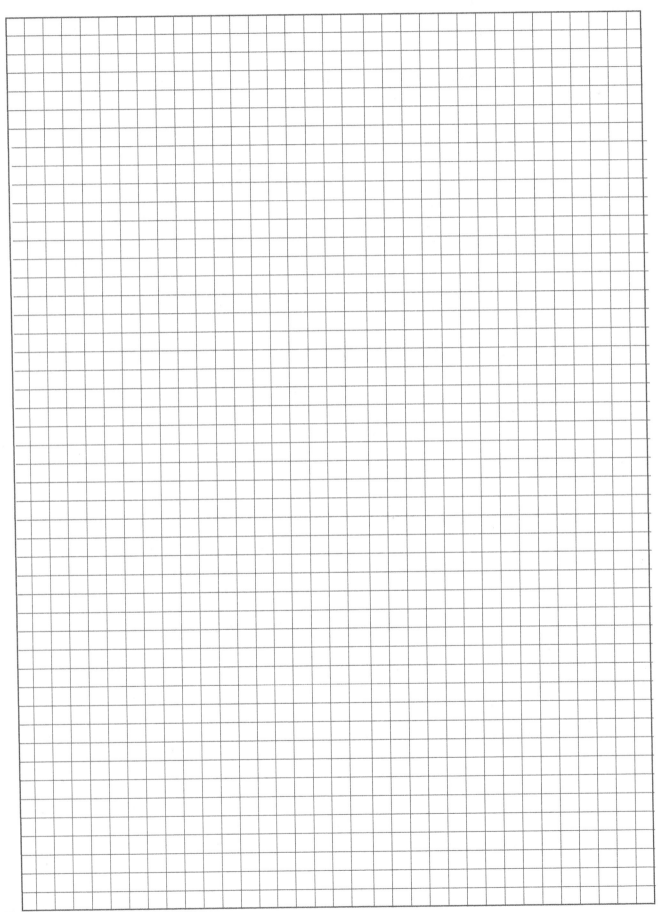

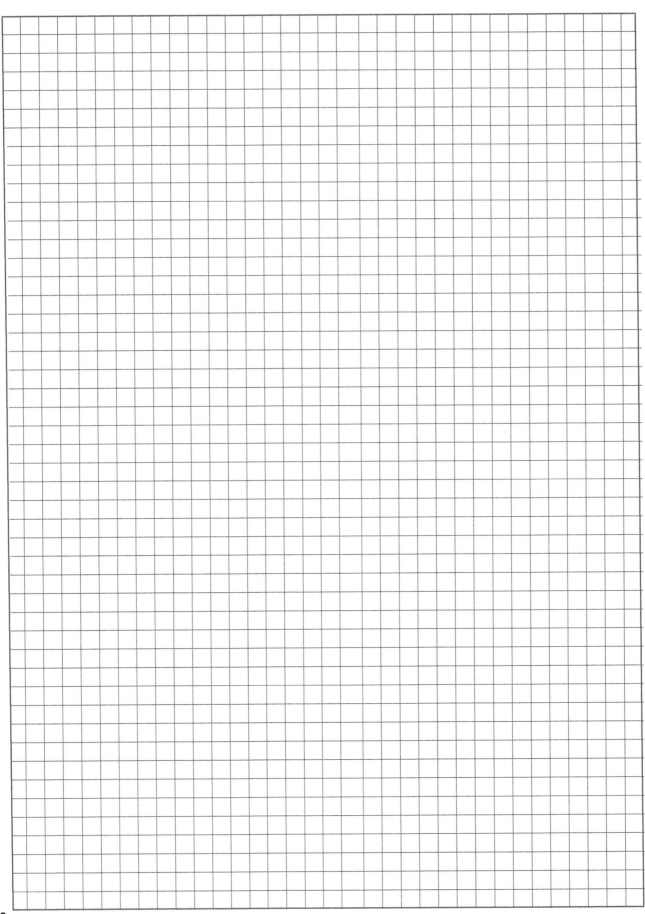

# Animal Behavior

## Laboratory Objectives

After completing this lab topic, you should be able to:

1. Define *ethology*.
2. Define and give an example of *taxis, kinesis, agonistic behavior,* and *reproductive behavior.*
3. State the possible adaptive significance of each of these behaviors.
4. Propose hypotheses, make predictions, design experiments to test hypotheses, collect and process data, and discuss results.
5. Present the results of your experiments in a scientific paper.

## Introduction

**Behavior,** broadly defined, is the sum of the responses of an organism to stimuli in its environment. In other words, behavior is what organisms do. **Ethology** is the study of animal behavior in the context of the evolution, ecology, social organization, and sensory abilities of an animal (Gould, 1982). Ethologists concentrate on developing accurate descriptions of animal behavior by carefully observing and experimentally analyzing overt behavior patterns and by studying the physiology of behavior (Barnett, 1981).

Explaining a particular behavior in the broad, multivariable context of evolution or ecology can become a complex undertaking. It is often necessary, therefore, to study behavior in animals that have a limited range of behaviors and for which more is known about their evolution, ecology, and sensory abilities. Understanding simple and isolated behaviors is important in unraveling more complex behaviors.

There are two basic categories of behavior: **learned** and **innate** (inherited) behavior. Experimental evidence suggests that the basis of both lies in the animal's genes. As with all genetically controlled features of an organism, behavior is subject to evolutionary adaptation. As you study animal behavioral activities in this lab topic, think in terms of both **proximate causes,** the immediate physiological events that led to the behavior, and **ultimate causes,** the adaptive value and evolutionary origin of the behavior. To illustrate, a fiddler crab will respond to human intrusion into its feeding area by running into its burrow. The proximate cause of this behavior might be the vibration caused by footsteps stimulating sensory receptors and triggering nervous impulses. The nervous impulses control muscle contractions in the crab's legs. Ultimate causes are the adaptive value of retreating from predators to avoid being eaten.

From *Investigating Biology Laboratory Manual,* Sixth Edition, Judith G. Morgan and M. Eloise Brown Carter. Copyright © 2008 by Pearson Education, Inc. Published by Benjamin Cummings, Inc. All rights reserved.

Note that you will be asking **causal** questions in your investigations. It is inappropriate to ask **anthropomorphic** questions—that is, questions that ascribe human attributes to the animal. Consider, for example, a behavior that places an animal in its best environment. An anthropomorphic explanation for this behavior would be that the animal makes a conscious choice of its environment. There is no way for us to come to this conclusion scientifically. The causal explanation would be that the animal is equipped with a sensory system that responds to environmental stimuli until the favorable environment is reached.

Ethologists have categorized behavioral patterns based on the particular consequence of that behavior for the organism. **Orientation behaviors** place the animal in its most favorable environment. Two categories of orientation behaviors are **taxis** (plural, **taxes**) and **kinesis.** A taxis is movement directly toward or away from a stimulus. When the response is toward a stimulus, it is said to be *positive;* when it is away from the stimulus, it is *negative.* Prefixes such as *photo, chemo,* and *thermo* can be added to the term to describe the nature of the stimulus. For example, an animal that responds to light may demonstrate positive phototaxis and is described as being *positively phototactic.*

A kinesis differs from a taxis in that it is undirected, or random, movement. A stimulus initiates the movement but does not necessarily orient the movement. The intensity of the stimulus determines the rate, or velocity, of movement in response to that stimulus. If a bright light is shined on an animal and the animal responds by moving directly away from it, the behavior is a taxis. But if the bright light initiates random movement or stimulates an increase in the rate of turning with no particular orientation involved, the behavior is a kinesis. The terms *positive* and *negative* and the prefixes mentioned earlier are also appropriately used with *kinesis.* An increase in activity is a positive response; a decrease in activity is a negative response.

Another complex of behaviors observed in some animals is **agonistic behavior.** In this case, the animal is in a conflict situation where there may be a threat or approach, then an attack or withdrawal. Agonistic behaviors in the form of force are called **aggression;** those of retreat or avoidance are called **submission.** Often the agonistic behavior is simply a display that makes the organism look big or threatening. It rarely leads to death and is thought to help maintain territory so that the dominant organism has greater access to resources such as space, food, and mates.

Mating, or **reproductive behavior,** can involve a complex sequence of activities, sometimes spectacular, that facilitate finding, courting, and mating with a member of the same species. It is an adaptive advantage that reproductive behaviors are species-specific. Can you suggest reasons why?

For the first hour of lab, you will perform Experiment A in each of the exercises that follow, briefly investigating the four behaviors just discussed: taxis in brine shrimp, kinesis in pill bugs, agonistic behavior in Siamese fighting fish, and reproductive behavior in fruit flies. After completing every Experiment A, your team will choose one of the systems discussed and perform Experiment B in that exercise. To begin Experiment B, you will propose one or more testable hypotheses and design a simple experiment by which to test your hypotheses. Then you will spend the remainder of the laboratory period carrying out your experiments.

Near the end of the laboratory period, several of you may be asked to present your team's results to the class for discussion. One part of the scientific process involves persuading your colleagues that your experimental design is sound and that your results support your conclusions (either negating or supporting your hypothesis). Be prepared to describe your results in a brief presentation in which you will use your experimental evidence to persuade the other students in your class.

You may be required to submit a laboratory report describing your experiment and results in the format of a scientific paper. You should discuss results and come to conclusions with your team members; however, you must turn in an originally written lab report. Your Materials and Methods section and your tables and figures may be similar, but your Introduction, Results, and Discussion sections must be the product of your own library research and creative thinking.

Remember, first complete Experiment A in each exercise. Then discuss with your research team a possible question for your original experiment, choosing one of the animals investigated in Experiment A as your experimental organism. Be certain you can pose an interesting question from which you can develop a testable hypothesis. Then turn to Experiment B in the exercise for your chosen organism and design and execute an experiment.

## EXERCISE 1
# Taxis in Brine Shrimp

Brine shrimp (*Artemia salina*) are small crustaceans that live in salt lakes and swim upside down using 11 pairs of appendages. Their sensory structures include two large compound eyes and two pairs of short antennae (Figure 1). They are a favorite fish food and can be purchased in pet stores.

**Figure 1.**
**Brine shrimp (*Artemia salina*) magnified about 20✕.** A type of fairy shrimp, brine shrimp live in inland salt lakes such as the Great Salt Lake in Utah.

# Experiment A. Brine Shrimp Behavior in Environments with Few Stimuli

## Materials

brine shrimp
2 large test tubes
black construction paper

1 small finger bowl
salt water
dropper

## Introduction

In this experiment, you will place brine shrimp in a test tube of salt water similar to the water of their normal environment. You will not feed them or disturb them in any way. You will observe their behavior in this relatively stimulus-free environment. Notice their positions in the test tube. Are they in groups, or are they solitary? Are they near the top or near the bottom? You should make careful observations of their behavior, asking questions about possible stimuli that might initiate taxes in these animals.

## Hypothesis

Hypothesize about the behavior of brine shrimp in an environment with few stimuli.

## Prediction

Predict the result of your experiment based on the hypothesis (if/then).

## Procedure

1. Place six brine shrimp in a test tube filled two-thirds with salt water. Rest the test tube in the finger bowl in such a way that you can easily see all six shrimp. You may need to use black construction paper as a background.
2. Describe the behavior of the brine shrimp in the Results section; for example, are they randomly distributed throughout the test tube or do they collect in one area?
3. Record your observations in the Results section.

## Results

1. By describing the behavior of brine shrimp in an environment with relatively few stimuli, which component of experimental design are you establishing?

2. Describe the behavior of the brine shrimp.

## Discussion

On separate paper, list four stimuli that might initiate taxes in brine shrimp and predict the response of the animal to each. What possible adaptive advantage could this behavior provide?

# Experiment B. Student-Designed Investigation of Brine Shrimp Behavior

## Materials

supplies from Experiment A
piece of black cloth
lamp

dropper bottles—solutions of
   sugar, egg albumin, acid,
   and base

## Introduction

If your team chooses to perform your original experiment investigating taxes in brine shrimp, return to this experiment after you have completed all the introductory investigations (Experiment A of each exercise). Using the materials available and collaborating with other members of your research team, design a simple experiment to investigate taxes in brine shrimp.

## Hypothesis

State the hypothesis that you will investigate.

## Prediction

Predict the results of your experiment based on your hypothesis (if/then).

## Procedure

 Allow a conditioning period of several minutes after the shrimp have been disturbed or stimulated. If you add something to the water in one experiment, begin additional experiments with fresh water and shrimp.

1. On separate paper, list in numerical order each step of your procedure. Remember to include the number of repetitions, levels of treatment, the duration of each stimulus, and other time intervals when appropriate.
2. If you have an idea for an experiment that requires materials other than those available, ask your laboratory instructor. If possible, additional supplies will be made available.
3. Quantify your data whenever possible (count, weigh, measure, time).

## Results

On separate paper, record your data and describe your results. You should design at least one table and figure.

## Discussion

1. Among members of your team, discuss your results in light of your hypothesis. If possible, come to conclusions about the behaviors you have been investigating. Record your conclusions on a separate paper.
2. You may be asked to report the results of your experiments to the class.

EXERCISE 2

# Kinesis in Pill Bugs

Kinesis can be studied using a crustacean in the order Isopoda (called *isopods*). These animals are also called *pill bugs, sow bugs,* and *roly-polies* (Figure 2). Although most crustaceans are aquatic, pill bugs are truly terrestrial, and much of their behavior is involved with their need to avoid desiccation. They are easily collected in warm weather under flowerpots, in leaf litter, or in woodpiles. They often respond to mechanical stimuli by rolling up into a ball.

## Experiment A. Pill Bug Behavior in Moist and Dry Environments

### Materials

pill bugs
2 large petri dishes

filter paper
squirt bottle of water

**Figure 2.**
**Pill bugs magnified about 15×.**
These terrestrial isopods are also called *sow bugs* and *roly-polies*.

## Introduction

In this experiment, you will investigate pill bug behavior in moist and dry environments by observing the degree of their activity, that is, the number of times they circle and turn. As you observe their behavior, ask questions about possible stimuli that might modify this behavior.

## Hypothesis

Hypothesize about the degree of activity of pill bugs in moist and dry environments.

## Prediction

Predict the results of the experiment based on your hypothesis (if/then).

## Procedure

1. Prepare two large petri dishes, one with wet filter paper, the other with dry filter paper.
2. Place five pill bugs in each dish.
3. Place the dishes in a dark spot, such as a drawer, for 5 minutes.
4. After 5 minutes, carefully observe the pill bugs in the petri dishes. Before you open the drawer or uncover the petri dishes, assign each of the following procedures to a member of your team.
   a. Count the number of pill bugs moving in each dish.
   b. Choose one moving pill bug in each dish and determine the rate of locomotion by counting revolutions per minute (rpm) around the petri dish.

c. Determine the rate of turning by counting turns (reversal of direction) per minute for one pill bug in each dish.

## Results

Record your results in Table 1.

### Table 1
Kinesis in Pill Bugs: Response to Wet and Dry Environments

| Environmental Condition | Number Moving | Rate of Locomotion (rpm) | Rate of Turning (turn/min) |
|---|---|---|---|
| Moist | | | |
| Dry | | | |

## Discussion

1. Kinetic response to varying moisture in the environment is called *hygrokinesis*. What other environmental factors might influence the behavior of pill bugs?

2. On separate paper, list four factors that might initiate kineses in pill bugs and predict their response to each. What possible adaptive advantage could this behavior provide?

## Experiment B. Student-Designed Investigation of Pill Bug Behavior

### Materials

supplies from Experiment A
white enamel pan
wax pencils
beaker of water

construction paper
manila folder
large pieces of black cloth

### Introduction

If your team chooses to perform your original experiment investigating kineses in pill bugs, return to this experiment after you have completed all the introductory investigations (Experiment A of each exercise). Using the materials available and collaborating with other members of your research team, design a simple experiment to investigate kineses in pill bugs.

## Hypothesis

State the hypothesis that you will investigate.

## Prediction

Predict the results of the experiment based on your hypothesis (if/then).

## Procedure

1. On separate paper, list in numerical order each step of your procedure. Remember to include the number of repetitions, the levels of treatment, the duration of stimulus, and other time intervals where appropriate.
2. If you have an idea for an experiment that requires materials other than those available, ask your laboratory instructor. If possible, additional supplies will be made available.
3. Quantify your data whenever possible (count, weigh, measure, time).

## Results

On separate paper, record your data and describe your results. You should design at least one table and figure.

## Discussion

1. Among members of your team, discuss your results in light of your hypothesis. If possible, come to conclusions about the behaviors you have been investigating. Record your conclusions on a separate paper.
2. You may be asked to report the results of your experiments to the class.

EXERCISE 3

# Agonistic Display in Male Siamese Fighting Fish

The innate agonistic behavior of the male Siamese fighting fish (*Betta splendens*) has been widely studied (Simpson, 1968; Thompson, 1969). The sight of another male *Betta* or even its own reflection in a mirror will stimulate a ritualized series of responses toward the intruder. If two fish are placed in the same aquarium, their agonistic behavior usually continues until one fish is defeated or subordinated.

# Experiment A. Display Behavior in Male Siamese Fighting Fish

## Materials

male Siamese fighting fish in a 1- to 2-L flat-sided fishbowl
mirror

## Introduction

The purpose of this experiment is to describe the ritualized agonistic display of a male Siamese fighting fish after being stimulated by its own reflection in a mirror. Before you begin the experiment, become familiar with the fish's anatomy, identifying its dorsal fin, ventral fin, pectoral fin, gill cover, and tail (Figure 3).

When you begin the experiment, you will be looking for several possible responses: frontal approach (facing intruder), broadside display, undulating movements, increased swimming speed, fin elevation (dorsal, ventral, or pectoral), gill cover extension (angle may vary), tail expansion, and enhanced coloration in tail, fin, or body.

## Hypothesis

Hypothesize about the response of the fish to its image in the mirror.

## Prediction

Predict the result of the experiment based on your hypothesis (if/then).

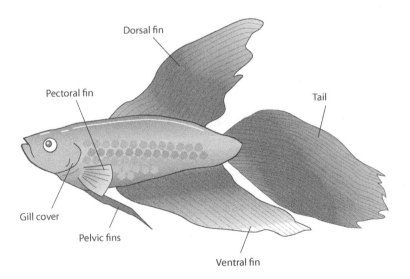

**Figure 3.**
**Male Siamese fighting fish (*Betta splendens*).**

## Procedure

1. Plan your strategy.

   a. Be ready with your pencil and paper to record your observations. Behaviors can happen very quickly. Your entire team should observe and record them.

   b. Each team member should be responsible for timing the duration of particular responses (listed in the Introduction). You might also take turns observing different behaviors, alternating from one behavior to another every 30 seconds.

2. Place the mirror against the fishbowl.

3. As the fish reacts to its reflection, list, in order and using the appropriate terminology, the series of responses. Be as quantitative as possible; for example, you might record "gill cover extended 90° for 30 seconds" or "broadside display for 60 seconds."

4. Compare collective results.

5. In the Results section, make a *sequential* list of the recognizable responses involved in the display.

6. Note in the Results section those responses that take place simultaneously.

## Results

1. Record your sequential list.

2. Record the responses that take place simultaneously.

## Discussion

1. Collaborating with your teammates, write a descriptive paragraph, as quantitative and detailed as possible, describing the agonistic display elicited in the Siamese fighting fish in response to its reflection.

2. What is the obvious adaptive advantage of complex agonistic displays that are not followed by damaging fights? Are there advantages that are not so obvious?

3. Name several other animals that demonstrate a strong display that is seldom followed by a damaging fight.

4. Name several animals that do engage in damaging fights.

# Experiment B. Student-Designed Investigation of Siamese Fighting Fish Behavior

## Materials

supplies from Experiment A
colored pencils
index cards

fish of different species in
    fishbowls
female Siamese fighting fish

## Introduction

If your team chooses to perform your original experiment investigating agonistic behavior in Siamese fighting fish, return to this experiment after you have completed all the introductory investigations (Experiment A of each exercise). Using the materials available and collaborating among your research team, design a simple experiment to investigate this behavior.

Discuss with your team members possible investigations that might be carried out. Several questions follow that might give you ideas.

1. What is the simplest stimulus that will initiate the response? Is color important? Size? Movement?

2. Is the behavior "released" by a specific stimulus or by a complex of all the stimuli?

3. Will another species of fish initiate the response?

4. Will a female *Betta* fish initiate the response, and, if so, how does the response compare with the response to a fish of a different species?

5. Is the response all or none—that is, are there partial displays with different stimuli?

6. Does the fish become "conditioned"—that is, after repeated identical stimuli, does the duration of the display change, or does the display cease?

7. Could chemical stimulation contribute to the response? (Transfer water from one fishbowl to another.)

## Hypothesis

After your team has decided on one or more questions to investigate, formulate a testable hypothesis.

## Prediction

Predict the results of the experiment based on your hypothesis (if/then).

## Procedure

1. On separate paper, list in numerical order each step of your procedure. Remember to include the number of repetitions, the levels of treatment, the duration of a stimulus, and other time intervals where appropriate.

2. If you have an idea for an experiment that requires materials other than those available, ask your laboratory instructor. If possible, additional supplies will be made available.

3. Quantify your data whenever possible (count, weigh, measure, time).

## Results

On separate paper, record your data and describe your results. You should design at least one table and figure.

## Discussion

1. Among members of your team, discuss your results in light of your hypothesis. If possible, come to conclusions about the behaviors you have been investigating. Record your conclusions on a separate paper.

2. You may be asked to report the results of your experiments to the class.

EXERCISE 4

# Reproductive Behavior in Fruit Flies

Spieth (1952, described in Marler, 1968) has classified the mating behavior of the fruit fly *Drosophila melanogaster* as being a complex of at least fourteen behaviors. Described below are ten of the most common and easily recognized of these behaviors. Read the list carefully and become familiar with the behaviors you will be required to recognize. Six of the behaviors are seen in males, four in females. The behavior sequence begins as the male orients his body toward the female (Figure 4a).

### Male Behaviors

1. *Tapping.* The forelegs are extended to strike or tap the female (Figure 4b).
2. *Waving.* The wing is extended and held 90° from the body, then relaxed without vibration (Figure 4c).
3. *Wing vibration.* The male extends one or both wings from the resting position and moves them rapidly up and down (Figure 4c).
4. *Licking.* The male licks the female's genitalia (on the rear of her abdomen) (Figure 4d).
5. *Circling.* The male postures and then circles the female, usually when she is nonreceptive.
6. *Stamping.* The male stamps forefeet as in tapping but does not strike the female.

### Female Behaviors

1. *Extruding.* A temporary, tubelike structure is extended from the female's genitalia.
2. *Decamping.* A nonreceptive female runs, jumps, or flies away from the courting male.
3. *Depressing.* A nonreceptive female prevents access to her genitalia by depressing her wings and curling the tip of her abdomen down.
4. *Ignoring.* A nonreceptive female ignores the male.

If the behavior display is successful, the flies will copulate (Figure 4e, f).

**a.** Orienting        **b.** Tapping        **c.** Waving and wing vibration

**d.** Licking        **e.** Attempting copulation        **f.** Copulation

Illustration by Suzanne Barnes.

**Figure 4.**
Mating behavior in fruit fly, *Drosophila melanogaster.*

## Experiment A. Reproductive Behavior in *Drosophila melanogaster*

### Materials

stereoscopic microscope
fly vials with 2 or 3 virgin female *D. melanogaster* flies
fly vials with 2 or 3 male *D. melanogaster* flies

### Introduction

In this experiment, you will place virgin female *D. melanogaster* flies in the same vial with male flies and observe the behavior of each sex. Working with another student, discuss the behaviors described in the introduction to this exercise and plan the strategy for your experiment. Identify mating behaviors of *D. melanogaster* and record their sequence and duration (when appropriate). As you observe the behavior of the flies, discuss possible original experiments investigating reproductive behavior in flies.

### Hypothesis

Hypothesize about the presence of flies of the opposite sex in the same vial.

## Prediction

Predict the results of the experiment based on your hypothesis (if/then).

## Procedure

1. Set up the stereoscopic microscope.
2. Have paper and pencil ready. The behaviors can happen very rapidly. One person should call out observations while the other person records.
3. Obtain one vial containing virgin females and one vial containing males, and gently tap the male flies into the vial containing females.
4. Observe first with the naked eye. Once flies have encountered each other, use the stereoscopic microscope to make observations.

## Results

1. Describe, in sequence, the response of the male to the female and the female to the male. Quantify your observations. To do this, you may consider counting the number of times a behavior takes place and timing the duration of behaviors.

2. Describe rejection if this takes place.

3. In the margin of your lab manual, note any behaviors that can be analyzed quantitatively.

## Discussion

Speculate about the adaptive advantage of elaborate courtship behaviors in animals.

# Experiment B. Student-Designed Investigation of Reproductive Behavior in Fruit Flies

## Materials

supplies from Experiment A
fly vials with 2 or 3 virgin females of an alternate fly species (other than *D. melanogaster*)

fly vials with 2 or 3 males of the alternate species

## Introduction

If your team chooses to perform your original experiment investigating reproductive behavior in fruit flies, continue with this experiment after you have completed all the introductory investigations (Experiment A of each exercise). Using the materials available and collaborating with your research partner, design a simple experiment to investigate reproductive behavior. Several questions follow that might provide ideas.

1. Will reproductive behavior in another species be identical to that in *D. melanogaster*?
2. Will males placed in the same vial demonstrate courtship behaviors?
3. Will males respond to dead females?
4. What is the response of a male *D. melanogaster* to females of a different species?
5. Do males compete?

Quantify your observations. To do this, you may consider counting the number of times a behavior takes place or timing the duration of behaviors.

## Hypothesis

After your team has decided on one or more questions to investigate, formulate a testable hypothesis.

## Prediction

Predict the results of your experiment based on your hypothesis (if/then).

## Procedure

1. On a separate paper, list in numerical order each step of your procedure. Remember to include the number of repetitions, the levels of treatment, the duration of stimulus, and other time intervals where appropriate.
2. If you have an idea for an experiment that requires materials other than those available, ask your laboratory instructor. If possible, additional supplies will be made available.
3. Quantify your data whenever possible (count, weigh, measure, time).

## Results

On a separate paper, record your data and describe your results. You should design at least one table and figure.

## Discussion

1. Within your team, discuss your results in light of your hypothesis. If possible, come to conclusions about the behaviors you have been investigating. Record your conclusions on a separate paper.

2. You may be asked to report the results of your experiments to the class.

## Questions for Review

Define, compare, and give examples for each item in the following pairs:

1. Learned behavior—innate behavior

2. Proximate cause of behavior—ultimate cause of behavior

3. Causal explanation for a behavior—anthropomorphic explanation for a behavior

4. Taxis—kinesis

## Applying Your Knowledge

1. Adult male European robins have red feathers on their breasts. A male robin will display aggressive behavior and attack another male robin that invades his territory during mating season. Immature male robins with all brown feathers do not elicit this behavior in the adult robin. How could you explain this behavior? Design an experiment to test your explanation (hypothesis).

2. In the spring, distinctive and elaborate male cardinal songs may be heard throughout most eastern deciduous forests. You suspect that the function of a bird's song at this time of year has something to do with territorial defense and finding a mate. You also suspect that there must be some environmental trigger that affects the bird's endocrine system leading to the behavior. In lab today, you learned that it is possible to explain behaviors based on anthropomorphic causes but that scientists base explanations on proximate and ultimate causes (see Lab Topic Introduction). In the space below, propose explanations (hypotheses) based on these three perspectives—anthropomorphic, proximate, and ultimate—and then propose a research project for those hypotheses that can be tested scientifically.

a. Anthropomorphic causes:

Possible research project:

b. Proximate causes:

Possible research project:

c. Ultimate causes:

Possible research project:

# Student Media Activities and Investigations

**Activities**—Ch. 51: Honeybee Waggle Dance Video
**Investigations**—Ch. 51: How Can Pillbug Responses to Environments Be Tested?
www.masteringbio.com

# References

Alcock, J. *Animal Behavior: An Evolutionary Approach,* 8th ed. Sunderland, MA: Sinauer Associates, 2005.

Campbell, N., and J. Reece. *Biology,* 8th ed. San Francisco, CA: Benjamin Cummings, 2008.

Greenspan, R. J. "Understanding the Genetic Construction of Behavior." *Scientific American,* 1995, vol. 272, no. 4, p. 72.

Johnson, R. N. *Aggression in Man and Animals.* Philadelphia, PA: Saunders College Publishing, 1972.

Marler, P. "Mating Behavior of *Drosophila.*" In *Animal Behavior in Laboratory and Field,* editor A. W. Stokes. San Francisco: Freeman, 1968.

Raham, G. "Pill Bug Biology." *The American Biology Teacher,* 1986, vol. 48, no. 1.

Simpson, M. J. A. "The Threat Display of the Siamese Fighting Fish, *Betta splendens.*" *Animal Behavior Monograph,* 1968, vol. 1, p. 1.

Thompson, T. "Aggressive Behavior of Siamese Fighting Fish," in *Aggressive Behavior,* editors S. Garattini and E. B. Sigg. Proceedings of the International Symposium on the Biology of Aggressive Behavior. New York, NY: Wiley, 1969.

Waterman, M., and E. Stanley. *Biological Inquiry: A Workbook of Investigative Cases.* San Francisco, CA: Benjamin Cummings, 2008. In this supplement to Campbell and Reece, 8th ed., see "Back to the Bay," a case study applying principles of animal behavior to an environmental problem.

# Websites

Animal Behavior Society Website:
http://www.animalbehavior.org

Overview of topics in animal behavior:
http://cas.bellarmine.edu/tietjen/
animal_behavior_and_ethology.htm

J. Kimball's online discussion of innate behavior:
http://users.rcn.com/jkimball.ma.ultranet/BiologyPages/
I/InnateBehavior.html

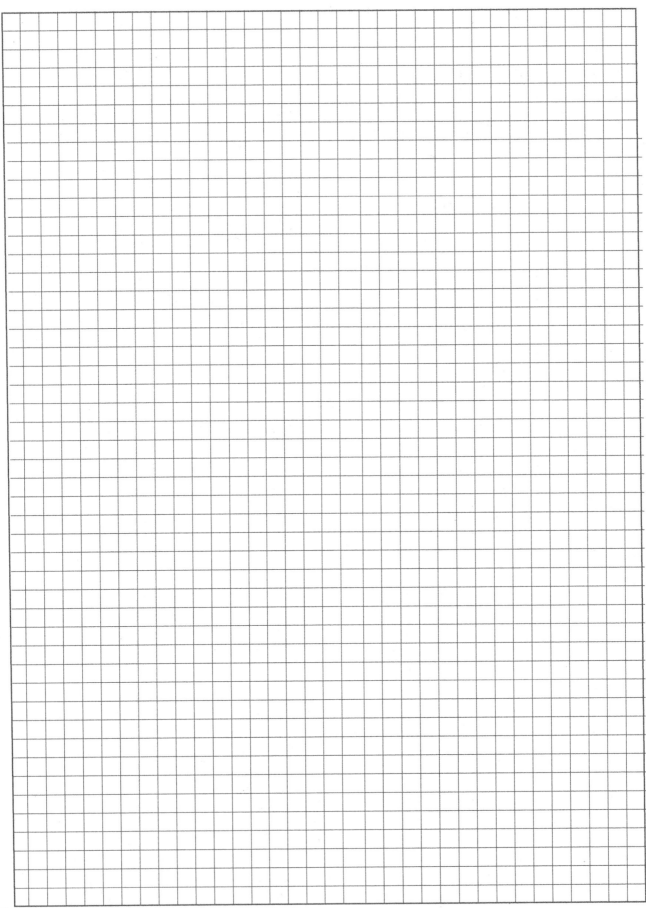

# Plant Anatomy

## Laboratory Objectives

After completing this lab topic, you should be able to:

1. Identify and describe the structure and function of each cell type and tissue type.
2. Describe the organization of tissues and cells in each plant organ.
3. Relate the function of an organ to its structure.
4. Describe primary and secondary growth and identify the location of each in the plant.
5. Relate primary and secondary growth to the growth habit (woody or herbaceous).
6. Discuss adaptation of land plants to the terrestrial environment as illustrated by the structure and function of plant anatomy.
7. Apply your knowledge of plants to the kinds of produce you find in the grocery store.

## Introduction

Vascular plants have been successful on land for over 420 million years, and their success is related to their adaptations to the land environment. An aquatic alga lives most often in a continuously homogeneous environment: The requirements for life are everywhere around it, so relatively minor structural adaptations have evolved for functions such as reproduction and attachment. In contrast, the terrestrial habitat, with its extreme environmental conditions, presents numerous challenges for the survival of plants. Consequently, land plants have evolved structural adaptations for functions such as the absorption of underground water and nutrients, the anchoring of the plant in the substrate, the support of aerial parts of the plant, and the transportation of materials throughout the relatively large plant body. In angiosperms, the structural adaptations required for these and other functions are divided among three vegetative plant organs: stems, roots, and leaves. Unlike animal organs, which are often composed of unique cell types (for example, cardiac muscle fibers are found only in the heart, osteocytes only in bone), plant organs have many tissues and cell types in common, but they are organized in different ways. The structural organization of basic tissues and cell types in different plant organs is directly related to their different functions. For example, leaves function as the primary photosynthetic organ and generally have thin, flat blades that maximize light absorption and gas

From *Investigating Biology Laboratory Manual,* Sixth Edition, Judith G. Morgan and M. Eloise Brown Carter. Copyright © 2008 by Pearson Education, Inc. Published by Benjamin Cummings, Inc. All rights reserved.

exchange. Specialized cells of the root epidermis are long extensions that promote one of the root functions, absorption. The interrelationship of structure and function is a major theme in biology, and you will continue to explore it in this lab topic.

Use the figures in this lab topic for orientation and as a study aid. Be certain that you can identify all items by examining the living specimens and microscope slides. These, and not the diagrams, will be used in the laboratory evaluations.

## Summary of Basic Plant Tissue Systems and Cell Types

The plant body is constructed into **tissue systems** based on their shared structural and functional features. There are three tissue systems—**dermal, ground**, and **vascular**—that are continuous throughout the organs of roots, stems, and leaves. The plant tissues that actively divide by mitosis are called **meristematic tissues.** These are located in specific regions—for example the root tip. Following is a review of plant tissue systems and the most common types of cells seen in plant organs, as well as their functions. Other specialized cells will be described as they are discussed in lab. Refer back to this summary as you work through the exercises.

### Dermal Tissue System: Epidermis

The **epidermis** forms the outermost layer of cells, usually one cell thick, covering the entire plant body. The epidermal cells are often flattened and rectangular in shape (Figure 1a and 1b). Specialized epidermal cells include the **guard cells** of the stomata, hairs called **trichomes,** and unicellular **root hairs.** Most epidermal cells on aboveground structures are covered by a waxy **cuticle,** which prevents water loss. The epidermis provides protection and regulates movement of materials.

### Ground Tissue System: Parenchyma, Collenchyma, and Sclerenchyma

The ground tissue system is distributed throughout the plant beneath the epidermis and surrounding vascular tissues. Parenchyma, collenchyma, and/or sclerenchyma cells are typically found in ground tissue as seen in the cross-section of a pumpkin stem (Figure 1c).

**Parenchyma** cells are the most common cell in plants and are characteristically thin-walled with large vacuoles. These cells may function in photosynthesis, support, storage of materials, and lateral transport.

**Collenchyma** cells are usually found near the surface of the stem, leaf petioles, and veins. These living cells are similar to parenchyma cells but are characterized by an uneven thickening of cell walls. They provide flexible support to young plant organs.

**Sclerenchyma** cells have thickened cell walls that may contain lignin. They provide strength and support to mature plant structures and may be dead at functional maturity. The most common type of sclerenchyma cells are long, thin **fibers.**

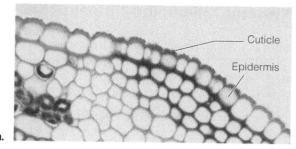

Cuticle

Epidermis

**a.**

Judith Morgan and Eloise Carter

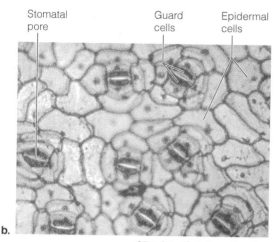

Stomatal pore

Guard cells

Epidermal cells

**b.**

©Eric Grave/Photo Researchers, Inc.

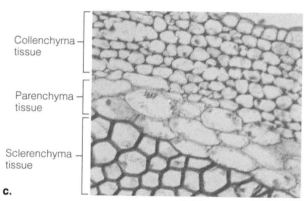

Collenchyma tissue

Parenchyma tissue

Sclerenchyma tissue

**c.**

Judith Morgan and Eloise Carter

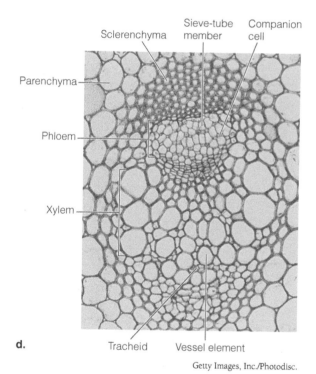

Sclerenchyma

Sieve-tube member

Companion cell

Parenchyma

Phloem

Xylem

**d.**

Tracheid

Vessel element

Getty Images, Inc./Photodisc.

One phloem sieve-tube member

Vessel element

Cell wall of vessel with pits

Sieve plate

**e.**

Spiral cell wall thickenings in xylem

Judith Morgan and Eloise Carter

## Figure 1.

**Plant tissue systems and cell types.**
(a) Dermal tissue—a single layer of
epidermis covered by waxy cuticle;
(b) Leaf surface showing epidermis
with stomata and guard cells;
(c) Ground tissue—cross section of
pumpkin stem;
(d) Vascular tissue—cross section of a
vascular bundle in a buttercup stem;
(e) Long section through xylem and
phloem of pumpkin stem.

# Vascular Tissue System: Xylem and Phloem

The vascular tissue system functions in the transport of materials throughout the plant body. Xylem tissue and phloem tissue are complex tissues (composed of several cell types) seen in the cross section of a buttercup stem (Figure 1d) and a long section of a pumpkin stem (Figure 1e).

**Xylem** cells form a complex vascular tissue that functions in the transport of water and minerals throughout the plant and provides support. **Tracheids** and **vessel elements** are the primary water-conducting cells. Tracheids are long, thin cells with perforated tapered ends. Vessel elements are larger in diameter, open-ended, and joined end to end, forming continuous transport systems referred to as **vessels.** Parenchyma cells are present in the xylem and function in storage and lateral transport. Fibers in the xylem provide additional support.

**Phloem** tissue transports the products of photosynthesis throughout the plant as part of the vascular tissue system. This complex tissue is composed of living, conducting cells called **sieve-tube members,** which lack a nucleus and have **sieve plates** for end walls. The cells are joined end to end throughout the plant. Each sieve-tube member is associated with one or more adjacent **companion cells,** which are thought to regulate sieve-tube member function. Phloem parenchyma cells function in storage and lateral transport, and phloem fibers provide additional support.

## Meristematic Tissue: Primary Meristem, Cambium, and Pericycle

**Primary meristems** consist of small, actively dividing cells located in buds of the shoot and in root tips of plants. These cells produce the primary tissues along the plant axis throughout the life of the plant. You will study primary meristems in the apical bud in Exercise 2 (Figure 3).

**Pericycle** is a layer of meristematic cells just outside the vascular cylinder in the root. These cells divide to produce lateral branch roots (Exercise 3 Lab Study B, Figure 6c).

**Vascular cambium** is a lateral meristem also composed of small, actively dividing cells that are located between the xylem and phloem vascular tissue. These cells divide to produce secondary growth, which results in an increase in girth (Exercise 4, Figure 10).

**Cork cambium** is a lateral meristem located just inside the cork layer of a woody plant. These cells divide to produce secondary growth (Exercise 4, Figure 10).

This lab topic begins with a study of the shape and form of the whole plant, then moves to an investigation of the primary plant body derived from apical meristems. You will look at a slide of the apical bud from the tip of the stem. Next you will look at the structure of the three organs of the primary plant body: stems, roots, and leaves. Some plants continue to grow from lateral meristems producing secondary tissues, which you will investigate in stems of a woody plant. The lab topic concludes with an application of your knowledge to plants commonly found in the grocery store.

EXERCISE 1
# Plant Morphology

## Materials

living bean or geranium plant       paper towel
squirt bottle of water

## Introduction

As you begin your investigation of the structure and function of plants, you need an understanding of the general shape and form of the whole plant. In this exercise, you will study a bean or geranium plant, identifying basic features of the three vegetative organs: roots, stems, and leaves. In the following exercises, you will investigate the cellular structure of these organs as viewed in cross sections. Refer to the living plant for orientation before you view your slides.

## Procedure

1. Working with another student, examine a living **herbaceous** (non-woody) plant and identify the following structures in the shoot (stems and leaves):

   a. **Nodes** are regions of the stem from which leaves, buds, and branches arise and which contain meristematic tissue (areas of cell division).

   b. **Internodes** are the regions of the stem located between the nodes.

   c. **Terminal buds** are located at the tips of stems and branches. They enclose the shoot apical meristem, which gives rise to leaves, buds, and all primary tissue of the stem. Only stems produce buds.

   d. **Axillary,** or **lateral, buds** are located in the leaf axes at nodes; they may give rise to lateral branches.

   e. Leaves consist of flattened **blades** attached at the node of a stem by a stalk, or **petiole.**

2. Observe the root structures by gently removing the plant from the pot and loosening the soil from the root structure. You may need to rinse a few roots with water to observe the tiny, active roots. Identify the following structures:

   a. **Primary** and **secondary roots.** The primary root is the first root produced by a plant embryo and may become a long taproot. Secondary roots arise from meristematic tissue deep within the primary root.

   b. Root tips consist of a **root apical meristem** that gives rise to a **root cap** (protective layer of cells covering the root tip) and to all the primary tissues of the root. A short distance from the root tip is a zone of **root hairs** (specialized epidermal cells), the principal site of water and mineral absorption.

## Results

1. Label Figure 2.
2. Sketch in the margin of your lab manual any features not included in this diagram that might be needed for future reference.

**Figure 2.**
**A herbaceous plant.** The vegetative plant body consists of roots, stems, and leaves. The buds are located in the axils of the leaves and at the shoot tip. The roots also grow from meristem tissues in the root tip. Label the diagram based on your observations of a living plant and the structures named in Exercise 1.

## Discussion

1. Look at your plant and discuss with your partner the possible functions of each plant organ. Your discussion might include evidence observed in the lab today or prior knowledge. Describe proposed functions (more than one) for each organ.

   Stems:

   Roots:

   Leaves:

2. Imagine that you have cut each organ—roots, stems, and leaves—in cross section. Sketch the overall shape of that cross section in the margin of your lab manual. Remember, you are not predicting the internal structure, just the overall shape.

EXERCISE 2

# Plant Primary Growth and Development

## Materials

prepared slides of *Coleus* stem (long section)
compound microscope

## Introduction

Plants produce new cells throughout their lifetime as a result of cell divisions in meristems. Tissues produced from apical meristems are called **primary tissues,** and this growth is called **primary growth.** Primary growth occurs along the plant axis at the shoot and the root tip. Certain meristem cells divide in such a way that one cell product becomes a new body cell and the other remains in the meristem. Beyond the zone of active cell division, new cells become enlarged and specialized for specific functions (resulting, for example, in vessels, parenchyma, and epidermis). The investigation of the genetic and biochemical basis of this cell differentiation continues to be an area of exciting biological research.

In this exercise, you will examine a longitudinal section through the tip of the stem, observing the youngest tissues and meristems at the apex, then moving down the stem, where you will observe more mature cells and tissues.

## Procedure

1. Examine a prepared slide of a longitudinal section through a terminal bud of *Coleus.* Use low power to get an overview of the slide; then increase magnification. Locate the **apical meristem,** a dome of tissue nestled between the **leaf primordia,** young developing leaves. Locate the axillary **bud primordial** between the leaf and the stem.

2. Move the specimen under the microscope so that cells may be viewed at varying distances from the apex. The youngest cells are at the apex of the bud, and cells of increasing maturity and differentiation can be seen as you move away from the apex. Follow the early development of vascular tissue, which differentiates in relation to the development of primordial leaves.

   a. Locate the narrow, dark tracks of **undifferentiated vascular tissue** in the leaf primordia.

   b. Observe changes in cell size and structure of the vascular system as you move away from the apex and end with a distinguishable vessel element of the **xylem,** with its spiral cell wall thickening in the older leaf primordia and stem. You may need to use the highest power on the microscope to locate these spiral cell walls.

## Results

1. Label Figure 3, indicating the structures visible in the young stem tip.
2. Modify the figure or sketch details in the margin of the lab manual for future reference.

## Discussion

1. Describe the changes in cell size and structure in the stem tip. Begin at the youngest cells at the apex and continue to the xylem cells.

2. The meristems of plants continue to grow throughout their lifetime, an example of **indeterminate growth.** Imagine a 200-year-old oak tree, with active meristem producing new buds, leaves, and stems each year. Contrast this with the growth pattern in humans.

# EXERCISE 3
# Cell Structure of Primary Tissues

All **herbaceous** (nonwoody) flowering plants produce a complete plant body composed of primary tissue, derived from apical primary meristem. This plant body consists of *organs*—roots, stems, leaves, flowers, fruits, and seeds—and *tissue systems*—**dermal, ground,** and **vascular.** In this exercise, you will investigate the cellular structure and organization of plant organs and tissues by examining microscopic slides. You will make your own thin cross sections of stems, and view prepared slides of stems, roots, and leaves. Woody stems will be examined in Exercise 4.

## Lab Study A. Stems

### Materials

prepared slide of herbaceous
    dicot stem
dropper bottle of distilled water
small petri dish with 50% ethanol
dropper bottle of 50% glycerine
dropper bottle of 0.2% toluidine
    blue stain
nut-and-bolt microtome

warm paraffin
living plant for sections
new single-edged razor blade
forceps
microscope slides
coverslips
compound microscope
dissecting needles

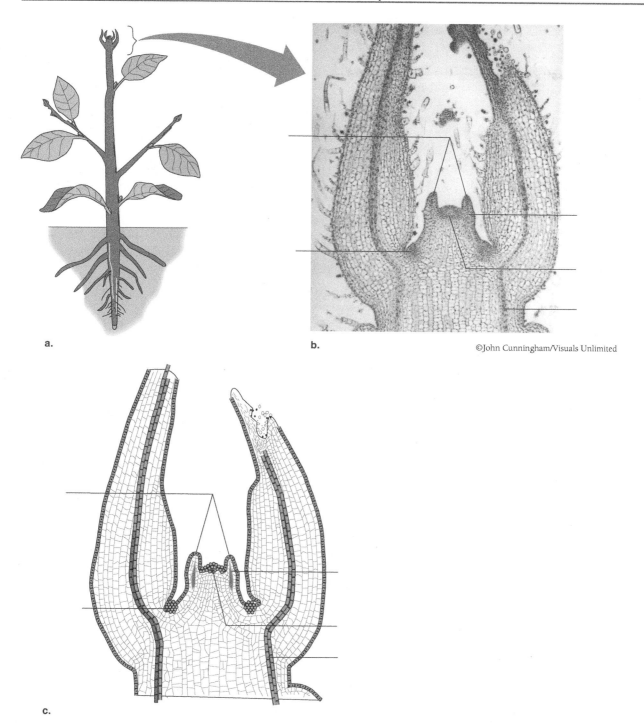

©John Cunningham/Visuals Unlimited

a.

b.

c.

**Figure 3.**
*Coleus* **stem tip.** (a) Diagram of entire plant body. (b) Photomicrograph of a longitudinal section through the terminal bud. (c) Line diagram of the growing shoot tip with primordial leaves surrounding the actively dividing apical meristem. The most immature cells are at the tip of the shoot and increase in stages of development and differentiation farther down the stem. Label the cells and structures described in Exercise 2.

## Introduction

A stem is usually the main stalk, or axis, of a plant and is the only organ that produces buds and leaves. Stems support leaves and conduct water and inorganic substances from the root to the leaves and carbohydrate products of photosynthesis from the leaves to the roots. Most herbaceous stems are able to photosynthesize. Stems exhibit several interesting adaptations, including water storage in cacti, carbohydrate storage in some food plants, and thorns that reduce herbivory in a variety of plants.

You will view a prepared slide of a cross section of a stem, and, working with another student, you will use a simple microtome—an instrument used for cutting thin sections for microscopic study—to make your own slides. You will embed the stem tissue in paraffin and cut thin sections. You will stain your sections with toluidine blue, which will help you distinguish different cell types. This simple procedure is analogous to the process used to make prepared slides for subsequent lab studies.

 Read through the procedure and set up the materials before beginning.

## Procedure

1. Embed the sections of the stem.
   a. Using a new single-edged razor blade, cut a 0.5 cm section of a young bean stem.
   b. Obtain a nut-and-bolt microtome. The nut should be screwed just into the first threads of the bolt. Using forceps, carefully hold the bean stem upright inside the nut.
   c. Pour the warm paraffin into the nut until full. Continue to hold the top of the stem until the paraffin begins to harden. While the paraffin completely hardens, continue the exercise by examining the prepared slide of the stem.
2. Examine a prepared slide of a cross section through the herbaceous dicot stem. As you study the stem tissues and cells, refer to "Summary of Basic Plant Tissue Systems and Cell Types," and Figure 1.
3. Identify the **dermal tissue system,** characterized by a protective cell layer covering the plant. It is composed of the **epidermis** and the **cuticle.** Occasionally, you may also observe multicellular **trichomes** on the outer surface of the plants.
4. Locate the **ground tissue system,** background tissue that fills the spaces between epidermis and vascular tissue. Identify the **cortex region** located between the vascular bundles and the epidermis. It is composed mostly of **parenchyma,** but the outer part may contain **collenchyma** as well.

5. Next find the **pith region,** which occupies the center of the stem, inside the ring of vascular bundles; it is composed of parenchyma. In herbaceous stems, these cells provide support through turgor pressure. This region is also important in storage.

6. Now identify the **vascular system,** a continuous system of xylem and phloem providing transport and support. In your stems and in many stems, the **vascular bundles** (clusters of xylem and phloem) occur in rings that surround the pith; however, in some groups of flowering plants, the vascular tissue is arranged in a complex network.

7. Observe that each bundle consists of phloem tissue toward the outside and xylem tissue toward the inside. A narrow layer of vascular cambium, which may become active in herbaceous stems, is situated between the xylem and the phloem. Take note of the following information as you make your observations.

**Phloem tissue** is composed of three cell types:

a. Dead, fibrous, thick-walled **sclerenchyma cells** that provide support for the phloem tissue and appear in a cluster as a **bundle cap.**

b. **Sieve-tube members,** which are large, living, elongated cells that lack a nucleus at maturity. They become vertically aligned to form sieve tubes, and their cytoplasm is interconnected through sieve plates located at the ends of the cells. Sieve plates are not usually seen in cross sections.

c. **Companion cells,** which are small, nucleated parenchyma cells connected to sieve-tube cells by means of cytoplasmic strands.

**Xylem tissue** is made up of two cell types:

a. **Tracheids,** which are elongated, thick-walled cells with closed, tapered ends. They are dead at functional maturity, and their lumens are interconnected through pits in the cell walls.

b. **Vessel elements,** which are cylindrical cells that are large in diameter and dead at functional maturity. They become joined end to end, lose their end walls, and form long, vertical vessels.

**Vascular cambium** is a type of tissue that is located between the xylem and the phloem and which actively divides to give rise to secondary tissues.

8. Complete the Results section on the next page for this slide, then return to step 9 to prepare and observe your own handmade sections of stem preparations.

9. Cut the stem sections in the hardened paraffin.

a. Support the nut-and-bolt microtome with the bolt head down and, using the razor blade, carefully slice off any excess paraffin extending above the nut. Be careful to slice in a direction away from your body and to keep your fingers away from the edge of the razor blade (Figure 4).

 Be careful to keep fingers and knuckles away from the razor blade. Follow directions carefully.

b. Turn the bolt *just a little,* to extend the stem/paraffin above the edge of the nut.

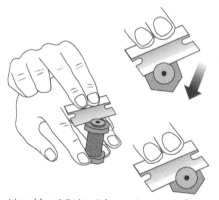

Adapted from J. Dickey, *Laboratory Investigations for General Biology* (Redwood City, CA: Benjamin Cummings, 1994) © 1994 The Benjamin/Cummings Publishing Company.

**Figure 4.**

**Using the nut-and-bolt microtome.**
A piece of stem is embedded in paraffin in the bolt. As you twist the bolt up, slice thin sections to be stained and viewed. Slide the entire blade through the paraffin to smoothly slice thin sections. Follow the directions in Exercise 3, Lab Study A carefully.

c. Produce a thin section by slicing off the extension using the full length of the razor blade, beginning at one end of the blade and slicing to the other end of the blade (see Figure 4).

d. Transfer each section to a small petri dish containing 50% ethanol.

e. Continue to produce thin sections of stem in this manner. The thinnest slices may curl, but this is all right if the stem section remains in the paraffin as you make the transfer. Cell types are easier to identify in very thin sections or in the thin edges of thicker sections.

10. Stain the sections.

a. Leave the sections in 50% ethanol in the petri dish for 5 minutes. The alcohol *fixes,* or preserves, the tissue. Using dissecting needles and forceps, carefully separate the tissue from the surrounding paraffin.

b. Using forceps, move the stem sections, free of the paraffin, to a clean slide.

c. Add several drops of toluidine blue to cover the sections. Allow the sections to stain for 10 to 15 seconds.

d. Carefully draw off the stain by placing a piece of paper towel at the edge of the stain.

e. Rinse the sections by adding several drops of distilled water to cover the sections. Draw off the excess water with a paper towel. Repeat this step until the rinse water no longer looks blue.

f. Add a drop of 50% glycerine to the sections and cover them with a coverslip, being careful not to trap bubbles in the preparation.

g. Observe your sections using a compound microscope. Survey the sections at low or intermediate power, selecting the specimens with the clearest cell structure. You may have to study more than one specimen to see all structures.

11. Follow steps 3–7 above and identify all structures and cells. Incorporate your observations into the Results section (step 4).

## Results

1. Label the stem section in Figure 5b and c.

2. Were any epidermal trichomes present in your stem?

3. Note any features not described in the procedure. Sketch these in the margin of your lab manual for future reference. Return to Procedure step 9 in this lab study and complete the preparation of hand sections of the bean stem.

4. Compare your hand sections with the prepared slide. Modify Figure 5 or sketch your hand section in the margin. Is there any evidence of vascular cambium and secondary growth (Exercise 4)? Compare your results with those of other students.

 **The functions of cells were described in the Summary of Basic Plant Tissue Systems and Cell Types, which appeared near the beginning of this lab topic (Figure 1).**

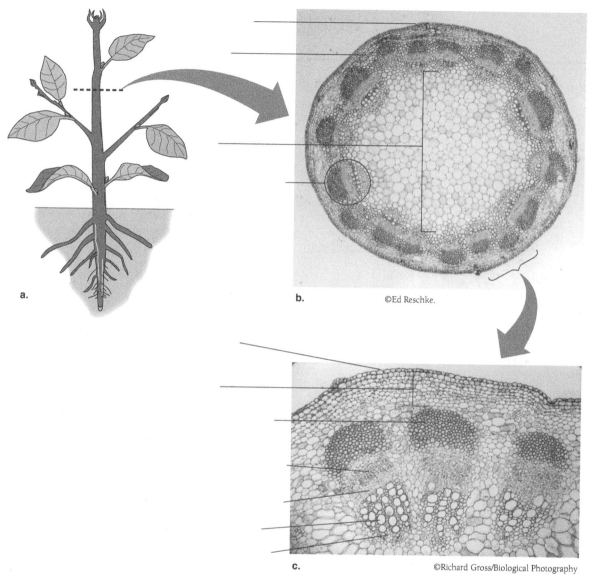

**Figure 5.**
**Stem anatomy.** (a) Diagram of whole plant. (b) Photomicrograph of cross section through the stem portion of the plant. (c) Enlargement of one vascular bundle as seen in cross section of the stem.

## Discussion

1. Which are larger and more distinct, xylem cells or phloem cells?

2. What types of cells provide support of the stem? Where are these cells located in the stem?

3. For the cells described in your preceding answer, how does their observed structure relate to their function, which is support?

4. What is the function of xylem? Of phloem?

5. The pith and cortex are made up of parenchyma cells. Describe the many functions of these cells. Relate parenchyma cell functions to their observed structure.

6. What differences did you observe in the prepared stem sections and your hand sections? What factors might be responsible for these differences?

## Lab Study B. Roots

### Materials

prepared slide of buttercup (*Ranunculus*) root (cross section)
demonstration of fibrous roots and taproots
colored pencils
compound microscope

### Introduction

Roots and stems often appear to be similar, except that roots grow in the soil and stems above the ground. However, some stems (rhizomes) grow underground, and some roots (adventitious roots) grow aboveground. Roots and stems may superficially appear similar, but they differ significantly in their functions.

What are the primary functions of stems?

Roots have four primary functions:

1. anchorage of the plant in the soil
2. absorption of water and minerals from the soil
3. conduction of water and minerals from the region of absorption to the base of the stem
4. starch storage to varying degrees, depending on the plant

## Hypothesis

The working hypothesis for this investigation is that the *structure* of the plant body is related to particular *functions*.

## Prediction

Based on the hypothesis, make a prediction about the similarity of root and stem structures that you expect to observe (if/then).

You will now test your hypothesis and predictions by observing the external structure of roots and their internal cellular structure and organization in a prepared cross section. This activity is an example of collecting evidence from observations rather than conducting a controlled experiment.

## Procedure

1. Examine the external root structure. When a seed germinates, it sends down a **primary root**, or **radicle**, into the soil. This root sends out side branches called lateral roots, and these in turn branch out until a root system is formed.

   If the primary root continues to be the largest and most important part of the root system, the plant is said to have a **taproot** system. If many main roots are formed, the plant has a **fibrous root** system. Most grasses have a fibrous root system, as do trees with roots occurring within 1 m of the soil surface. Carrots, dandelions, and pine trees are examples of plants having taproots.

   a. Observe examples of fibrous roots and taproots on demonstration in the laboratory.

   b. Sketch the two types of roots in the margin of your lab manual.

2. Examine the internal root structure.

   a. Study a slide of a cross section through a buttercup (*Ranunculus*) root. Note that the root lacks a central pith. The vascular tissue is located in the center of the root and is called the **vascular cylinder** (Figure 6b).

   b. Look for a cortex. The **cortex** is primarily composed of large parenchyma cells filled with numerous purple-stained organelles. Which of the

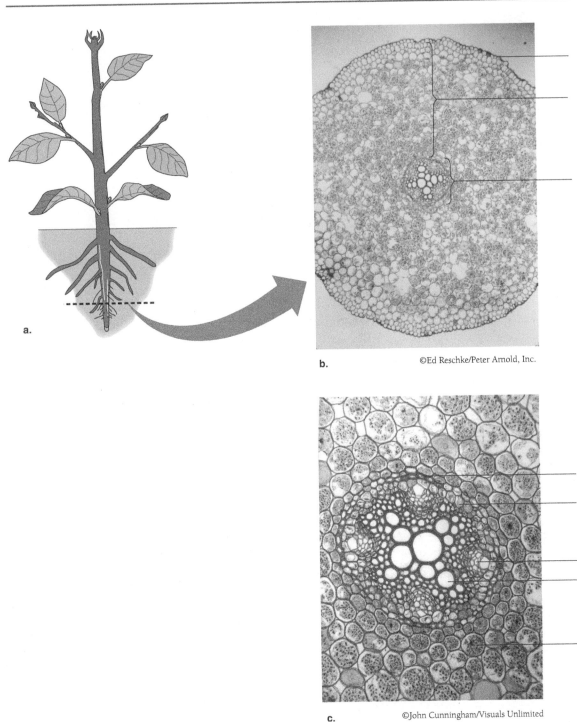

b.

c.

**Figure 6.**
**Cross section of the buttercup root.** (a) Whole plant. (b) Photomicrograph of a cross section of a root. (c) Enlargement of the vascular cylinder. Label the root based on your observations of a prepared microscope slide.

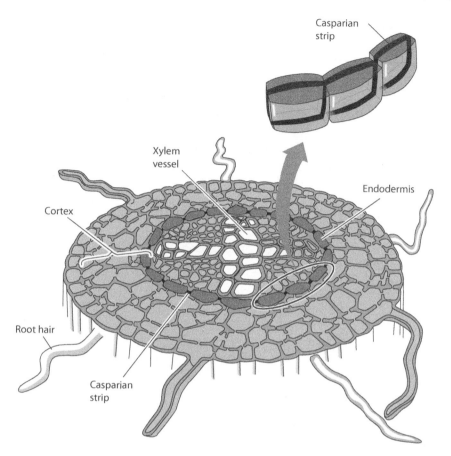

Casparian strip

Xylem vessel

Cortex

Endodermis

Root hair

Casparian strip

**Figure 7.**
**Root endodermis.** The endodermis is composed of cells surrounded by a band containing *suberin,* called the *Casparian strip* (seen in enlargement), that prevents the movement of materials along the cells' walls and intercellular spaces into the vascular cylinder. Materials must cross the cell membrane before entering the vascular tissue.

four functions of roots listed in the introduction to this lab study do you think is related to these cortical cells and their organelles?

c. Identify the following tissues and regions and label Figure 6b and c accordingly: **epidermis,** parenchyma of **cortex, vascular cylinder, xylem, phloem, endodermis,** and **pericycle.** The endodermis and the pericycle are unique to roots. The endodermis is the innermost cell layer of the cortex. The walls of endodermal cells have a band called the **Casparian strip**—made of **suberin,** a waxy material— that extends completely around each cell, as shown in Figure 7. This strip forms a barrier to the passage of anything moving between adjacent cells of the endodermis. All water and dissolved materials absorbed by the epidermal root hairs and transported inward through the cortex must first pass through the living cytoplasm of endodermal cells before entering the vascular tissues. The pericycle is a layer of dividing cells immediately inside the endodermis; it gives rise to lateral roots. Refer to "Summary of Basic Plant Tissue Systems and Cell Types" and Figure 1.

## Results

1. Review Figure 6 and note comparable structures in Figure 7.
2. Using a colored pencil, highlight the representations of structures or cells found in the root but not seen in the stem.

## Discussion

1. Suggest the advantage of taproots and of fibrous roots under different environmental conditions.

2. Did your observations support your hypothesis and predictions?

3. Compare the structure and organization of roots and stems. How do these two organs differ?

4. Explain the relationship of structure and function for two structures or cells found only in roots.

5. Note that the epidermis of the root lacks a cuticle. Can you explain why this might be advantageous?

6. What is the function of the endodermis? Why is the endodermis important to the success of plants in the land environment?

 **Student Media Video—Ch. 35: Root Growth in a Radish Seed (time-lapse)**

# Lab Study C. Leaves

## Materials

prepared slide of lilac (*Syringia*) leaf
slides
compound microscope
coverslips

dropper bottles of water
leaves of purple heart (*Setcreasia*)
    kept in saline and DI water

## Introduction

Leaves are organs especially adapted for photosynthesis. The thin blade portion provides a very large surface area for the absorption of light and the uptake of carbon dioxide through stomata. The leaf is basically a layer of parenchyma cells (the **mesophyll**) between two layers of epidermis. The loose arrangement of parenchyma cells within the leaf allows for an extensive surface area for the rapid exchange of gases. Specialized epidermal cells called guard cells allow the exchange of gases and evaporation of water at the leaf surface. Guard cells are photosynthetic (unlike other epidermal cells), and are capable of changing shape in response to complex environmental and physiological factors. Current research indicates that the opening of the stomata is the result of the active uptake of $K^+$ and subsequent changes in turgor pressure in the guard cells.

In this lab study, you will examine the structure of a leaf in cross section. You will observe stomata on the leaf epidermis and will study the activity of guard cells under different conditions.

## Procedure

1. Before beginning your observations of the leaf cross section, compare the shape of the leaf on your slide with Figure 8a and b on the next page.

2. Observe the internal leaf structure.

    a. Examine a cross section through a lilac leaf and identify the following cells or structures: **cuticle** (a waxy layer secreted by the epidermis), **epidermis** (upper and lower), parenchyma with chloroplasts (**mesophyll**), **vascular bundle** with **phloem** and **xylem**, and **stomata** with **guard cells** and **substomatal chamber**. Refer to "Summary of Basic Plant Tissue Systems and Cell Types" and Figure 1.

    b. The vascular bundles of the leaf are often called **veins** and can be seen in both cross section and longitudinal sections of the leaf. Observe the structure of cells in the central midvein. Is xylem or phloem on top in the leaf?

    c. Observe the distribution of stomata in the upper and lower epidermis. Where are they more abundant?

    d. Label the cross section of the leaf in Figure 8.

3. Observe the leaf epidermis and stomata.

    a. Obtain two *Setcreasia* leaves, one placed in saline for an hour and the other placed in distilled water for an hour.

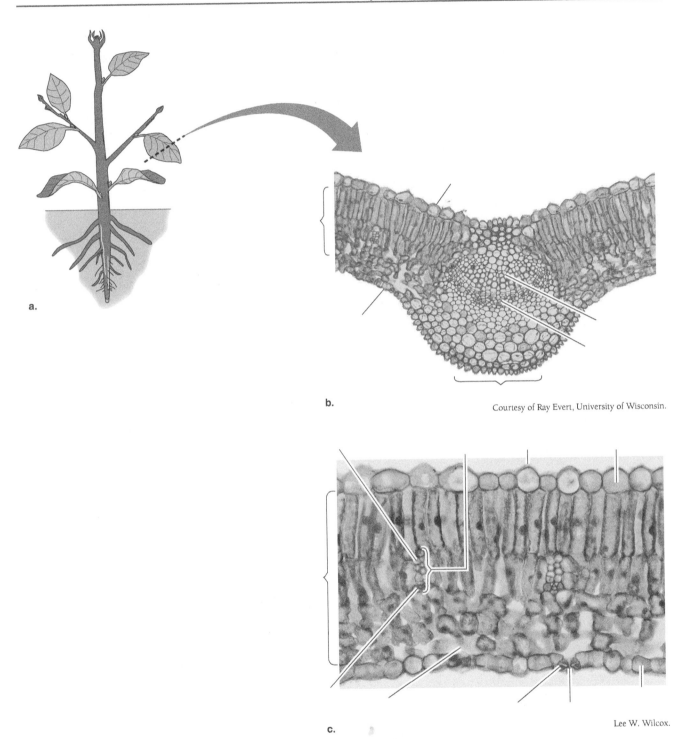

a.

b.

Courtesy of Ray Evert, University of Wisconsin.

c.

Lee W. Wilcox.

**Figure 8.**
**Leaf structure.** (a) Whole plant. (b) Photomicrograph of a leaf cross section through the midvein. (c) Photomicrograph of a leaf cross section adjacent to the midvein.

b. Label two microscope slides, one "saline" and the other "H₂O."

c. To remove a small piece of the lower epidermis, fold the leaf in half, with the lower epidermis to the inside. Tear the leaf, pulling one end toward the other, stripping off the lower epidermis (Figure 9). If you do this correctly, you will see a thin purple layer of lower epidermis at the torn edge of the leaf.

d. Remove a small section of the epidermis from the leaf in *DI water* and mount it in water on the appropriate slide, being sure that the outside surface of the leaf is facing up. View the slide at low and high power on your microscope, and observe the structure of the stomata. Sketch your observations in the margin of your lab manual.

e. Remove a section of the epidermis from the leaf in *saline* and mount it on the appropriate slide in a drop of the *saline.*Make sure that the outside surface of the leaf is facing up. View the slide with low power on your microscope, and observe the structure of the stomata. Sketch your observations in the margin of your lab manual.

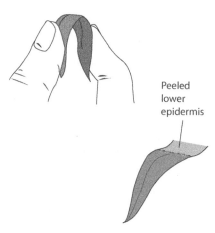

Peeled lower epidermis

**Figure 9.**

**Preparation of leaf epidermis peel.**
Bend the leaf in half and peel away the lower epidermis. Remove a small section of lower epidermis and make a wet mount.

## Results

1. Review the leaf cross section in Figure 8.
2. Describe the structure of the stomata on leaves kept in DI water.

3. Describe the structure of the stomata on leaves kept in saline.

## Discussion

1. Describe the functions of leaves.

2. Provide evidence from your observations of leaf structure to support the hypothesis that structure and function are related. Be specific in your examples.

3. Explain the observation that more stomata are found on the lower surface of the leaf than on the upper.

4. Explain the differences observed, if any, between the stomata from leaves kept in DI water and those kept in saline. Utilize your knowledge of osmosis to explain the changes in the guard cells. (In this activity, you stimulated stomatal closure by changes in turgor pressure due to saline rather than $K^+$ transport.)

---

E X E R C I S E  4

# Cell Structure of Tissues Produced by Secondary Growth

## Materials

prepared slides of basswood (*Tilia*) stem
compound microscope

## Introduction

Secondary growth arises from meristematic tissue called cambium. Vascular cambium and cork cambium are two types of cambium. The vascular cambium is a single layer of meristematic cells located between the secondary phloem and secondary xylem. Dividing cambium cells produce a new cell at one time toward the xylem, at another time toward the phloem. Thus, each cambial cell produces files of cells, one toward the inside of the stem, another toward the outside, resulting in an increase in stem girth (diameter). The secondary phloem cells become differentiated into sclerenchyma fiber cells, sieve-tube members, and companion cells. Secondary xylem cells become differentiated into tracheids and vessel elements. Certain cambial cells produce parenchyma ray cells that can extend radially through the xylem and phloem of the stem.

The cork cambium is a type of meristematic tissue that divides, producing cork tissue to the outside of the stem and other cells to the inside. The cork cambium and the secondary tissues derived from it are called periderm. The periderm layer replaces the epidermis and cortex in stems and roots with secondary growth. These layers are continually broken and sloughed off as the woody plant grows and expands in diameter.

## Procedure

1. Examine a cross section of a woody stem.
   a. Observe the cork cambium and periderm in the outer layers of the stem. The outer **cork** cells of the periderm have thick walls impregnated with a waxy material called **suberin.** These cells are dead at

maturity. The thin layer of nucleated cells that may be visible next to the cork cells is the **cork cambium.** The **periderm** includes the layers of cork and associated cork cambium. The term **bark** is used to describe the periderm and phloem on the outside of woody plants.

b. Observe the cellular nature of the listed tissues or structures, beginning at the periderm and moving inward to the central pith region. **Sclerenchyma fibers** have thick, dark-stained cell walls and are located in bands in the phloem. **Secondary phloem** cells with thin cell walls alternate with the rows of fibers. The **vascular cambium** appears as a thin line of small, actively dividing cells lying between the outer phloem tissue and the extensive secondary xylem. **Secondary xylem** consists of distinctive open cells that extend in layers to the central **pith** region. Lines of parenchyma cells one or two cells thick form **lateral rays** that radiate from the pith through the xylem and expand to a wedge shape in the phloem, forming a **phloem ray.**

2. Note the **annual rings** of xylem, which make up the **wood** of the stem surrounding the pith. Each annual ring of xylem has several rows of **early wood,** thin-walled, large-diameter cells that grew in the spring and, outside of these, a few rows of **late wood,** thick-walled, smaller-diameter cells that grew in the summer, when water is less available.

3. By counting the annual rings of xylem, determine the age of your stem. Note that the phloem region is not involved with determining the age of the tree.

## Results

1. Review Figure 10 on the next page.
2. Sketch in the margin of your lab manual any details not represented in the figure that you might need for future reference.
3. Indicate on your diagram the region where primary tissues can still be found.

## Discussion

1. What has happened to the several years of phloem tissue production?

2. Based on your observations of the woody stem, does xylem or phloem provide structural support for trees?

3. What function might the ray parenchyma cells serve?

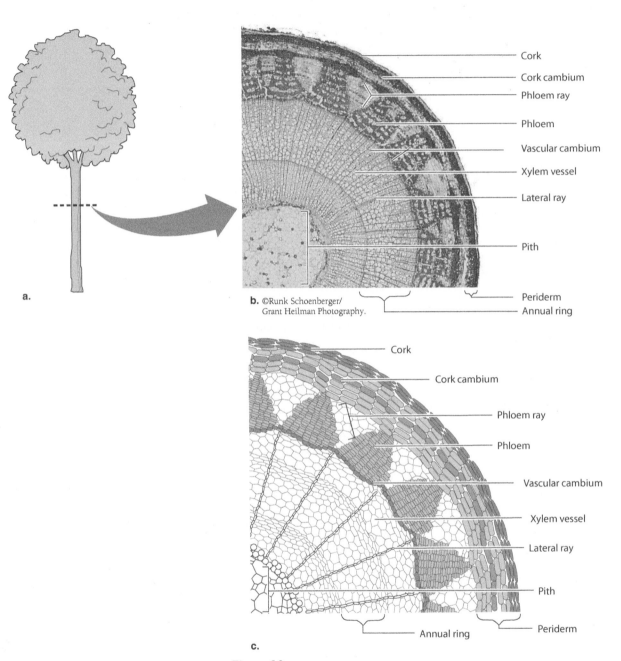

a.

b. ©Runk Schoenberger/
Grant Heilman Photography.

Cork
Cork cambium
Phloem ray
Phloem
Vascular cambium
Xylem vessel
Lateral ray
Pith
Periderm
Annual ring

Cork
Cork cambium
Phloem ray
Phloem
Vascular cambium
Xylem vessel
Lateral ray
Pith
Annual ring
Periderm

c.

**Figure 10.**

**Secondary growth.** (a) Whole woody plant. (b) Photomicrograph of a cross section of a woody stem. (c) Compare the corresponding diagram with your observations of a prepared slide. If necessary, modify the diagram to correspond to your specimen.

4. How might the structure of early wood and late wood be related to seasonal conditions and the function of the cells? Think about environmental conditions during the growing season.

# EXERCISE 5
# Grocery Store Botany: Modifications of Plant Organs

## Materials

variety of produce: squash, lettuce, celery, carrot, white potato, sweet potato, asparagus, onion, broccoli, and any other produce you wish to examine

## Introduction

Every day you come into contact with the plant world, particularly in the selection, preparation, and enjoyment of food. Most agricultural food plants have undergone extreme selection for specific features. For example, broccoli, cauliflower, cabbage, and brussels sprouts are all members of the same species that have undergone selection for different features. In this exercise, you will apply your botanical knowledge to the laboratory of the grocery store.

## Procedure

1. Working with another student, examine the numerous examples of root, stem, and leaf modifications on demonstration. (There may be some reproductive structures as well.)

2. For each grocery item, determine the type of plant organ, its modification, and its primary function. How will you decide what is a root, stem, or leaf? Review the characteristics of these plant organs and examine your produce carefully.

## Results

Complete Table 1 on the next page.

## Discussion

1. What feature of the white potato provided key evidence in deciding the correct plant organ?


2. Based on your knowledge of the root, why do you think roots have been selected so often as food sources?

**Table 1**
Grocery Store Botany

| Name of Item | Plant Organ (Root, Stem, Leaf, Flower, Fruit) | Function/Features (Storage, Support, Reproduction, Photosynthesis |
|---|---|---|
|  |  |  |
|  |  |  |
|  |  |  |
|  |  |  |
|  |  |  |
|  |  |  |
|  |  |  |
|  |  |  |
|  |  |  |

# Questions for Review

1. Use Table 2 to describe the structure and function of the cell types seen in lab today. Indicate the location of these in the various plant organs examined. Refer to "Summary of Tissue Systems and Cell Types" and Figure 1.

2. Some tissues are composed of only one type of cell; others are more complex. List the cell types observed in xylem and in phloem.

   Xylem:

   Phloem:

| Cell Type | Structure | Function | Plant Organ |
|---|---|---|---|
| Epidermis | | | |
| Guard cells | | | |
| Parenchyma | | | |
| Collenchyma | | | |
| Sclerenchyma | | | |
| Tracheids | | | |
| Vessels | | | |
| Sieve tubes | | | |
| Endodermis | | | |
| Primary meristems | | | |
| Vascular cambium | | | |
| Pericycle | | | |
| Periderm | | | |
| Ray parenchyma | | | |

**Table 2**
Structure and Function of Plant Cells

3. What characteristic of sieve-tube structure provides a clue to the role of companion cells?

4. Compare primary and secondary growth. What cells divide to form primary tissue? To form secondary tissue? Can a plant have both primary growth and secondary growth? Explain, providing evidence to support your answer.

## Applying Your Knowledge

1. Cells of the epidermis frequently retain a capability for cell division. Why is this important? (*Hint:* What is their function?)

2. Why is the endodermis essential in the root but not in the stem?

3. In the summer of 1998, after extremely hot, dry weather, the Georgia corn harvest was expected to be reduced by at least 25%. Using your knowledge of the dual functions of guard cells relative to water retention and gas exchange, explain the reduction in photosynthetic productivity.

4. The belt buckle of a standing 20-year-old man may be a foot higher than it was when he was 10, but a nail driven into a 10-year-old tree will be at the same height 10 years later. Explain.

5. The number of annual rings in trees growing in temperate climates corresponds to the age of the trees. Scientists use tree ring analysis (dendrochronology) to age trees. By comparing patterns of tree ring size in cores from living trees with patterns in older dead trees and even samples of wood from old buildings, scientists have been able to piece together a chronology back thousands of years. Scientists in Europe are

working collaboratively to develop a history of climate change for the last 10,000 years using tree ring analysis (dendroclimatology). How would regional climate changes affect the growth of trees? What features of secondary growth in trees would provide evidence for scientists to determine regional climate change? Why do you think this research is being conducted in temperate forests, but not in tropical forests?

6. The oldest living organisms on Earth are plants. Some bristlecone pines are about 4,600 years old, and a desert creosote bush is known to be 10,000 years old. What special feature of plants provides for this incredible longevity? How do plants differ from animals in their pattern of growth and development?

7. Many of the structural features studied in this laboratory evolved in response to the environmental challenges of the terrestrial habitat. Complete Table 3 naming the cells, tissues, and organs that have allowed vascular plants to adapt to each environmental factor.

**Table 3**
Adaptations of Plant Cells and Structures to the Land Environment

| Environmental Factor | Adaptations to Land Environment |
|---|---|
| Desiccation | |
| Transport of materials between plant and environment | |
| Gas exchange | |
| Anchorage in substrate | |
| Transport of materials within plant body | |
| Structural support in response to gravity | |
| Sexual reproduction without water | |
| Dispersal of offspring from immobile parent | |

## Investigative Extensions

1. A walk across campus, through the forest or along the path at the botanical garden will reveal an amazing diversity in the structure of roots, stems, and leaves. This outward diversity is accompanied by anatomical diversity in structure that is directly related to the functioning of these organs. Using the "nut and bolt" technique in Exercise 3, you can investigate questions relating to structural diversity. For other techniques for studying plant anatomy see http://www.publicbookshelf.com/public_html/Methods_in_Plant_Histology. Develop an investigation based on your observations of plant structures or consider one of the following suggestions.

    a. C3 and C4 plants use different photosynthetic pathways with corresponding differences in leaf anatomy. Using Web and other resources identify C3 and C4 species that are commercially available and compare the leaf anatomy for two related species.

    b. Angiosperms are divided into several groups, including eudicots and monocots. One feature that distinguishes these two groups is the difference in the organization of stem and root tissues. Investigate differences in anatomy for monocots and eudicots.

2. Plants balance the complex problems of gas exchange, temperature regulation, and water loss through stomata opening and closing. Using techniques from this lab topic investigate microenvironmental (at the scale of the plant) factors, such as light, temperature, wind, or soil moisture that might affect stomata function. See Brewer (1992) for a method for making leaf casts using nail polish and then observing these surface replicas under the microscope.

## Student Media Activities and Investigations

**Activities**—Ch. 35: Root, Stem, and Leaf Sections; Primary and Secondary Growth
**Investigation**—Ch. 35: What Are Functions of Monocot Tissues?
www.masteringbio.com

## References

Berg L. *Introductory Botany: Plants, People, and the Environment,* 2nd ed. Belmont, CA: Thomson Brooks/Cole, 2007.

Brewer, C. A. "Responses by Stomata on Leaves to Microenvironmental Conditions," in *Tested Studies for Laboratory Teaching* (volume 12), Proceedings of the 13th Workshop/Conference of the Association for Biology Laboratory Education (ABLE), Corer A. Goldman, Editor.

Mauseth, J. D. *Botany: An Introduction to Plant Biology,* 3rd ed. Sudbury, MA: Jones and Bartlett Publishers, 2003.

Raven, P. H., R. F. Evert, and S. E. Eichorn. *Biology of Plants,* 7th ed. New York: W.H. Freeman Publishers, 2004.

Zeiger, E., G. D. Farquhar, and I. R. Cowan. *Stomatal Function.* Stanford, CA: Stanford University Press, 1987.

# Websites

Click on General Botany and browse this site for images of plant cells and tissues and plant organ anatomy: http://botit.botany.wisc.edu

NASA Virtual Astronaut. Descriptions of botanical research conducted by astronauts in space: http://virtualastronaut.jsc.nasa.gov/textonly/act25/text-plants.html

Methods in Plant Histology. An online book with techniques for studying plant anatomy: http://www.publicbookshelf.com/public_html/Methods_in_Plant_Histology

American Society of Plant Biologists website with links for undergraduates: http://www.aspb.org/resourcelinks/scripts/cats2.cfm?cat=65

Photomicrographs of plant organs can be viewed at this site: http://www.emc.maricopea.edu/faculty/farabee/BIOBK/BioBook PLANT ANATII.html

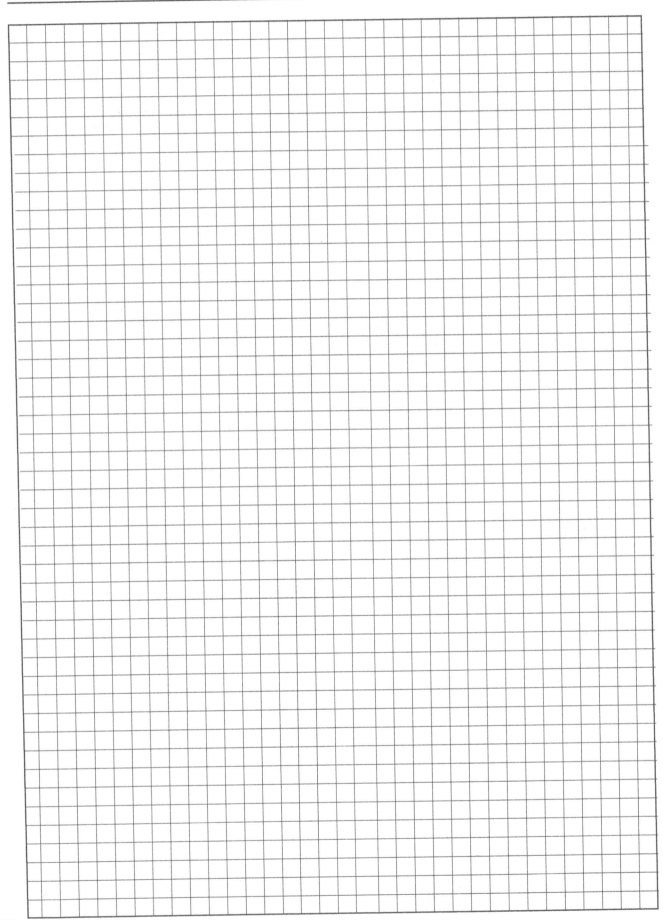

# Plant Growth

 This lab topic gives you another opportunity to practice the scientific process. Before going to lab, review scientific investigation and carefully read this Lab Topic. Be prepared to use this information to design an experiment for plant growth.

## Laboratory Objectives

After completing this lab topic, you should be able to:

1. Describe external and internal factors that influence the germination of angiosperm seeds.
2. Explain the effect of auxin on plant growth.
3. Explain the effect of gibberellins on the growth of dwarf corn seedlings.
4. Define and give examples of *phototropism* and *gravitropism*.
5. Design and execute an experiment testing factors that influence seed germination and plant growth.
6. Present the results of the experiment in oral or written form.

## Introduction

In the life cycle of angiosperms, fertilization of the egg in the female gametophyte results in an embryo protected in a **seed** consisting of the young embryonic sporophyte, food, and a protective seed coat. Seeds develop in the parent plant, and when they are mature, they are separated from the parent and dispersed. Most seeds go through a period of dormancy, but when a dormant seed finds a favorable environment, it will begin to **germinate;** that is, it renews its development and the embryo resumes its growth. Most plants continue to grow as long as they live, a condition known as **indeterminate growth.** Indeterminate growth is possible because of plant tissues called **meristems,** which remain embryonic as long as the plant lives. Seed germination and plant growth are regulated by external factors such as light, temperature, nutrients, and water availability. Plants respond to these environmental stimuli by internal mechanisms regulated by chemical messengers called **hormones.** A hormone, whether it is found in plants or

From *Investigating Biology Laboratory Manual,* Sixth Edition, Judith G. Morgan and M. Eloise Brown Carter. Copyright © 2008 by Pearson Education, Inc. Published by Benjamin Cummings, Inc. All rights reserved.

animals, is produced in small quantities in one part of the organism and transported to another site, where it causes some special effect.

In this lab topic, you will work in teams, investigating external stimuli and internal mechanisms that influence the germination of seeds and the growth of plants. You will be led through several brief introductory experiments (Experiment A of Exercises 1, 2, and 3); then your team will propose one or more testable hypotheses based on questions from the lab studies or your imagination. You will then design and carry out an independent investigation based on your hypotheses (Exercise 4). You may design an experiment that can be completed in the laboratory period. However, you should plan to make observations of your plants over several days or at the beginning of the next laboratory. Your instructor will tell you if you will be able to return to the lab to make observations or if you should carry your experiment elsewhere for observations. Before or during the first hour of the following laboratory period, you should have completed your observations and recorded your results. Your team should discuss the results and prepare an oral presentation. One member of your team will present your team's results to the class for discussion. This person should be prepared to persuade the class that your experimental design is sound and that your results support your conclusions. If required by the lab instructor, each of you will submit an independent laboratory report describing your experiment and results in the format of a scientific paper.

 First complete Experiment A in Exercises 1, 2, and 3. Then discuss possible questions for investigation with your research team. Be certain you can pose an interesting question from which you can develop a testable hypothesis. Design and initiate the experiment today. Complete the experiment and report your results during the following laboratory period.

# Germinating Seeds and Growing Plants for Independent Investigations

## Experimental Plants

You may choose plants used in the lab studies for your independent investigation. These include *Zea mays* (corn), *Phaseolus vulgaris* (pinto bean), *Phaseolus limensis* (lima bean), *Coleus blumei* (a common ornamental annual with colorful variegated leaves), and *Brassica rapa* (related to mustard and cabbage). If you decide to use different plant species, check with your laboratory instructor about the availability of additional plants.

## Germinating Bean and Pea Seeds

Bean and pea seeds can be germinated by first submerging them in a 10% sodium hypochlorite solution for 5 minutes to kill bacteria and fungus spores on their surfaces. Follow this with a distilled water rinse and plant the seeds 1 cm deep in flats of vermiculite, a clay mineral that looks like mica and is frequently used as a starting medium for seeds. Add water or a test solution to the flats daily.

## Growing Wisconsin Fast Plants

The *Brassica rapa* seeds used in this exercise were developed by Dr. Paul Williams of the Department of Plant Pathology, University of Wisconsin, Madison. Dr. Williams used traditional breeding techniques to produce plants, called Wisconsin Fast Plants™, that can complete an entire breeding cycle from seed to seed in 35 days (Figure 1). Because of the rapid growth and shortened breeding cycle of these plants, they are excellent investigative tools for use in plant growth experiments.

## *A. Seed Germination Exercises*

*Brassica rapa* seeds can be germinated by placing them on wet filter paper in the lid of a petri dish. Stand the dish, tilted on its end, in a water reservoir such as the bottom of a 2-L soft-drink bottle (Figure 2a). The dish and reservoir should be placed under fluorescent lights. Germination begins within 24 hours, and observations can be made for several days. It is important to keep the filter paper moist by carefully adding water. If you wish to make quantitative measurements of seed germination, tape a transparent grid sheet marked in measured increments to the outside of the petri dish lid. Place the wet filter paper in the lid, as before, and plant the seeds at a particular position in relation to the grid. As the seeds germinate and grow, you can easily use the grid to measure their size (Figure 2b).

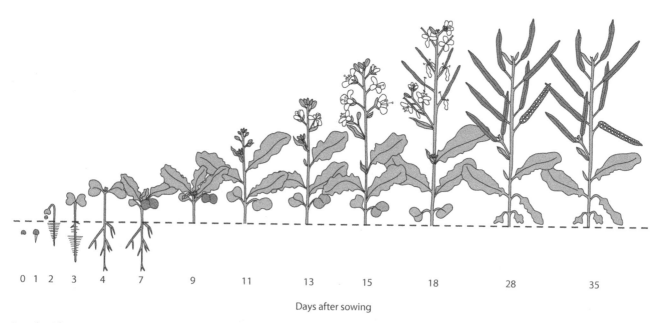

Days after sowing

**Figure 1.**
**Life cycle of Fast Plant *Brassica rapa*.** These plants can complete their entire life cycle from seed to seed in 35 days.

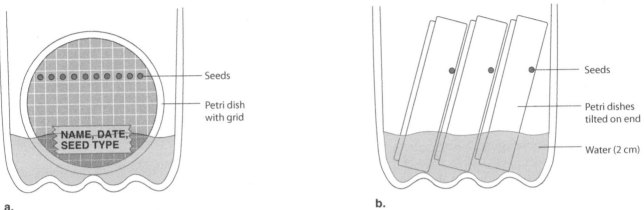

**Figure 2.**

**Germinating *Brassica rapa* seeds in a petri dish.** (a) Place the seeds on wet filter paper in the lid of a petri dish. Attach a grid to the outside of the lid for easy seedling measurement. (b) Stand the dishes on end in a water reservoir.

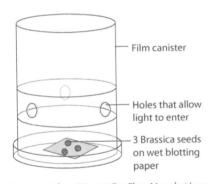

**Figure 3.**

**Growing *Brassica rapa* plants in film canisters.** Place seeds on moist blotting paper in the lid. Holes can be punched in the canister to allow light to enter the chamber.

## B. Tropism Studies

*Brassica rapa* seeds can be germinated in empty 35-mm clear or black film canisters (Figure 3). The canisters can be used as is or black canisters can be modified by punching holes in the sides to allow light to enter the chamber. Place small, appropriately sized squares of wet blotting paper in the lid, and place two or three seeds on the blotting paper. (Do not use filter paper; it dries out too quickly.) Invert the canister and snap it into the lid. Holes in the canister can be covered with different-colored filters, and the size of the holes can be varied to alter the quality or quantity of light hitting the plants.

## C. Growing Brassica rapa *Seedlings in Quads*

Scientists working with Wisconsin Fast Plants suggest germinating seeds in small, commercially available Styrofoam™ containers called *quads,* which contain four cells, or chambers. To germinate seeds in quads (Figure 4):

1. Add a wick to each cell to draw water from the source into the soil.
2. Add potting mix until each cell is about half full.
3. Add three fertilizer pellets.
4. Add more soil and press to make a depression.
5. Add two or three seeds to each cell and cover them with potting mix.
6. Carefully water each section using a pipette until water soaks through the potting mix and drips from the wick.
7. Place the quad on the watering tray under fluorescent lights.

After the seeds begin to germinate, you can manipulate the plants in many different ways to investigate plant growth.

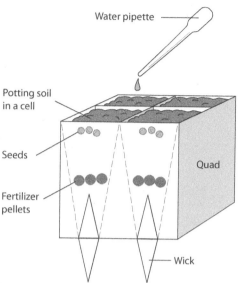

Reproduced from *Wisconsin Fast Plants Manual* with permission of Carolina Biological Supply, Burlington, NC 27215, and Wisconsin Alumni Research Foundation, Madison WI 53707. © 1989 Wisconsin Alumni Research Foundation.

**Figure 4.**
**Growing *Brassica rapa* plants in quads.** Pull a wick through the hole in each cell. Add potting soil, fertilizer, and seeds. Initially, water using a pipette.

# EXERCISE 1
# Factors Influencing Seed Germination

Seeds are the means of reproduction, dispersal, and, frequently, survival for a plant. Plants are immobile and can colonize new habitats and escape inhospitable weather only through the dispersal and dormancy of seeds. *Dormancy* is a special condition of arrested growth in which the seed cannot germinate without special environmental cues. In this exercise, you will observe germinating bean and *Brassica rapa* seeds. The beans have been germinating in a moist environment for several days. The *Brassica rapa* seeds are germinating on wet filter paper in the lid of a petri dish.

## Experiment A. Germinating Bean and *Brassica rapa* Seeds

### Materials

germinating bean seeds
petri dishes with germinating *Brassica rapa* seeds
stereoscopic microscope or hand lens

### Introduction

In this lab study, you will examine seed and seedling morphology. Working individually, you will identify seed parts in two plants, a species of bean and *Brassica rapa*. As you investigate the morphology of seeds, consider the role of each structure in facilitating the function of the seed.

### Procedure

1. Examine a germinating bean seed and identify the **seed coat, cotyledons** (seed leaves), and **embryo** consisting of the **radicle** (embryonic root),

**Figure 5.**
**The structure of a bean seed.** Add
the labels: *seed coat, cotyledons, radicle,
hypocotyl,* and *epicotyl.*

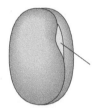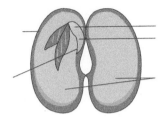

**hypocotyl** (plant axis below the cotyledons), and **epicotyl** with young
leaves (plant axis above the cotyledons).

2. Secure a petri dish with germinating *Brassica rapa* seeds. Carefully examine the seeds using a hand lens or the stereoscopic microscope and
   identify the **seed coat** (which may have been shed), **cotyledons** (how
   many?), **hypocotyl, primary root, root hairs,** and **young shoot.**

## Results

1. Label the parts of the bean seed in Figure 5.
2. Draw and label several germinating *B. rapa* seeds in the margin of your
   lab manual.

## Discussion

1. What is the function of the seed coat? From what does it develop?

2. How have the cotyledons developed, and from what? (Check your text;
   see, for example, Campbell and Reece, 2008, Chapter 38.)

3. How does the structure of the seed facilitate the dispersal and survival
   of the plant?

# Experiment B. Student-Designed Investigation of Seed Germination

## Materials

seeds of *Brassica rapa*

various other seeds—beans, corn, radish, okra, lettuce

35-mm film canisters—clear plastic, black, or black with holes punched in the sides

small squares of blotting paper soaking in water

red, green, and blue cellophane sheets

tape

water baths, oven, refrigerator

grid sheets that fit the lids of petri dishes

reservoir

forceps

scissors

waterproof pen

agar plates

empty petri dishes

sandpaper

various pH solutions

10% sodium hyperchlorite solution

solutions of gibberellin or other hormones

hole punch

## Introduction

If your team chooses to study seed germination for your independent investigation and report, use the available materials. Design a simple experiment to investigate factors involved in the germination of seeds.

## Procedure

1. Collaborating with your research team, read the following questions, check your text and other sources for supporting information, and choose a question to investigate, using this list or your own imagination.

   a. Do seeds need light to germinate? What effect will germination in total darkness have on the process? Is germination better in alternating light and dark, as in nature?

   b. Is germination different in different wavelengths (colors) of light?

   c. What effect does scarification (scratching the seed coat) have on germination of various seeds? How does scarification occur in nature?

   d. What temperature regimens are optimum for seed germination? Is germination affected by alternating temperatures (as in nature)? Is a constant temperature favorable?

   e. Does gibberellin (Exercise 3) promote or inhibit seed germination? What about other hormones—for example, cytokinins or abscisic acid? Check your text for other test substances.

   f. What effect will salt solutions or acid solutions have on seed germination? Why would questions such as these be of interest?

   g. Does seed size have an effect on germination rates? On seedling size?

   h. Some crops are limited in their distribution by cold soils that affect seed germination. Will changes in regional climate affect seed germination in okra, broccoli, or varieties of wheat?

2. Design your experiment, proposing hypotheses, making predictions, and determining procedures as instructed in Exercise 4.

EXERCISE 2
# Plant Growth Regulators: Auxin

Both plants and animals respond to environmental cues. Animals generally respond rapidly via the nervous system or more slowly via hormones secreted from endocrine glands. Plants lack a nervous system and respond to environmental stimuli via chemical messengers or hormones. Changes in these hormones lead to altered patterns of growth and development. **Auxin** is the name given to a complex of substances that promotes stem growth. The natural auxin, indoleacetic acid (IAA), is a hormone produced in apical meristems. It migrates down the stem from the zone of production. If the growing tip is removed, the stem will not elongate, but if the tip is replaced with a paste containing IAA, elongation will continue. At low concentrations, IAA facilitates cell elongation and promotes growth by breaking linkages among cellulose fibers and loosening the cell wall. In this exercise, you will investigate the role of auxin in stem curvature in response to light and gravity.

## Experiment A. Gravitropic and Phototropic Curvature in *Coleus blumei*

### Materials

(on demonstration)
*Coleus* plant placed on its side
*Coleus* plant in unilateral light
*Coleus* plant in upright position

### Introduction

In this exercise, you will investigate the growth of the stem in response to two environmental stimuli, gravity and light. **Gravitropism** (or geotropism) is the response of a plant to gravity. **Phototropism** is the response of a plant to light. Three *Coleus blumei* plants are on demonstration in the lab room. One was placed on its side several days ago. Another has been growing in unilateral light for several days. The third, the control, was left undisturbed in the greenhouse until lab time.

### Procedure

1. Study gravitropic curvature in *Coleus blumei*.
   a. Carry your lab notebook to the demonstration area and observe the *Coleus* plant placed on its side.
   b. Examine the plant, noting the appearance of different regions of the stems and roots (if visible). What part of each stem has curved? To what degree?
   c. Compare this plant with the control plant left in an upright position.
   d. Describe your observations and answer the questions in the Results section.

2. Study phototropic curvature in *Coleus blumei*.

    a. Examine the plant growing in unilateral light, noting the appearance of different regions of the stems.

    b. Compare the plant to the control plant, which has received light from all directions in the greenhouse.

    c. Record your observations and answer the questions in the Results section.

## Results

1. Describe the appearance of the plant lying on its side. *Sketch* the plant in the margin of your lab manual. How does this compare with the appearance of the control plant?

2. What is the extent of the response to gravity? How could you measure or quantify the response?

3. Describe the appearance of the plant in unilateral light. Sketch the plant in the margin of your lab manual. Compare this plant with the control plant.

4. What is the extent of the response to the light? How could you measure or quantify the response?

5. What part of the plant specifically is being affected? Can you explain why?

## Discussion

1. What type of response would you expect to see if you reoriented the plant lying on its side? Explain.

2. How do plants detect the force of gravity (according to current theory)? Consult your text, if necessary.

3. Review with your team members the physiological basis for the growth response. How is auxin involved in gravitropism? Where is it produced? Consult your text, if necessary.

4. Is curvature of the stem in response to gravity and light the result of additional cell division or cell elongation? How do you know, or how could you investigate this?

5. What is the role of auxin in phototropism? How is directional light detected in the plant? Use your text and discuss these items with members of your research team.

Student Media Videos—Ch. 39: Phototropism; Gravitropism

## Experiment B. Student-Designed Investigation of Auxins

### Materials

auxin solutions in various
   concentrations
auxin in lanolin paste
lanolin with no auxin
scissors
*Coleus* plants
glass containers for planting
*Brassica rapa* seedlings in quads

corn and bean seedlings in pots or flats
lamps
toothpicks
protractor
spray bottles
cotton-tipped applicators
aluminum foil

### Introduction

Having made observations of gravitropism and phototropism in the preceding experiment, discuss with your team members ways to use *Coleus*, *Brassica*, or corn or bean seedlings to further investigate these phenomena. If you choose to carry out your independent investigation with this system, the questions provided in the following Procedure section will be appropriate for your study. Using the materials available, design a simple experiment to investigate the role of auxin in plant growth or factors involved in phototropism and gravitropism.

### Procedure

1. Collaborating with your research team, read the following questions, check your text and other sources for supporting information, and choose a question to investigate, using this list or your own imagination.

   a. If only some wavelengths stimulate phototropic response, which ones do and which do not?

   b. If the apical meristem is removed, will plants respond to unilateral light?

   c. If the tip of the root is removed, will roots respond to gravity? (Seedlings can be planted close to the wall in glass containers so that root growth can be viewed.)

   d. Can these tropisms be altered by applying auxin paste to the plant?

   e. What will happen if the tips of the plants (root or stem) are covered with aluminum foil?

   f. How else does auxin affect plants? How does auxin affect apical dominance? Can auxin be used as an herbicide? (In what concentrations? What is the effect on plants?) What concentration of auxin produces the largest roots on cut stems? (What horticultural application would this have?)

g. Will seedlings growing in the dark respond to auxin applied to the side of the stem? At all locations on the stem?

h. The herbicide 2,4-dichlorophenoxyacetic acid (2,4-D), used to control weeds, is described as a synthetic auxin. How does 2,4-D affect plant growth? What plants are affected or unaffected by 2,4-D and at what concentrations?

2. Design your experiment, proposing hypotheses, making predictions, and determining procedures as instructed in Exercise 4.

# EXERCISE 3
# Plant Growth Regulators: Gibberellins

**Gibberellins** are another group of important plant growth hormones found in high concentrations in seeds and present in varying amounts in all plant parts. In some plants, gibberellins produce rapid elongation of stems; in others they produce **bolting**, the rapid elongation of the flower stalk. Produced near the stem apex, gibberellins work by increasing both the number of cell divisions and the elongation of cells produced by those divisions. The effects of gibberellins can be induced by artificially applying solutions to plant parts. Not all plants respond to the application of gibberellins, however, and in this exercise, you will investigate the effect of applying gibberellin solutions to normal and to dwarf (mutant) corn seedlings.

## Experiment A. Effects of Gibberellins on Normal and Dwarf Corn Seedlings

### Materials

2 pots each with 4 tall (normal) corn seedlings
2 pots each with 4 dwarf (mutant) corn seedlings
calculator

### Introduction

The seedlings used in this exercise are approximately the same age, but they exist in two phenotypes, tall and dwarf (Figure 6). The tall seedlings are wild type, or normal. A genetic mutation produces dwarf plants that lack gibberellins. Each team of students has four pots, each with four corn seedlings. Your instructor has previously treated the plants with either water or a gibberellin solution. In this experiment, you will investigate the effects of these treatments on the corn plants.

### Procedure

1. Several days ago, your instructor sprayed the plants with either distilled water or a gibberellin solution, as follows:

| *Control* | *Treated* |
|---|---|
| Pot 1: normal corn, water treatment | Pot 2: normal corn, gibberellin treatment |
| Pot 3: dwarf corn, water treatment | Pot 4: dwarf corn, gibberellin treatment |

©Grant Heilman/Grant Heilman Photography

Figure 6.
Normal corn plants and recessive dwarf mutants.

2. Observe the results of the treatments.

3. Measure the height of each of your plants and record these data in Table 1.

**Table 1**
Height of Normal and Dwarf Corn Seedlings
with and Without Gibberellin Treatment

|  | Normal Control (Pot 1) | Normal Treated (Pot 2) | Dwarf Control (Pot 3) | Dwarf Treated (Pot 4) |
|---|---|---|---|---|
| Plant 1 Height |  |  |  |  |
| Plant 2 Height |  |  |  |  |
| Plant 3 Height |  |  |  |  |
| Plant 4 Height |  |  |  |  |
| Mean Height |  |  |  |  |

## Results

1. Determine and record the mean height of plants in each category in Table 1.

2. Using the mean height for each category of plants, calculate the percentage difference in the mean height of treated normal plants and control normal plants. Then calculate the percentage difference in the mean height of treated dwarf plants and control dwarf plants. Use the given formula for your calculations:

$$\text{Normal \% difference} = \frac{\text{treated} - \text{control}}{\text{control}} \times 100 = \underline{\hspace{2cm}}\%$$

$$\text{Dwarf \% difference} = \frac{\text{treated} - \text{control}}{\text{control}} \times 100 = \underline{\hspace{2cm}}\%$$

3. Record your data for the average percentage difference in the mean values for both normal and dwarf plants from Table 1 on the class master sheet. Then calculate the average percentage differences for the entire class.

|  | *Your Data* | *Class Data* |
|---|---|---|
| Average % difference: normal | _____ | _____ |
| dwarf | _____ | _____ |

## Discussion

1. How do values for percentage difference compare for dwarf versus normal treated and untreated plants?

2. What is the action of gibberellins? Discuss your results with your group, and consult your text or other references in the laboratory.

# Experiment B. Student-Designed Investigation of Gibberellins

## Materials

normal and dwarf *Brassica rapa* seedlings
(*petite* and *rosette* strains)
normal and dwarf corn seedlings
normal and dwarf pea seedlings
(Little Marvel peas, *Pisum sativum*)

solutions of gibberellin
dropper bottles
sprayers
cotton-tipped applicators

## Introduction

Having seen the effect of gibberellins on the growth of normal and dwarf corn seedlings in the preceding experiment, discuss with your team members possible questions for further study of this group of hormones. If you choose to carry out your independent investigation with this system, the questions provided in the following Procedure section will be appropriate for your study. Using the materials available, design a simple experiment to investigate the actions of gibberellins in plant growth or seed germination.

## Procedure

1. Collaborating with your research team, read the following questions, check your text and other sources for supporting information, and choose a question to investigate, using this list or your own imagination.

   a. Plant scientists have discovered a mutant strain of *Brassica rapa* in which plants are dwarf. In these plants, the internodes do not elongate, and plants consist of a cluster of leaves spreading close to the soil. Flowers cluster close to the leaves. What could be the cause of this phenotype?

   b. Would other plant hormones produce the same response in dwarf corn seedlings as do gibberellins?

   c. In the demonstration experiment, the gibberellin solution was sprayed on all parts of the plant. If the gibberellin solution were added only to specific regions, such as the roots or apical meristem, would the effect be the same?

   d. Would the results in the corn experiment differ with different concentrations of gibberellin solution?

   e. What effect do gibberellins have on seed germination?

   f. What effect do gibberellins have on root growth on cut stems?

   g. Is the dwarf condition seen in certain strains of peas (Little Marvel peas) due to the lack of gibberellins?

   h. There are two dwarf forms of *Brassica rapa*—*rosette* and *petite*. Is dwarfism in these mutant strains due to insufficient gibberellin or to some other factor?

   i. *Brassica rapa* mutant, *tall* (ein/ein genotype) produces an excess of gibberellins. Can the elongated growth in this mutant be inhibited by growth regulator, Cyocel™? Can growth be further stimulated by applying gibberellins? Research the mode of action for Cyocel™.

2. Design your experiment, proposing hypotheses, making predictions, and determining procedures as instructed in Exercise 4.

## EXERCISE 4
# Designing and Performing an Open-Inquiry Investigation

### Materials

See each Experiment materials list.

### Introduction

Be ready to assign tasks to members of your lab team. Be sure that everyone understands the techniques that will be used. Your experiment will be successful only if you plan carefully, cooperate with your team members, perform lab techniques accurately and systematically, and record and report data accurately.

 You and your lab partner are responsible for the care and maintenance of your plants. Remember to check the water. The success of your investigation depends on the plants' survival.

### Procedure

1. **Decide on one or more questions to investigate.** Suggested questions are included in Experiment B of Exercises 1, 2, and 3 as a starting point.

   **Question:**

2. **Formulate a testable hypothesis.**

   **Hypothesis:**

3. **Summarize the essential elements of the experiment.** (Use separate paper.)

4. **Predict the results of your experiment based on your hypothesis.**
   **Prediction:** (If/then)

5. **Outline the procedures used in the experiment.**

   a. Review and modify the procedures used in Experiment A (see Germinating Seeds, Auxin, or Gibberellin). List each step in your procedure in numerical order.

   b. Critique your procedure: check for replicates, level of treatment, controls, duration of experiment, growing conditions, glassware, and age and size of plants. Review measurements and intervals between measurements. Assign team members to check plants periodically and water if needed.

   c. If your experiment requires materials other than those provided, ask your instructor about their availability. If possible, submit requests in advance.

   d. Create a table for data collection. Using examples in this lab topic as a model or design your own. If computers are available, create your table in Excel. Remember to include space for general observations of plant growth.

6. **Perform the experiment,** making observations and collecting data for analysis.

7. **Record observations and data** in your data table. Make notes about experimental conditions and observations. Do not rely on your memory for information that you will need when reporting your results.

8. **Prepare your discussion.** Discuss your results in light of your hypothesis.

   a. Review your prediction. Did your results correspond to the prediction you made? If not, explain how your results are different from your predictions, and why this might have occurred.

   b. Review your hypothesis. Review your results (tables and graphs). Do your results support or falsify your hypothesis? Explain your answer, using your data for support.

   c. If you had problems with the procedure or questionable results, explain how they might have influenced your conclusion.

   d. If you had an opportunity to repeat and expand this experiment to make your results more convincing, what would you do?

   e. Summarize the conclusion you have drawn from your results.

9. **Be prepared to report your results to the class.** Prepare to persuade your fellow scientists that your experimental design is sound and that your results support your conclusions.

10. If your instructor requires it, **submit a written laboratory report** in the form of a scientific paper. Keep in mind that although you have performed the experiments as a team, you must turn in a lab report of *your original writing*. Your tables and figures may be similar to those of your team members, but your paper must be the product of your own literature search and creative thinking.

## Questions for Review

1. Having completed this lab topic, you should be able to define and use the following terms, providing examples when appropriate: *seed, seedling, seed coat, cotyledon, endosperm, radicle, hypocotyl, epicotyl, germination, dormancy, phototropism, gravitropism, apical dominance, auxin, gibberellins, bolting.*

2. Students investigating plant growth and the effects of hormones removed the seeds from developing strawberries and compared the size and time of fruit development. The strawberries failed to enlarge and become red and fleshy in plants where the seeds were removed. Research the roles of auxin and gibberellin and determine which hormone is responsible for fruit development.

## Applying Your Knowledge

1. Auxin is directly or indirectly responsible for apical dominance in plants. In this phenomenon, the growth of lateral or axillary buds is inhibited by the auxin that moves down the stem from the apical meristem. It has long been the practice of horticulturists to clip off the apical meristems of certain young houseplants. What impact should this practice have on subsequent plant growth and appearance?

2. Dormancy is often caused by various germination-inhibiting chemicals that may be present in seeds. These water-soluble inhibitors are more common in plants growing in regions with prolonged wet and dry seasons. Suggest an adaptive advantage of the presence of these inhibitors.

3. Heliotropism, or solar tracking, is a plant movement whereby some plants orient their leaves or flowers to follow the position of the sun over the course of the day. Based on your investigations, what hormone do you predict might be involved in solar tracking? Briefly describe an experiment to test whether a particular plant species demonstrates solar tracking.

4. In *Brassica rapa* there are two known mutations for dwarfism, *petite* and *rosette*. When grown, both produce a cluster of leaves on the surface of the soil, but the stem does not elongate even during flowering. These mutations could be related to the production of gibberellin or to some other factor affecting development. Design an experiment to test the hypothesis that dwarfism in *petite* and *rosette B. rapa* are due to deficiency in gibberellin. Consider controlled variables, control treatment, replication, how you will measure plant growth, and the time period for making measurements and observations. State your prediction based on the experiment you design.

# Student Media Activities and Investigations

**Investigation**—Ch. 39: What Plant Hormones Affect Organ Formation? www.masteringbio.com

## References

Berg, L. *Introductory Botany: Plants, People, and the Environment,* 2nd ed. Belmont, CA: Thomson Brooks/Cole, 2007.

Campbell, N., and J. Reece. *Biology,* 8th ed. San Francisco, CA: Benjamin Cummings, 2008.

Mauseth, J. D. *Botany. An Introduction to Plant Biology.* Sudbury, MA: Jones and Bartlett Publishers, 2003.

Taiz, L., and E. Zeiger. *Plant Physiology,* 4th ed. Sunderland, MA: Sinauer, 2006.

*Wisconsin Fast Plants Manual.* Burlington, NC: Carolina Biological Supply, 1989.

## Websites

Plant Hormones:
http://www.plant-hormones.bbsrc.ac.uk/

Planting Science. Botanical Society of America website connecting scientists and students in collaborative research:
http://www.plantingscience.org/index.php

American Society of Plant Biologists website with links for undergraduates:
http://www.aspb.org/resourcelinks/scripts/cats2.cfm?cat=65

NASA Virtual Astronaut. Descriptions of botanical research conducted by astronauts in space:
http://virtualastronaut.jsc.nasa.gov/textonly/act25/text-plants.html

North Carolina State University Extension Office site with information on plant propagation:
http://www.ces.ncsu.edu/depts/hort/hil/hil-8702.html

*Plant Physiology* is a journal of the American Society of Plant Biologists. Current research in plant physiology:
http://www.plantphysiol.org/

USDA website with agricultural applications and information on plants, growth, and hormones:
http:www.usda.gov/wps/portal/usdahome

Wisconsin Fast Plants:
http://www.fastplants.org/

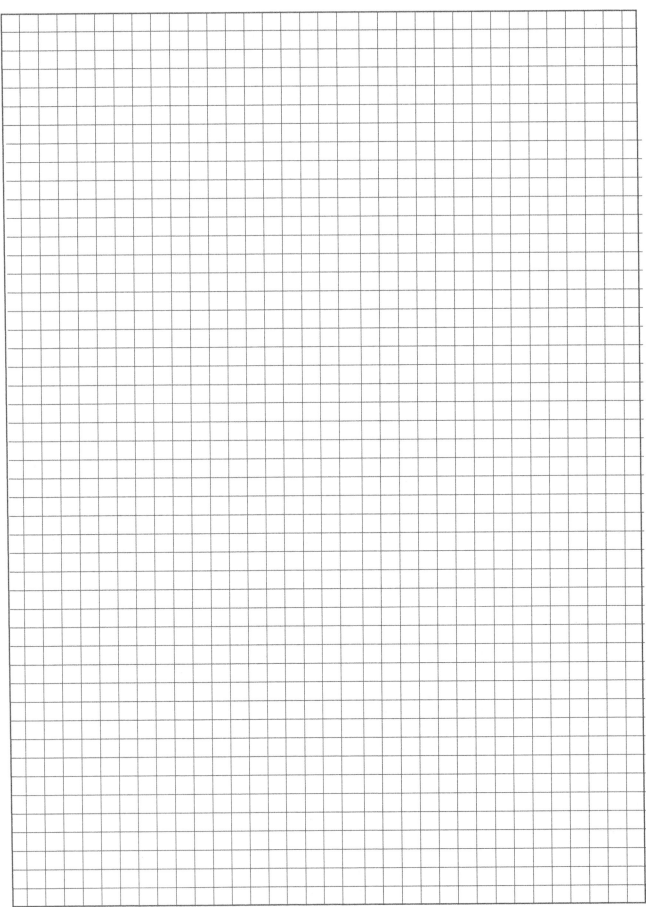

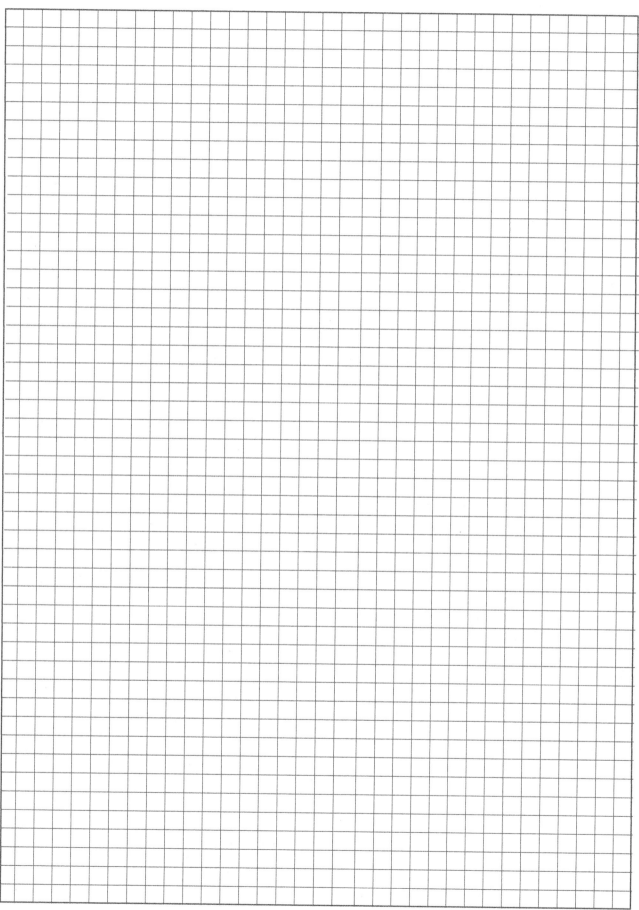

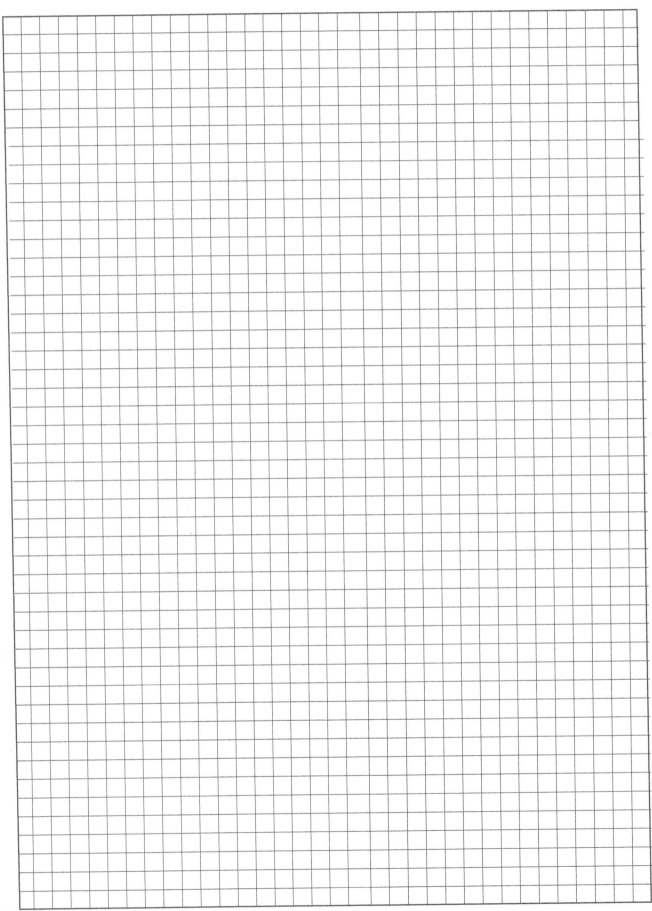

# Vertebrate Anatomy: The Skin and Digestive System

## Overview of Vertebrate Anatomy Labs

You have investigated several major themes in biology as illustrated by biodiversity in the animal kingdom. One of these themes is the relationship between form and function in organ systems. In this lab topic, you will continue to expand your understanding of this theme as you investigate the relationship between form, or structure, and function in vertebrate organ systems. For these investigations, you will be asked to view prepared slides and to dissect a representative vertebrate, the fetal pig. The purpose of these investigations is not to complete a comprehensive study of vertebrate morphology but rather to use several select vertebrate systems to analyze critically the relationship between form and function.

You will explore the listed concepts in the designated exercises.

1. The specialization of cells into tissues with specific functions makes possible the development of functional units, or organs (Exercise 1, Histology of the Skin).

2. Multicellular heterotrophic organisms must obtain and process food for body maintenance, growth, and repair (Exercise 3, The Digestive System in the Fetal Pig).

3. Because of their size, complexity, and level of activity, vertebrates require a complex system to transport nutrients and oxygen to body tissues and to remove waste from all body tissues.

4. Reproduction is the ultimate objective of all metabolic processes. Sexual reproduction involves the production of two different gametes, the bringing together of the gametes for fertilization, and limited or extensive care of the new individual.

5. Complex animals with many organ systems must coordinate the activities of the diverse parts. Coordination is influenced by the endocrine and nervous systems. Integration via the endocrine system is generally slower and more prolonged than that produced by the nervous system, which may receive stimuli, process information, and elicit a response very quickly.

## Laboratory Objectives

After completing this lab topic, you should be able to:

1. Describe the four main categories of tissues and give examples of each.
2. Identify tissues and structures in mammalian skin.
3. Describe the function of skin. Describe how the morphology of skin makes possible its functions.
4. Identify structures in the fetal pig digestive system.
5. Describe the role played by each digestive structure in the digestion and processing of food.
6. Relate tissue types to organ anatomy.
7. Apply knowledge and understanding acquired in this lab to problems in human physiology.
8. Apply knowledge and understanding acquired in this lab to explain organismal adaptive strategies.

## Introduction to Tissues

All animals are composed of **tissues**, groups of cells that are similar in structure and that perform a common function. During the embryonic development of most animals, the body is composed of three tissue layers: ectoderm, mesoderm, and endoderm. (Recall that animals in the phylum Porifera lack true tissue organization and that animals in the phylum Cnidaria have only two tissue layers— ectoderm and endoderm.) It is from these embryonic tissue layers that all other body tissues develop. There are four main categories of tissues: epithelium, connective tissue, muscle, and nervous tissue. Organs are formed from these tissues, and usually all four will be found in a single organ.

Tissues are composed of cells and intercellular substances. The intercellular substances are secreted by the cells. **Epithelial tissue** has cells in close aggregates with little intercellular substance (see Figure 1). These cells may be in one continuous layer, or they may be in multiple layers. They generally cover or line an external or internal surface. If formed from single layers of cells, the epithelium is called **simple**. If cells are in multiple layers, the epithelium is called **stratified**. If epithelial cells are flat, they are called **squamous**. If they are cube-shaped, they are called **cuboidal**. Tall, prismatic cells are called **columnar**. Thus, epithelium can be stratified squamous (as in skin), simple cuboidal (as in kidney tubules), or in other combinations of characteristics. Epithelial layers may be derived from embryonic ectoderm, mesoderm, or endoderm.

In **connective tissue**, cells are widely separated by intercellular substances consisting of **fibers** embedded in an amorphous **ground substance**, which may be solid, gelatinous, or liquid (Figure 2). **Loose fibrous connective tissue**, embedded in a liquid ground substance, binds together other tissues and organs and helps hold organs in place. Adipose tissue is another connective tissue consisting of adipose cells with fibers in a soft, liquid intercellular matrix. Adipose cells store droplets of fat causing the cells to swell and forcing the nuclei to one side. **Bone** and **cartilage** are specialized connective tissues found in the skeleton with, respectively, hard and gelatinous ground substances. In bone, the ground substance is secreted by cells called **osteocytes**. The ground substance in cartilage is secreted by cells

## Epithelial tissue

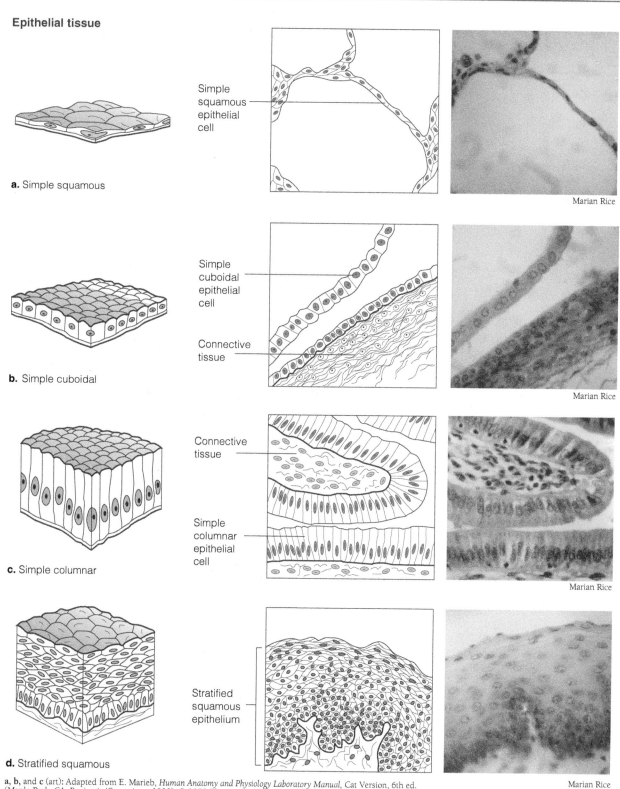

**a.** Simple squamous

Simple squamous epithelial cell

Marian Rice

**b.** Simple cuboidal

Simple cuboidal epithelial cell

Connective tissue

Marian Rice

**c.** Simple columnar

Connective tissue

Simple columnar epithelial cell

Marian Rice

**d.** Stratified squamous

Stratified squamous epithelium

Marian Rice

**a, b,** and **c** (art): Adapted from E. Marieb, *Human Anatomy and Physiology Laboratory Manual,* Cat Version, 6th ed. (Menlo Park, CA: Benjamin/Cummings, 1999), © 1999 The Benjamin/Cummings Publishing Company.
**1d** (art): Adapted from N. Campbell, J. Reece, and L. Mitchell, *Biology,* 5th ed. (Menlo Park, CA: Benjamin/Cummings, 1999), © 1999 The Benjamin/Cummings Publishing Company.

## Figure 1.

**Epithelial tissue.** Epithelial tissue has closely packed cells with little intercellular matrix. Cells may be (a) squamous (flat), (b) cuboidal (cube-shaped), or (c) columnar (elongated). They may be simple (in single layers) or (d) stratified (in multiple layers).

**Connective tissue**

**a.** Loose fibrous connective tissue

Fiber
Cell
Ground substance

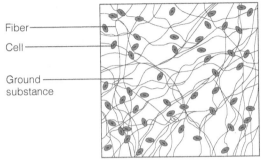
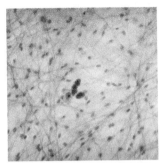

Marian Rice

**b.** Adipose tissue

Nucleus of adipose cell
Fat globule
Cytoplasm of adipose cell

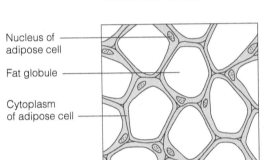
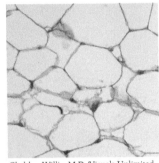

Gladden Willis, M.D./Visuals Unlimited

**c.** Bone

Osteocytes
Hard ground substance

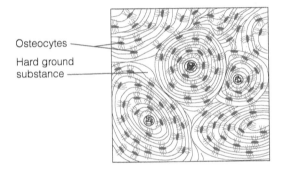
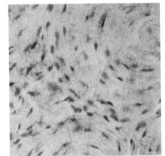

Marian Rice

**d.** Cartilage

Gelatinous ground substance
Chondrocytes

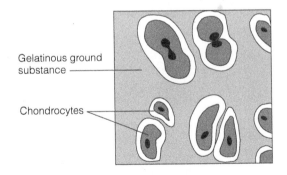
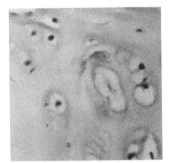

**e.** Blood

Platelet
Erythrocyte
Leukocytes
Liquid ground substance

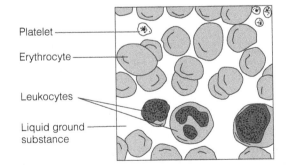
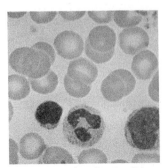

Biophoto Associates/Science Source/Photo Researchers, Inc.

**Muscle tissue**

**a.** Skeletal muscle

Muscle fiber

Nuclei

Marian Rice

**b.** Cardiac muscle

Nucleus

Intercalated discs

Marian Rice

**c.** Smooth muscle

Smooth muscle cell

Nuclei

Marian Rice

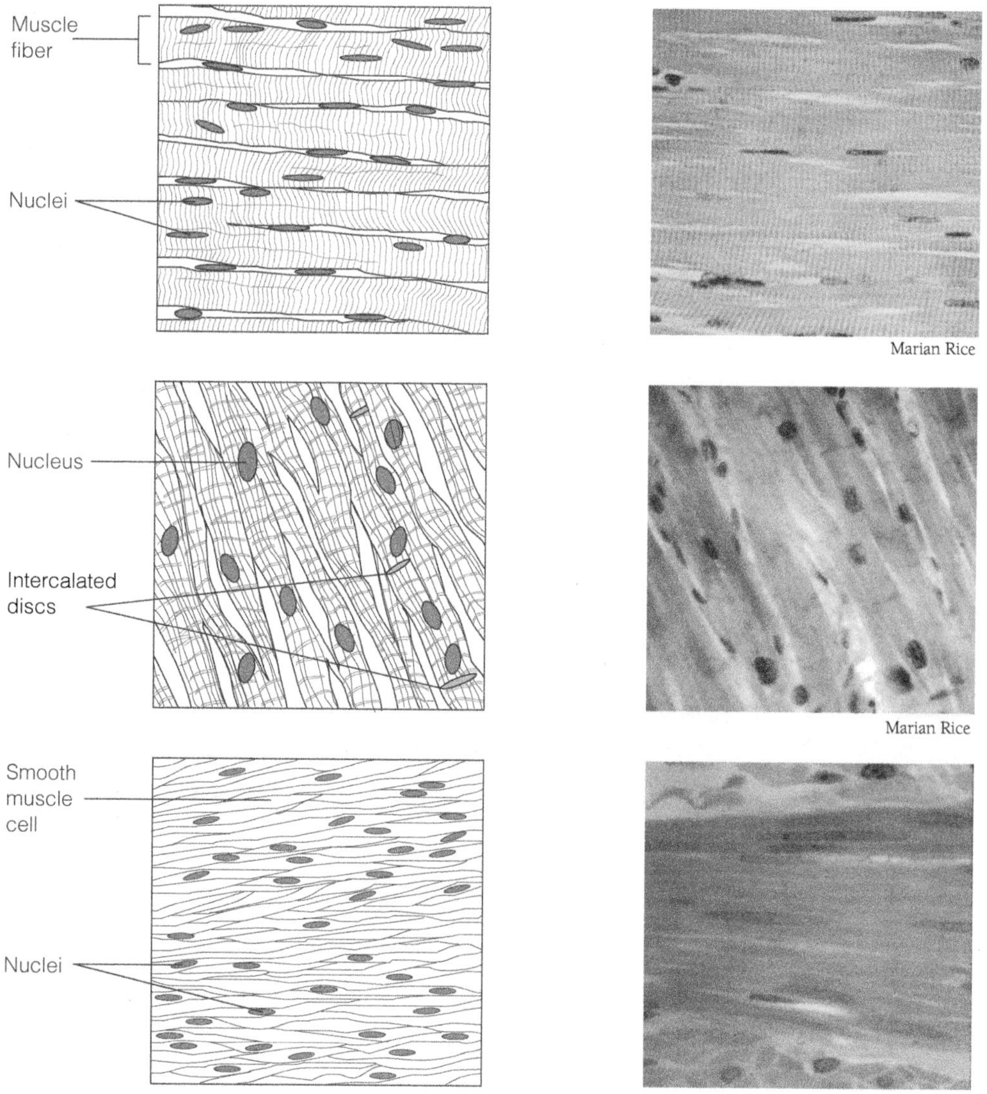

**Figure 3.**

**Muscle tissue.** Muscle tissue is either striated or smooth. (a) Skeletal muscle is striated. (b) Cardiac muscle is also striated. (c) Smooth, or visceral, muscle is not striated.

3a and c (art): Adapted from E. Marieb, *Human Anatomy and Physiology Laboratory Manual,* Cat Version, 6th ed. (Menlo Park, CA: Benjamin/Cummings, 1999), © 1999 The Benjamin/Cummings Publishing Company;

called **chondrocytes. Blood** is a connective tissue consisting of cellular components called **erythrocytes** (red blood cells), **leukocytes** (white blood cells), and **platelets** (cell fragments) in a liquid ground substance called **plasma.** Other connective tissues fill the spaces between various tissues, binding them together or performing other functions. Connective tissues are derived from mesoderm.

**(☛)Figure 2.**

**Connective tissue.** (a) In loose connective tissue, cells are embedded in a liquid fibrous matrix. (b) Adipose tissue stores fat droplets in adipose cells. (c) In bone, cells are embedded in a solid fibrous matrix. (d) In cartilage, cells are embedded in a gelatinous fibrous matrix. (e) In blood, cells are embedded in a liquid matrix.

**2a** (art): E. Marieb, *Human Anatomy and Physiology Laboratory Manual,* Cat Version, 5th ed. (Menlo Park, CA: Benjamin/Cummings, 1996), © 1996 The Benjamin/Cummings Publishing Company;
**2c:** Adapted from E. Marieb, *Human Anatomy and Physiology Laboratory Manual,* Cat Version, 6th ed. (Menlo Park, CA: Benjamin/Cummings, 1999), © 1999 The Benjamin/Cummings Publishing Company.
**2d** (art): E. Marieb, *Human Anatomy and Physiology Laboratory Manual,* Cat Version, 3rd ed. (Menlo Park, CA: Benjamin/Cummings, 1989), © 1989 The Benjamin/Cummings Publishing Company;
**2e** (art): E. Marieb, *Human Anatomy and Physiology Laboratory Manual,* Cat Version, 4th ed. (Menlo Park, CA: Benjamin/Cummings, 1993), © 1993 The Benjamin/Cummings Publishing Company.

**Figure 4.**

**Nervous tissue.** Neurons and glial cells.

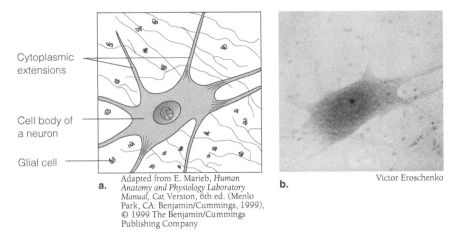

Cytoplasmic extensions

Cell body of a neuron

Glial cell

a. Adapted from E. Marieb, *Human Anatomy and Physiology Laboratory Manual*, Cat Version, 6th ed. (Menlo Park, CA: Benjamin/Cummings, 1999), © 1999 The Benjamin/Cummings Publishing Company

b. Victor Eroschenko

**Muscle tissue** may be **striated**, showing a pattern of alternating light and dark bands, or **smooth**, showing no banding pattern (Figure 3). There are two types of striated muscle, skeletal and cardiac. **Skeletal** muscle moves the skeleton and the diaphragm and is made of muscle fibers formed by the fusion of several cells end-to-end. **Cardiac** muscle, found only in the wall of the heart, is also striated, but the cells do not fuse. Cells are attached by **intercalated discs.** Smooth muscle, also called **visceral** muscle, is found in the skin and in the walls of organs such as the stomach, intestine, and uterus. Muscle, like connective tissue, is derived from mesoderm.

**Nervous tissue** is found in the central nervous system (brain and spinal cord) and in the peripheral nervous system consisting of nerves (Figure 4). Nervous tissue is found in every organ throughout the body. There are two basic cell types, neurons and glial cells. **Neurons** are capable of responding to physical and chemical stimuli by creating an **impulse,** which is transmitted from one locality to another. **Glial cells** support and protect the neurons. Nervous tissue is derived from ectoderm.

The organs that you will investigate in the following exercises are made up of the four basic tissues. The tissues, each with a specific function, are organized into a functional organ unit.

---

## EXERCISE 1
# Histology of the Skin

### Materials

compound microscope
prepared slide of pig and/or monkey skin

### Introduction

Tissues are structurally arranged to function together in **organs**, which are adapted to perform specific functions. Organs are found in all but the simplest animals. The largest organ of the vertebrate body, the skin, illustrates the organization of tissues, each with a specific function, into a functioning organ (Figure 5). The skin protects the body from dehydration and bacterial invasion, assists in regulating body temperature, and receives stimuli from the environment. As you work through this exercise, ask how the unique function

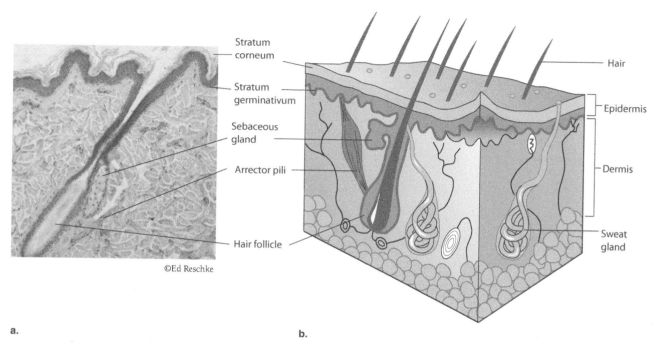

Stratum
corneum

Stratum
germinativum

Sebaceous
gland

Arrector pili

Hair follicle

©Ed Reschke

Hair

Epidermis

Dermis

Sweat
gland

a.

b.

**Figure 5.**
**Mammalian skin structure.** (a) Photomicrograph of a cross section of the skin.
(b) A diagram detailing the skin structure.

of each tissue produces the functioning whole—the skin. Review information
about each observed tissue type in "Introduction to Tissues".

## Procedure

1. Obtain a prepared slide of mammalian skin (pig or monkey). View it using
   the low and intermediate power objectives on the compound microscope.

2. Identify the two main layers of the skin. The thin outer layer, the
   **epidermis,** consists of **stratified squamous epithelium** (Figure 1d);
   the thicker inner layer, the **dermis,** consists mainly of **dense connective
   tissue** and scattered **blood vessels.** The dermis merges into layers of
   loose connective tissue (Figure 2a) and smooth muscle (Figure 3c),
   which are not considered part of the skin.

3. Locate **hair follicles** extending obliquely from the epidermis into the
   dermis. In the living animal, each follicle contains a hair, but the hair
   shaft may or may not be visible in every follicle on your slide, depending on the plane of the section through the follicle. The follicle is lined
   by epithelial cells continuous with the epidermis. Carefully observe several hair follicles. You may be able to find a band of smooth muscle cells
   attached to the side of a follicle. This muscle, called the **arrector pili,**
   attaches the hair follicle to the outermost layer of the dermis. When
   stimulated by cold or fright, it pulls the hair erect, causing "goose
   bumps." In furry animals this adaptation increases the thickness of the
   coat to provide additional temperature insulation. Clusters of secretory
   cells making up **sebaceous glands** are also associated with hair follicles.
   These are more obvious in monkey skin slides than in pig skin slides.

4. Focus your attention on the epidermis and locate the outermost layer,
   the **stratum corneum,** a layer of dead, keratinized cells, impermeable
   to water. This layer is continually exfoliated and replaced. The thickness

of the stratum corneum varies, depending on the location of the skin. This layer is very thick on the soles of feet or palms of human hands.

5. The innermost layer of cells in the epidermis is called the **basal layer** or the **stratum germinativum.** These cells divide mitotically and produce new cells, which, as they mature, are pushed to higher and higher layers of the epidermis, until they fill with keratin and form the stratum corneum. Scattered through the basal layer (though not seen on your slide) are cells called **melanocytes** that produce **melanin,** a pigment that produces brown or black hues in the skin. The melanin is inserted into newly forming epidermal cells as they are pushed outward. Regular exposure to sunlight stimulates melanocytes to produce more melanin, helping protect the body against the potentially harmful effects of sun exposure.

6. In addition to hair follicles, coiled tubular **sweat glands** lined with **cuboidal epithelium** (Figure 1b) extend from the epidermis into the dermis. They appear as circular clusters in cross section and may be easily located in pig skin but are less numerous or absent in furry animals, such as monkeys. The tubular secretory portion is convoluted into a ball, which connects with a narrow unbranched tube leading to the skin surface. It is unlikely that you will see an entire intact sweat gland in one section.

7. Look for connective tissue and blood vessels, which often contain red blood cells in the dermis. Look for adipose tissue (Figure 2b) below the dermis.

## Results

In Table 1, list the tissues you have identified in the skin and indicate the specific function of each.

**Table 1**
Tissues of the Skin and Their Functions

| Tissue | Function |
|--------|----------|
|        |          |
|        |          |
|        |          |
|        |          |
|        |          |
|        |          |

## Discussion

1. How does the skin prevent dehydration?

2. How does the skin protect from bacterial invasion?

3. Discuss how each of the following helps regulate body temperature: blood vessels in the dermis, sweat glands, adipose tissue below the dermis, hair, and hair follicles.

---

EXERCISE 2

# Introduction to the Fetal Pig

---

## Materials

preserved fetal pig        disposable gloves
dissecting pan             preservative

## Introduction

Fetal, or unborn, pigs are obtained from pregnant sows being slaughtered for food. The size of your pig will vary, depending on its stage of gestation, a total period of about 112 to 115 days. After being embalmed in a formaldehyde- or phenol-based solution, pigs are stored in a preservative that usually does not contain formaldehyde, although the smell of formaldehyde may remain. Most preserving solutions are relatively harmless; however, they will dry the skin, and occasionally a student may be allergic to the solutions. For these reasons, you should not handle the pigs with your bare hands, and you should perform your dissections in a well-ventilated room.

---

 **Wear disposable gloves when handling the pig and other preserved animals.**

---

In this exercise, you will become familiar with the external anatomy of the fetal pig, noting the regions of its body and the surface structures. The skin, just studied in microscopic sections, will be the first organ observed.

Each student, working independently (unless otherwise instructed), will dissect a fetal pig; however, we encourage you to engage in collaborative discussions with your lab partner. Discuss results and conclusions and compare dissections.

 Read carefully the rules and techniques for dissection before you begin your study of the fetal pig.

## Procedure

1. Obtain a fetal pig and place it in a dissecting pan. Add a small amount of preservative to the pan. Do not allow the pig to dry out at any time. However, use the preservative, not water, to moisten the tissue unless otherwise instructed.

 Your pig may have been injected with red and blue latex. The red was injected into arteries through one of the umbilical arteries; the blue was injected into veins through the external jugular vein through an incision in the neck.

2. With your lab partner, locate your pig's left and right, dorsal and ventral, and anterior (cranial) and posterior (caudal) regions. Use the terms *proximal* and *distal* to compare positions of several structures.

3. Locate the body regions on your pig. The pig has a **head, neck, trunk, and tail** (Figure 6a). The trunk is divided into an anterior **thorax,** encased by ribs, and a posterior **abdomen.** The thoracic and abdominal regions of the body house corresponding cavities that are divisions of the body cavity, or coelom. The **thoracic cavity** is in the thorax, and the **abdominal (peritoneal) cavity** is in the abdomen.

4. Examine the head with its concentration of sensory receptors. Identify the mouth; **external nostrils** on the end of the snout; ears, each with an external flap supported by cartilage (Figure 2d), the **auricle;** eyes with two eyelids, as in humans, and a third eyelid, the **nictitating membrane,** near the inside corner of each eye.

5. Examine the pig's skin and review its functions. In a fetal pig, an outer embryonic skin, the **epitrichium,** lies over the skin. You may find pieces of this layer on your pig. Is hair present on your pig?

6. Locate the cut **umbilical cord** on the ventral surface of the abdomen. Blood vessels pass from the placenta, attached to the wall of the mother's uterus, to the fetal pig through this cord. If your pig's umbilical cord is collapsed, use scissors to make a fresh transverse cut and examine the end more closely. Identify the cut ends of two round, thick-walled **umbilical arteries;** one larger, flattened **umbilical vein;** and one very small, round **allantoic stalk.** You may remember that

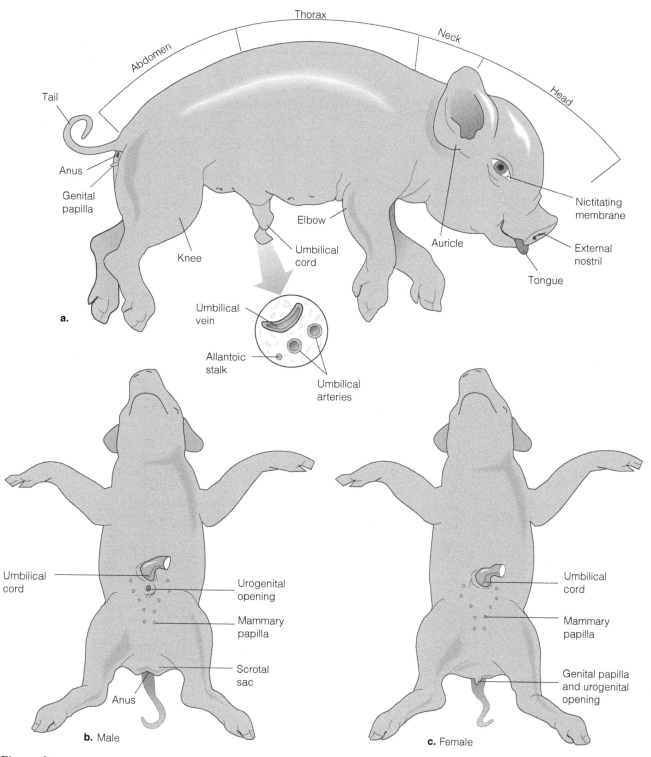

**Figure 6.**
**Fetal pig.** (a) Body regions and external structures of the fetal pig with an enlarged cross section of the umbilical cord. (b) Posterior region of male pig. (c) Posterior region of female pig.

blood vessels carrying blood away from the heart of the animal are called **arteries.** Blood vessels carrying blood back to the heart are called **veins.** In fetal circulation, the umbilical arteries carry blood from the fetus to the placenta. The umbilical vein carries blood from the placenta to the fetus. The allantois is an extension of the urinary bladder of the fetus into the umbilical cord. Speculate about the nature of blood in the umbilical arteries and the umbilical vein. Explain your conclusions.

a. Which vessel—umbilical artery or umbilical vein—would carry blood *high* in oxygen (oxygen-rich blood)?

b. Which vessel would carry blood *low* in oxygen (oxygen-poor blood)?

c. Which vessel would carry blood high in nutrients?

d. Which vessel would carry blood high in metabolic waste?

7. Look just caudal to the umbilical cord to determine the sex of your pig. If it is a male (Figure 6b), you will see the **urogenital opening** in this position. This opening is located below the tail in the female. Locate the **anus** just ventral to the base of the tail in both sexes. In the male, **scrotal sacs** will be present ventral to the anus and caudal to the hind legs. In the female pig (Figure 6c), the **urogenital opening** is located ventral to the anus. Folds, or **labia,** surround this opening, and a small protuberance, the **genital papilla,** is visible just ventral to the urogenital opening. The urogenital opening is a common opening from the urinary and reproductive tracts. Notice that **mammary papillae** are present in pigs of both sexes. Locate a pig of the opposite sex for comparison. Having determined the sex of your pig, you are now ready to begin your dissection.

## Results

1. List structures observed in the fetal pig that are no longer present in the pig after birth.

2. Modify Figure 6 or make a sketch in the margin of your lab manual with any additional details needed for future reference.

## Discussion

Review the definition of the term *cephalization*, and describe how the pig demonstrates this phenomenon.

---

EXERCISE 3

# The Digestive System in the Fetal Pig

---

## Materials

supplies from Exercise 2
dissecting instruments
twine

plastic bag with twist tie and label
stereoscopic microscope or hand lens

## Introduction

Most internal organs, including the entire digestive system, are located in the body cavity, or coelom. A large muscular structure, the **diaphragm,** divides the body cavity into the **thoracic** cavity and the **abdominal (peritoneal)** cavity. The **thoracic** cavity includes two additional cavities, the **pleural** cavity housing the lungs and the **pericardial** cavity housing the heart. **Coelomic epithelial membranes** line these cavities and cover the surface of all organs. Those epithelial membranes *lining the wall* of the cavity are called **parietal** (L., *pariet,* "wall"). Epithelial membranes *covering organs* are called **visceral** (L., *viscera,* "bowels"). Each epithelial membrane lining in the coelom is named according to its cavity and location (lining the wall or covering the organ). Thus, the epithelial membrane covering the lungs would be the **visceral pleura.** The epithelial membrane lining the wall of the pleural cavity would be the **parietal pleura.** Likewise, the lining of the abdominal (peritoneal) cavity is **parietal peritoneum.** The epithelium covering organs in the peritoneal cavity is **visceral peritoneum.** What would be the name of the epithelium covering the heart?

Use this convention to complete Table 2, naming coelomic epithelial membranes. As you open each body cavity described in these lab topics, return to this table to check your answers.

**Table 2**
Divisions of the Body Cavity and Associated Membranes

| Body Cavity | Divisions | Epithelial Membrane Lining the Cavity Wall | Epithelial Membrane Covering the Organs | Organs |
|---|---|---|---|---|
| Thoracic | Pleural | Parietal pleura | Visceral pleura | Lungs |
| | Pericardial | | | |
| Abdominal | Abdominal (peritoneal) | | Visceral peritoneum | Stomach, pancreas, spleen, liver, gallbladder, intestines |

More complex animals have a tubular digestive system with an anterior opening, the mouth, and a posterior opening, the anus. This pattern in the digestive system allows specialization to take place along the length of the tract, resulting in the development of specific organs that carry out specific functions. As you investigate the digestive system in the fetal pig, ask how each structure or region solves a particular problem in nutrition procurement and processing. Remember that memorizing the names of structures is meaningless unless you understand how the morphology is related to the function of the organ.

## Procedure

1. Hold the pig ventral side up in the dissecting pan and use twine to tie the two anterior legs together and the two posterior legs together, leaving enough twine between to slip under the dissecting pan. The pig should be positioned "spread-eagle" in the pan, ventral side up.

2. To expose structures in the mouth cavity, use heavy, sharp-pointed scissors to cut at the corners of the mouth along the line of the tongue. Continue to cut until the lower jaw can be lowered, being careful not to cut into the tissues in the roof of the mouth cavity. Continue to cut, pulling down on the lower jaw until your cuts reach the muscle and tissue at the back of the mouth. Cut through this muscle until lowering the jaw exposes the back of the mouth cavity.

   a. Identify structures in the mouth cavity (Figure 7). Locate the **teeth;** the **tongue** covered with **papillae,** which house taste buds; and the roof of the mouth, composed of the **hard palate** supported by bone (Figure 2c) and the **soft palate.** The hard palate is anterior to the soft palate and is marked by ridges.

   b. Identify structures and openings at the rear of the mouth cavity: the **glottis,** the space in the beginning of the respiratory passageway; the **epiglottis,** a small flap of tissue supported by cartilage (Figure 2d) that covers the glottis when swallowing; the **esophagus,** the beginning of the digestive tube (alimentary canal); and the **opening into the nasal chamber.** All these open into the **pharynx,** the chamber located posterior to the mouth.

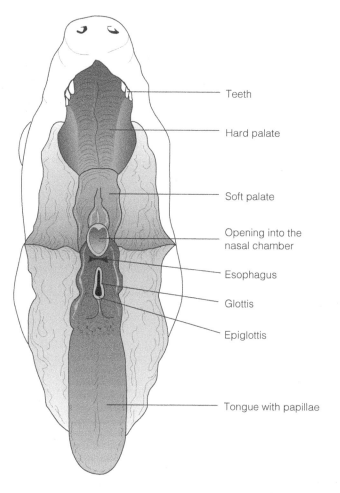

Teeth

Hard palate

Soft palate

Opening into the nasal chamber

Esophagus

Glottis

Epiglottis

Tongue with papillae

**Figure 7.**
**The mouth cavity.**
Openings into the pharynx in the rear of the mouth cavity lead to the respiratory system, the digestive system, and the nasal cavity. The tongue occupies the floor of the mouth, and the roof of the mouth consists of the hard and soft palates.

Adapted from Stephen Gilbert, *Pictorial Anatomy of Fetal Pig,* 2nd ed. © 1966 University of Washington Press. Reprinted by permission of the University of Washington Press.

  c. Probe into the nasal chamber through the opening at the rear of the soft palate, the esophagus just posterior and ventral to the opening into the nasal chamber, and the glottis. Notice that the opening into the esophagus lies dorsal to the opening into the respiratory tract.

3. Expose the digestive organs in the abdominal region by opening the posterior portion of the abdominal cavity.

  a. Begin the dissection by using the scalpel to make a shallow midventral incision from the base of the throat to the umbilical cord (Figure 8, incision 1). Cut lateral incisions (Figure 8, incision 2) around each side of the umbilical cord and continue the two incisions, one to the medial surface of each leg.

  b. Now use the scissors to cut deep into one of the lateral incisions beside the cord until you penetrate into the abdominal cavity, piercing the parietal peritoneum. At this point, fluid in the cavity should begin to seep out. Use the scissors to cut through the body wall along the two lateral incisions to the legs and around the umbilical cord.

  c. Pull lightly on the umbilical cord. If your dissection is correct, you will see that the umbilical cord and ventral wedge of body wall could be reflected, or pulled back, toward the tail, except for a blood vessel, the **umbilical vein.** This vein passes from the umbilical cord anteriorly toward a large brown organ, the liver. Cut through this vein, leaving a stub at each end. Tie a small piece of string around each stub so you can find them later. This should free the flap of body wall, which may now be reflected toward the tail, exposing the abdominal organs.

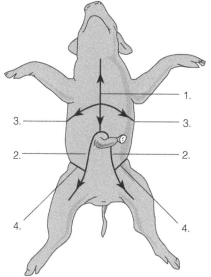

1.

3. 3.

2. 2.

4. 4.

**Figure 8.**
**Incisions to open the abdominal cavity.** Incision 1 makes a shallow midventral incision from the base of the throat to the umbilical cord. Incision 2 cuts around the umbilical cord to the medial surface of each leg. Incision 3 cuts through the body wall laterally just posterior to the diaphragm. Incision 4 cuts laterally at the posterior margin of the abdominal cavity.

241

4. Open the anterior portion of the abdominal cavity.

   a. Cut anteriorly through the body wall along the midventral incision until you reach the diaphragm, separating the thoracic and abdominal cavities.

   b. Make four lateral cuts, two adjacent to the rib cage just posterior to the diaphragm (incision 3) and two at the posterior margin of the abdominal cavity (incision 4). This will produce two flaps of body wall that can be folded back like the lids of a box.

   c. If your specimen contains coagulated blood or free latex from the injection, pull out the latex and rinse the body cavity under running water.

5. Identify the various structures in the abdominal cavity (Figure 9).

   a. Shiny epithelial membranes line the cavity and cover the organs. The **parietal peritoneum** lines the cavity, and the **visceral peritoneum** covers the organs. Speculate about the contents of the space between these two membranes and its function.

   b. The **diaphragm** is a large domed, striated (skeletal, Figure 3a) muscle forming the transverse cranial wall of the abdominal cavity, separating this from the thoracic cavity. Only mammals have a diaphragm. The contraction and relaxation of this muscle and muscles between the ribs cause the thoracic cavity to expand and contract, changing the pressure in the cavity and lungs, thus facilitating movement of air into and out of the lungs.

   c. The **liver** is the large brown organ that appears to fill the abdominal cavity. Notice that it consists of several lobes. Pull it cranially and locate the **gallbladder,** a small, thin-walled, paddle-shaped sac embedded in its ventral surface. The liver has many functions, including processing nutrients and detoxifying toxins and drugs. Its main digestive function is the production of **bile,** a substance that emulsifies fats. Bile is stored in the gallbladder until needed.

   d. The **stomach** is a large, saclike organ lying dorsal to the liver (Figure 9b). Reflect the liver cranially to get a better view. The larger upper-left portion of the stomach tapers down to a narrower portion to the right. The **esophagus** passes through the diaphragm and enters the upper medial border of the stomach. Locate the **spleen,** a dark organ lying along the **greater curvature** of the stomach (the lateral convex border). The spleen filters blood.

   e. Cut into the stomach along the greater curvature. Rinse out the stomach contents and identify the numerous longitudinal folds, called **gastric rugae.** Speculate about the role played by these folds.

   f. Food enters the stomach from the esophagus through the **cardiac valve,** or **cardiac sphincter.** A sphincter valve is a circular band of muscle that encircles an opening. Locate this valve between the esophagus and stomach and speculate about its function.

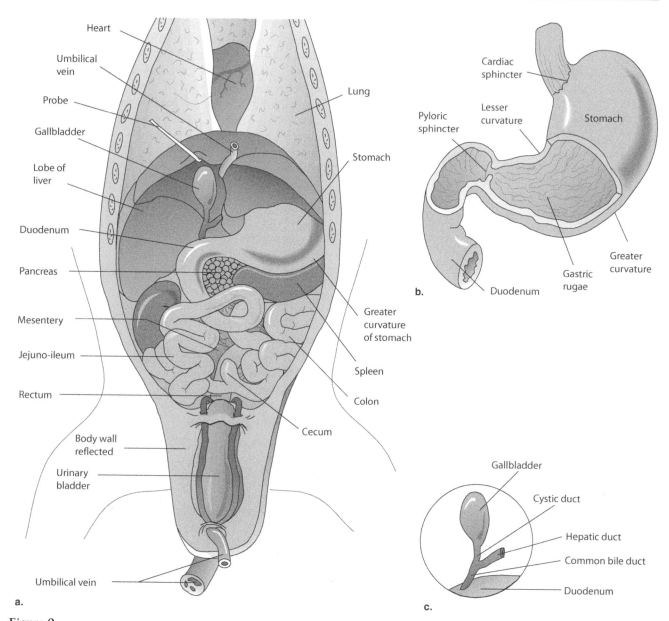

**Figure 9.**

**Digestive organs of the abdominal cavity.** (a) The liver is reflected cranially to expose deeper-lying organs. The stomach leads into the duodenum of the small intestine. The jejuno-ileum continues from the duodenum and empties into the colon near the cecum. (b) Cutaway view of stomach showing internal gastric rugae. (c) Enlargement of gallbladder and associated ducts.

    The stomach mechanically churns food and mixes it with water, mucus, hydrochloric acid, and protein-digesting enzymes.

g. From the stomach, food then passes into the **small intestine,** which joins the stomach at its extreme right narrow portion. Locate another valve, the **pyloric sphincter,** which lies between the stomach and small intestine. This sphincter is closed when food is present in the stomach, preventing food from entering the small intestine prematurely.

h. The **duodenum** is the portion of the small intestine connecting with the stomach (Figure 9b). The **pancreas,** an irregular, granular-looking gland, lies in a loop of the duodenum. As food passes through the duodenum, enzymes from the pancreas and the duodenal wall are added to it along with bile, which is produced in the liver and stored in the gallbladder. Using your forceps and a blunt probe to pick away surrounding tissue, locate and separate the **common bile duct,** which enters the duodenum. It is formed by the confluence of the **hepatic duct** passing from the liver and the **cystic duct** leading from the gallbladder (Figure 9c).

i. The **jejuno-ileum** is the extensive, highly convoluted portion of the small intestine extending from the duodenum to the colon (Figure 9a). Whereas the jejunum and the ileum are separate anatomical regions, macroscopically (without a microscope) it is difficult to distinguish between the two in the pig except by position. The duodenum joins the jejunum, which leads to the ileum. The ileum joins the colon.

Most digested food is absorbed into the circulatory system through the walls of the jejuno-ileum. The surface area of the lining of this organ is increased by the presence of microscopic **villi** and **microvilli,** greatly enhancing its absorbing capacity.

Spread apart folds in the jejuno-ileum and notice the thin membrane called **mesentery,** which supports the folds. Do you see blood vessels in this mesentery? Speculate about the relationship between these vessels and food processing.

j. Cut out a 1-cm-long segment of the jejuno-ileum and cut it open to expose the inner surface. Use a stereoscopic microscope or hand lens to examine this surface. Can you see villi?

k. Follow the ileum to its junction with the large intestine, or **colon.** The diameter of the colon is slightly greater than that of the small intestine, and it is tightly coiled and held together by mesentery. Look for a small outpocketing or fingerlike projection of the colon at its proximal end. This projection is the **cecum,** which is much larger in herbivores than in carnivores. In animals with a large cecum, it probably assists in digestion and absorption. In humans, a **vermiform** (wormlike) appendix extends from the cecum.

One of the important activities in the colon is the reabsorption of water that has been added, along with enzymes and mucus, to the food mass as it passes down the digestive tract. Water conservation is one of the most critical problems in terrestrial animals.

l. The distal portion of the colon is the **rectum,** which passes deep into the caudal portion of the abdominal cavity and to the outside of the body at the anus. Water reabsorption continues in the rectum.

6. After you complete the dissection, use an indelible pen to prepare two labels with your name, lab day, and room. Tie one label to your pig and place the pig in a plastic bag with the label in view. Add preservative from the lab stock and securely close the plastic bag. Tie the second label to the outside of the bag.

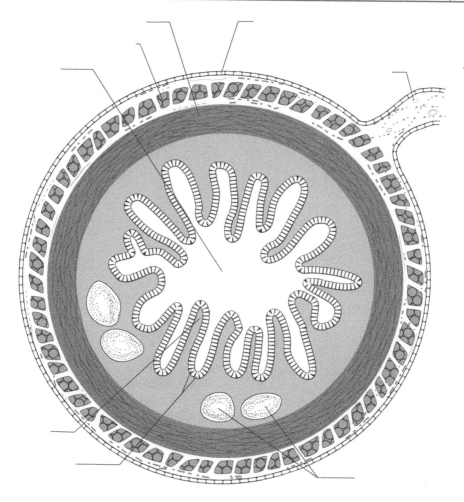

**Figure 10.**
**Cross section through the pig jejuno-ileum.** Label the cells and structures described in Exercise 3, Procedure section, step 7.

7. Using the compound microscope, study a prepared microscope slide of a section through a region of the jejuno-ileum (Figure 10).

   a. Use the lowest power on the microscope and scan the section, finding the smooth outer surface and then the **lumen,** or central cavity, located within the intestine. Food passing through the intestine passes through the lumen. Sketch the outline of the section in the margin of your lab manual.

   b. The fingerlike **villi** previously observed are now easily discernible, projecting into the lumen of the intestine. Switch to 10× magnification and focus on the simple **columnar epithelial** tissue lining each villus (Figure 1c). This tissue functions in the absorption of nutrients into the circulatory system. Capillaries and lacteals (small lymph vessels) are located within each villus. These vessels are not usually visible.

   c. Continue your observations, scanning outward toward the surface of the intestine. You will pass through regions with **loose fibrous connective tissue** containing many blood vessels. You may see large masses of cells that are lymphocytes in **lymph nodules.**

   d. On the outer surface of the section, locate a thin layer of simple squamous epithelium (Figure 1a), called the **visceral peritoneum,** or **serosa.** Two large bands of smooth muscle lie just inside the visceral peritoneum.

e. Locate the outermost muscle layer, composed of smooth muscle fibers extending longitudinally along the intestine. This muscle layer is called the **longitudinal muscle layer.** Since this is a cross section, the longitudinal nature of the fibers will not be apparent. Look just inside the longitudinal muscle layer to see a wide band of muscle, the **circular muscle layer** (appears as in Figure 3c). These muscle fibers encircle the intestine.

Imagine each band of muscle contracting as a unit, and speculate about the function of these muscles. Do you know the special name given to the waves of contraction of these muscles?

f. Turn to high power and locate nuclei in both the longitudinal and the circular muscle fibers.

g. Label Figure 10.

## Results

1. The digestive tract of many invertebrates is described as a "tube-within-a-tube"—a tubular digestive tract within a "tubular" body. The pig digestive tract has this tubular design. Which structures and organs of the pig digestive system develop as tubes or chambers within its tubular digestive tract?

2. Which organs in the digestive system lie outside the "digestive tube" but are important in the digestive process?

## Discussion

1. Conservation of water is a critical problem faced by terrestrial organisms. Given the water requirements for digestion, how is the digestive tract anatomy adapted to life on land?

2. Speculate about the outcome if food passes too slowly or too rapidly through the colon.

3. Consult a text and describe the process of food absorption in the small intestine, relating it to the structures observed in this exercise.

 Student Media Video—Ch. 41: Whale Eating a Seal

## Questions for Review

In Table 3, beginning with the mouth, list each region or organ through which food passes in the pig and describe for each the primary digestive functions, the enzymes active in that chamber, and the macromolecules affected, when appropriate. Consult your text if necessary.

**Table 3**
Organs of the Pig Digestive Tract and Their Functions

| Region/Organ | Function/Macromolecule Digested | Enzymes |
|---|---|---|
|  |  |  |
|  |  |  |
|  |  |  |
|  |  |  |
|  |  |  |
|  |  |  |
|  |  |  |

## Applying Your Knowledge

1. The Peachtree Road Race is over, and you have just been awarded the coveted T-shirt. Your body is dripping wet and your skin appears bright red. Explain, from a physiological perspective, what is happening to your body.

2. What happens to your skin when you get a "sunburn"? Describe the process of "getting a tan." Relate these processes to skin histology.

3. Tattooing is the risky and unregulated procedure of using a needle to deposit pigment in the skin. Where in the skin would it be necessary to deposit the pigment to make the tattoo permanent?

4. The three most common forms of skin cancer are (1) basal cell carcinoma, (2) squamous cell carcinoma, and (3) malignant melanoma. Using your knowledge of skin histology, predict the skin layers and/or cells that are involved in each of these cancers.

5. Give examples of structures supported by bone and by cartilage observed in this lab topic. What differences in flexibility and function have you noticed in these structures?

## Case Studies

You have just completed a study of the digestive tract, and now you know the names, structures, and have been introduced to the functions of each part. However, this information alone is just the beginning of understanding the role the digestive system plays in the body. This system functions to provide nourishment for optimum functioning of your tissues and organs. You eat carbohydrates, proteins, and fats and they are digested in the organs of your digestive system. But are all carbohydrates, proteins, and fats equally useful in providing nourishment? Should your diet include more of one component and less of another?

Over 10 years ago the U.S. Department of Agriculture created a "Food Guide Pyramid" with the goal of giving advice on the best diet for healthy living. In recent years, however, many health professionals have criticized this pyramid, pointing out that it was not based on sound scientific research and its design was influenced by the food industry. Recently, new food pyramids have been created with a stronger foundation in scientific evidence linking diet and health.

The "freshman 15" (refers to the number of pounds that many students gain their first year in college) is an indication that many college students are unaware or choose to ignore the wealth of information now available to help plan a healthy diet. This may be due to erratic eating patterns, high stress levels, sedentary lifestyles, or any number of factors of college life. The objective of this study is to encourage you to examine your diet and become familiar with the latest guidelines for healthy living.

1. As you begin, read the online article from the Harvard School of Public Health that gives the history of food pyramids. See "The Healthy Eating Pyramid," from *Eat, Drink and Be Healthy* by Walter C. Willett, M.D. http://hsph.harvard.edu/nutritionsource/pyramids.html. This pyramid and the subsequent discussion presented in this article are based on sound scientific evidence.

2. Next, compile a personal "meal log" for a typical 24-hour period. Create a table and record each food that you consume, keeping a record of numbers of servings and amounts (volume, e.g., ½ cup; or weight, e.g, one 6 oz. chocolate candy bar). Your table might look something like:

| Time | Item | Number and Amounts of Servings | Category in Food Pyramid |
|------|------|--------------------------------|--------------------------|
| 8:00 a.m. | Scrambled egg | 1 large | Fish, poultry, eggs |
| | Whole wheat toast | 2 sliced | Wholegrain foods |
| 10:00 a.m. | Banana | 1 | Fruits |
| | Yogurt, plain | ½ cup | Dairy |

3. Working with one or more classmates, evaluate your diets. Compare your diets to the content and proportions of a healthy diet presented in the Healthy Eating Pyramid. Make a list or write a paragraph describing changes you should make to improve your diet.

4. Survey the food available in the food services for your college or university. Based on what you have learned about healthy eating, write a recommended diet for college students from the menu of food available.

## Student Media Activities and Investigations

**Activities**—Ch. 40: Overview of Animal Tissues; Epithelial Tissue; Connective Tissue; Nervous Tissue; Muscle Tissue; Ch.41: Feeding Mechanisms of Animals; Digestive System Function
**Investigations**—Ch. 41: What Role Does Amylase Play in Digestion?
www.masteringbio.com

## References

Campbell, N., and J. Reece. *Biology,* 8th ed. Menlo Park, CA: Benjamin Cummings, 2008.

Fawcett, D. W., and W. Bloom. *A Textbook of Histology,* 12th ed. Philadelphia, PA: Saunders College Publishing, 1994.

Walker, W. F., Jr. *Anatomy and Dissection of the Fetal Pig,* 5th ed. New York: W. H. Freeman, 1998.

Marieb, E. N. *Human Anatomy and Physiology,* 6th ed. Menlo Park, CA: Benjamin Cummings, 2004.

## Websites

Photographs of fetal pig anatomy:
http://www.biologycorner.com/pig/fetal.html

"The Health Eating Pyramid":
http://hsph.harvard.edu/nutritionsource/pyramids.html

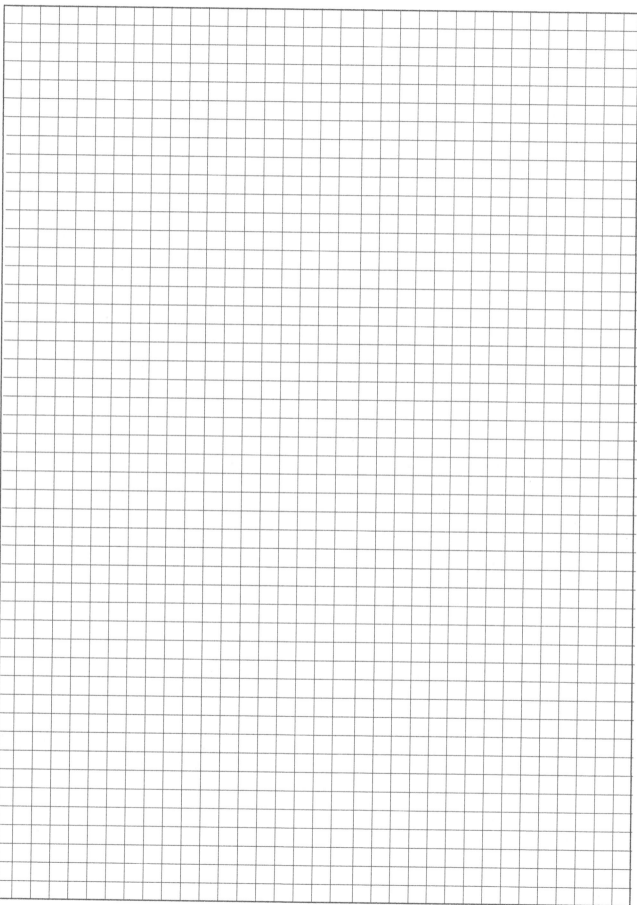

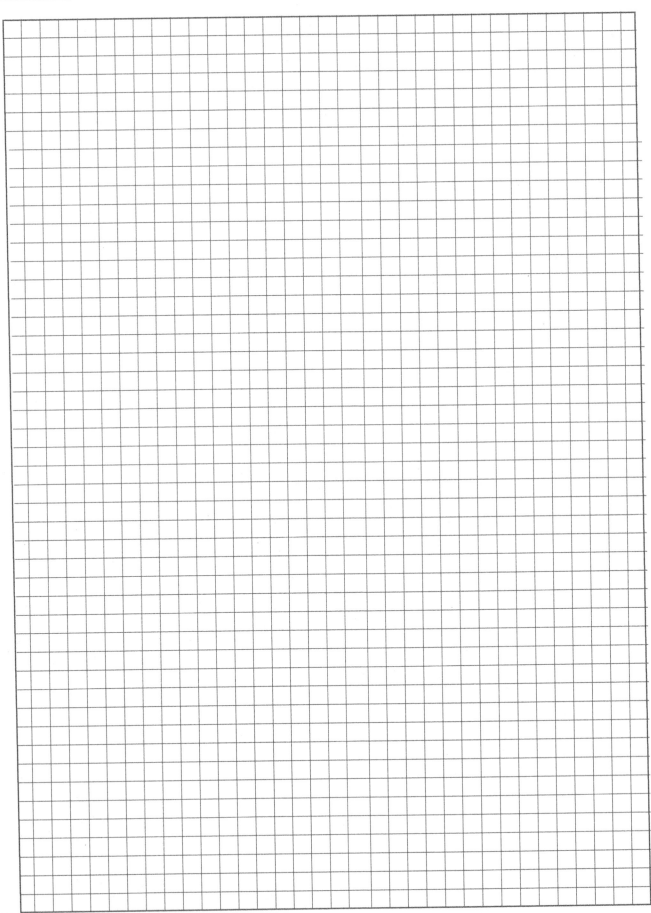

# Vertebrate Anatomy: The Circulatory and Respiratory Systems

## Laboratory Objectives

After completing this lab topic, you should be able to:

1. Identify and describe the function of the main organs and structures in the circulatory system and trace the flow of blood through the pulmonary and systemic circuits.

2. Identify and describe the function of the main organs and structures in the respiratory system and describe the exchange of oxygen and carbon dioxide in the lungs.

3. Describe how the circulatory and respiratory systems work together to bring about the integrated functioning of the body.

4. Apply knowledge and understanding acquired in this lab to problems in human physiology.

5. Apply knowledge and understanding acquired in this lab to explain organismal adaptive strategies.

## Introduction

Nutrients are taken into the digestive tract, where they are processed: chewed, mixed with water and churned to a liquid, mixed with digestive enzymes, and finally digested into the component monomers, or building blocks, from which they were synthesized. For an animal to receive the benefits of these nutrients, these products of digestion must pass across intestinal cells and into the circulatory system to be transported to all the cells of the animal's body. Oxygen is necessary for the release of energy from these digested products. Oxygen from the atmosphere passes into the respiratory system of the animal, where it ultimately crosses cells in the lungs (in a terrestrial vertebrate) or gills (in an aquatic vertebrate) and enters the circulatory system for transport to cells of all organs, to be utilized in nutrient metabolism. Waste products of cellular metabolism—carbon dioxide and urea—are transported from the tissues that produce them via the blood and are eliminated from the body through the lungs of the respiratory system and the kidney of the excretory system, respectively. Thus, the circulatory, respiratory, and excretory systems function collectively, utilizing environmental materials, eliminating wastes, and maintaining a stable internal environment.

From *Investigating Biology Laboratory Manual,* Sixth Edition, Judith G. Morgan and M. Eloise Brown Carter. Copyright © 2008 by Pearson Education, Inc. Published by Benjamin Cummings, Inc. All rights reserved.

In this lab topic, you will investigate the morphology of the circulatory, respiratory, and excretory systems in the fetal pig. As you dissect, relate the structure and specific function of each system to its role in the integrated body.

# EXERCISE 1

# Glands and Respiratory Structures of the Neck and Thoracic Cavity

## Materials

These materials will be used for the entire lab topic.

fetal pig
dissecting pan
dissecting instruments
twine

disposable gloves
plastic bag with twist tie and labels
preservative

## Introduction

To study the glands and respiratory structures of the neck, you must first open the thoracic cavity and then remove the skin and muscles in the neck region. This will expose several major glands that lie in the neck region in close proximity to the respiratory structures.

## Procedure

 **Wear disposable gloves when dissecting preserved animals.**

1. Begin the dissection by opening the thoracic cavity, which houses the heart and lungs, and making an incision that extends to the jaw.
   a. Use scissors to deepen the superficial incision previously made anterior to the abdominal cavity, and continue deepening this incision to the base of the lower jaw.
   b. Cut through the body wall in the region of the thorax, clipping through the ribs slightly to the right or left of the **sternum** (the flat bone lying midventrally to which ribs attach).
   c. Continue the incision past the rib cage to the base of the lower jaw.
2. Using the blunt probe to separate tissues, carefully remove the skin and muscles in the neck region. You will expose the **thymus gland** on each side of the neck (Figure 1). This gland is large in the fetal pig and in young mammals, but regresses with age. It plays an important role in the development of the bodys immune system.
3. Push the two thymus masses to the side to expose the **larynx** and **trachea** lying deep in the masses. Recall your knowledge about the **glottis**. The glottis leads into the larynx, an expanded structure through which air passes from the mouth to the narrower trachea. The larynx houses vocal cords.

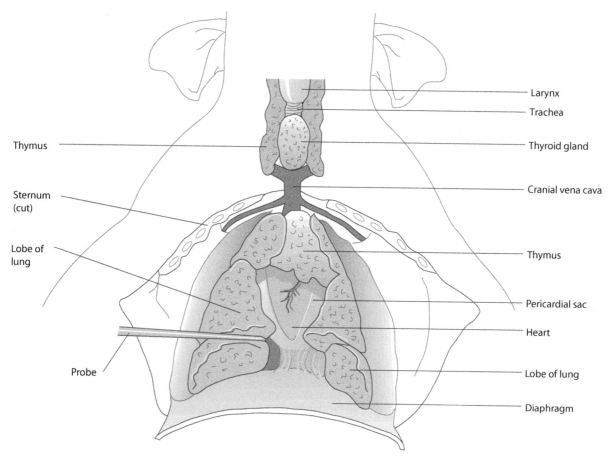

**Figure 1.**
**Ventral view of the anterior region of the pig,** showing structures in the neck region and the thoracic cavity. The pericardial sac encloses the heart.

4. A small reddish gland, the **thyroid gland,** covers the trachea. The thyroid gland secretes hormones that influence metabolism. Push this gland aside and observe the rings of cartilage that prevent the collapse of the trachea and allow air to pass to the lungs. Push aside the trachea to observe the dorsally located **esophagus.**

5. Do not continue the dissection of the neck and thoracic regions at this time. To prevent damage to blood vessels, you will complete the dissection of the remainder of the respiratory system (Exercise 5) following the dissection of the circulatory system.

## EXERCISE 2

# The Heart and the Pulmonary Blood Circuit

The heart and lungs lie in the **pericardial** and **pleural** (Gk. for "rib") cavities, respectively, within the thoracic cavity. In your dissection of the heart and blood vessels, you will distinguish the two circulatory pathways found in mammalian circulation: the **pulmonary circuit,** which carries blood from the heart to the lungs in arteries and back to the heart in veins; and the **systemic circuit,** which carries blood from the heart in arteries to all organs *but the lungs* and back to the heart in veins. This exercise investigates circulation in fetal and adult pig hearts and the pathway of blood to the lungs in the pulmonary circuit.

## Materials

isolated adult pig or sheep heart dissected to show chambers and valves, demonstration only
supplies from Exercise 1

## Procedure

 Although, generally, veins contain blue latex and arteries contain red latex, the colors can vary and should not be used as guides to distinguish veins from arteries or vessels carrying oxygen-rich blood from vessels carrying oxygen-poor blood.

1. In the fetal pig, expose the heart lying in the **pericardial cavity** between the two pleural cavities. Gently push open the rib cage, using scissors and a probe to cut through muscle and connective tissue. Another lobe of the thymus gland will be seen lying over the **pericardial sac** housing the heart. The wall of the pericardial sac is a tough membrane composed of two fused coelomic epithelial linings, the **parietal pericardium** and the **parietal pleura.**

2. Cut into and push aside the pericardial sac. Carefully dissect away membranes adhering to the heart until you can identify the four chambers of the heart (Figure 2). The walls of heart chambers consist of cardiac muscle.

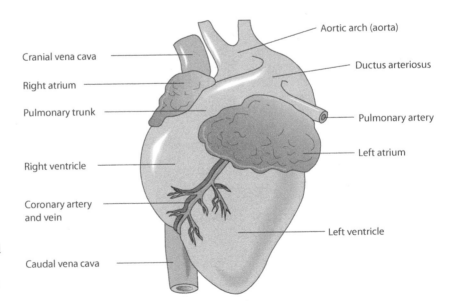

**Figure 2.**
**Enlarged ventral view of a fetal heart,** showing the four chambers and the major associated blood vessels. Compare this anatomy with that of an adult heart.

a. The **right atrium** and **left atrium** are small, dark, anteriorly located heart chambers that receive blood from the **venae cavae** and the pulmonary veins, respectively.

b. The **right ventricle** and **left ventricle** are large muscular heart chambers that contract to pump blood. A branch of the **coronary artery** may be seen on the heart surface where the left and right ventricles share a common wall. The coronary artery carries blood to heart tissue.

What is the name of the epithelial lining adhering to the heart surface?

3. Trace the pulmonary circuit. As the heart contracts, blood is forced from the right ventricle into the **pulmonary trunk,** a large vessel lying on the ventral surface of the heart. Another large vessel, the **aorta,** lies just dorsal to the pulmonary trunk.

a. Use forceps to pick away tissue around the pulmonary trunk and trace the pulmonary trunk as it curves cranially, giving off three branches: the right and left **pulmonary arteries** and the **ductus arteriosus.**

b. Identify the ductus arteriosus and the left pulmonary artery (the right pulmonary artery is not readily visible).

The right and left pulmonary arteries are relatively small at this stage of development. They conduct blood to the right and left lungs, respectively. The ductus arteriosus is the short, large-diameter vessel that connects the pulmonary trunk to the aorta. Because the small right and left pulmonary arteries and compact lung tissue present an extremely resistant blood pathway, the greatest volume of blood in the pulmonary trunk will flow through the ductus arteriosus and directly into the aorta and systemic circulation, bypassing the pulmonary arteries and lungs. At the time of the fetus's birth, when air enters the lungs and the tissues expand, blood will more easily flow into the lungs. The ductus arteriosus closes off and eventually becomes a ligament.

4. Observe the isolated adult pig or sheep heart on demonstration and locate the dorsal and ventral surfaces (Figure 2).

a. Identify the **right atrium** with associated **cranial** and **caudal venae cavae** and the **left atrium** with associated **pulmonary veins.**

b. Locate the **right** and **left ventricles** and the **atrioventricular valves** between the atria and the ventricles.

c. Locate the **pulmonary trunk,** which carries blood from the right ventricle, and the **aorta,** carrying blood from the left ventricle. The first two small branches of the aorta are **coronary arteries.** Locate these vessels and the **coronary veins** lying on the surface of the heart between the left and right ventricles. Coronary arteries and veins form a short circuit servicing heart tissues.

## Results

Review the heart chambers, blood vessels, and organs in the pathway of the pulmonary circuit in the *adult* heart. To facilitate this review, fill in the blanks in the next paragraph.

Blood entering the heart passes first into the right atrium. From there it flows into the right ventricle. When the heart contracts, this blood is forced out of the ventricle into the _____ trunk. Branches of this trunk called _____ carry blood to the lungs. After birth, the blood will become oxygen-rich in the lungs. Blood from the lungs passes back to the heart through _____, thus completing the circuit. It enters the left atrium of the heart.

### Discussion

1. Define *artery*. Define *vein*.

2. Why would pulmonary arteries be relatively small at the fetal stage of development?

3. Although a pulmonary circuit exists, the heart in amphibians and most reptiles is made up of only three chambers—two atria and one ventricle. The latter receives blood from both atria. Speculate about possible disadvantages to this circulatory pathway.

EXERCISE 3

# The Heart and the Systemic Circuit in the Thorax

Blood returning from the lungs collects in the left atrium and flows into the left ventricle. When the heart contracts, blood is forced out the **aorta,** the origin of which is obscured by the pulmonary trunk. The first branch from the aorta is the small **coronary artery,** previously identified, leading to the heart muscle. The larger volume of blood passes through the aorta to all organs of the body but the lungs. Blood returns to the heart from organs of the body through two large veins, the cranial and caudal venae cavae.

### Procedure

1. Identify the venae cavae and their major branches.
   a. Push the heart to the pigs left to see two large veins entering the right atrium; these are the **cranial** and **caudal venae cavae** (Figure 3).

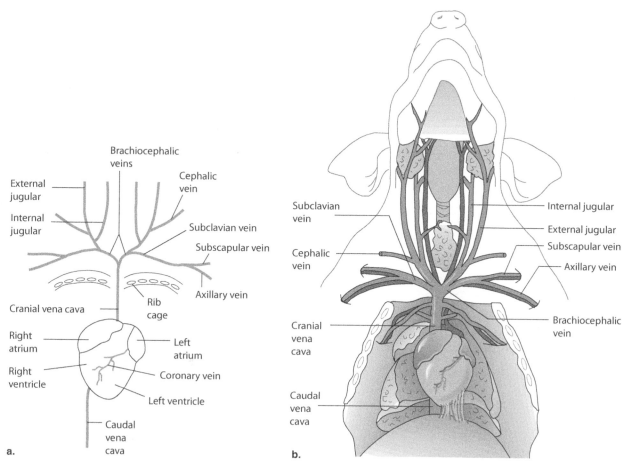

**Figure 3.**

**Veins near the heart.** The subclavian vein and the external and internal jugulars carry blood to the brachiocephalic veins, which unite into the cranial vena cava. The caudal vena cava carries blood from the posterior regions of the body.

b. Using the blunt probe to separate the vessels from surrounding tissues, follow the cranial vena cava toward the head and identify the two large **brachiocephalic veins**, which unite in the cranial vena cava.

c. Identify the three major veins that unite to form each brachiocephalic vein: the **external** and **internal jugulars** that carry blood returning from the head, and the **subclavian vein** that drains blood from the front leg and shoulder. Follow the subclavian vein into the front leg. Probe deep into the muscle covering the underside of the scapula (shoulder blade) and you should see the **subscapular vein,** draining blood from the shoulder region. The **axillary vein** carries blood from the front leg, becoming the subclavian vein at the subscapular branch. Occasionally, the subclavian vein is very short, and the subscapular and axillary veins unite close to the brachiocephalic vein. Another vein that is often injected and prominent in the shoulder area is the **cephalic vein.** This vein lies just beneath the skin on the upper front leg. It typically enters the external jugular near its base.

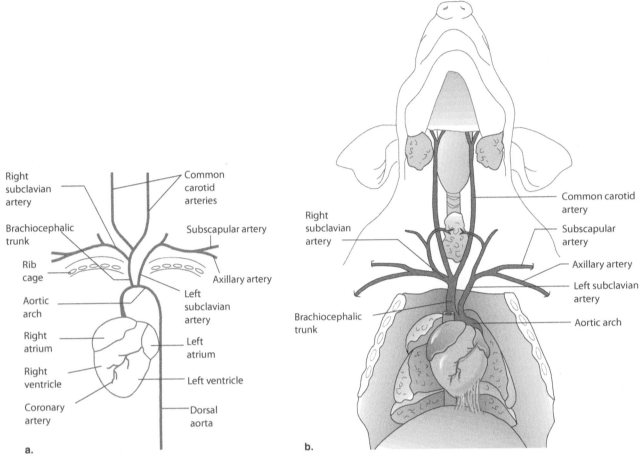

**Figure 4.**
**Branches of the aorta.** Branches from the aortic arch carry blood to the head and anterior limbs. The first branch, the brachiocephalic trunk, branches into the right subclavian artery to the right limb and two common carotid arteries to the head. The second branch is the left subclavian to the left limb.

2. Identify branches of the aorta near the heart (Figure 4).

   a. Push the pulmonary trunk ventrally and posteriorly to observe the curve of the aorta, the **aortic arch,** lying behind.

   b. Remove obscuring tissue and expose the first two major branches of the arch, which carry blood anteriorly. It may be necessary to remove the veins to do so. The larger of the branches, the **brachiocephalic trunk,** branches off first. The **left subclavian artery** branches off second.

   c. Identify the three major branches from the brachiocephalic trunk: the **right subclavian artery,** which gives off several branches that serve the right shoulder and limb area, and two **common carotid arteries,** which carry blood to the head. The common carotid arteries lie adjacent to the internal jugular veins.

   d. Trace the branches of the left subclavian artery into the left shoulder and front leg. The branch that passes deep toward the underside of the scapula is the **subscapular artery.** After the subscapular artery branches off, the left subclavian continues into the front leg as the left **axillary artery.** Additional branches of this artery complex may also be visible.

3. Pull the lungs to the pigs right side and trace the dorsal aorta as it extends posteriorly from the aortic arch along the dorsal thoracic wall. Notice again the **ductus arteriosus** connecting from the pulmonary trunk.

4. Note the small branches of the dorsal aorta carrying blood to the ribs. A large conspicuous vein, the **azygos vein,** lies near this region of the aorta. This vein carries blood from the ribs back to the heart.

## Results

Modify Figures 3 and 4 or sketch additional details in the margin of your lab manual to indicate particular features of your pigs circulatory system for future reference.

---

## EXERCISE 4
# The Systemic Circuit in the Abdominal Cavity

---

The dorsal aorta passes into the abdominal cavity, where it branches into arteries supplying the abdominal organs, the legs, and the tail. In fetal circulation, it also branches into two large umbilical arteries to the placenta. Blood from the legs, tail, and organs collects in veins that ultimately join the caudal vena cava to return to the heart. Blood draining from organs of the digestive system passes through additional vessels in the hepatic portal system before emptying into the caudal vena cava.

## Lab Study A. Major Branches of the Dorsal Aorta and the Caudal Vena Cava

In this lab study, you will identify the major blood vessels branching from the dorsal aorta and those emptying into the caudal vena cava.

### Procedure

1. Identify branches of the dorsal aorta (Figures 5 and 7).

   a. The first large branch of the aorta in the abdominal cavity exits the aorta at approximately the level of the diaphragm. Clip the diaphragm where it joins the body wall, pull all the organs (lungs and digestive organs) to the pig's right, and search for the **coeliac artery,** which carries blood to the stomach and the spleen. You may have to pick away pieces of the diaphragm that are attached to the aorta to see this vessel.

   b. Once you have identified the coeliac artery, look for the next branch of the aorta, the **cranial mesenteric artery,** arising slightly caudal to the coeliac artery and carrying blood to the small intestine. The cranial mesenteric artery ultimately branches to the **mesenteric arteries** you observed when you studied the digestive system.

   c. Following the dorsal aorta posteriorly, identify the two **renal arteries** leading to the kidneys.

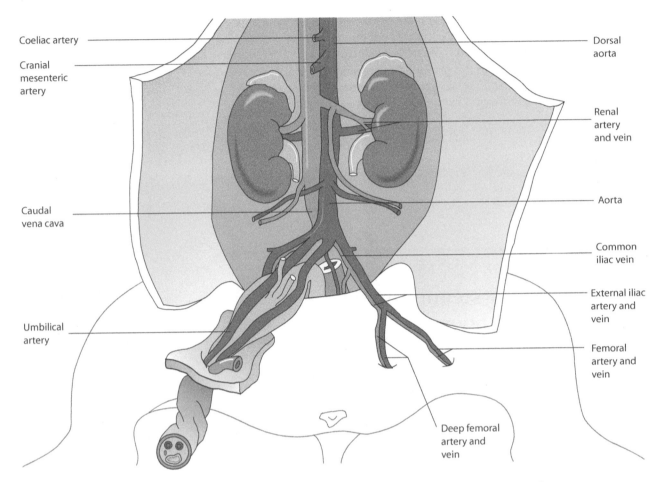

Coeliac artery

Cranial mesenteric artery

Caudal vena cava

Umbilical artery

Dorsal aorta

Renal artery and vein

Aorta

Common iliac vein

External iliac artery and vein

Femoral artery and vein

Deep femoral artery and vein

**Figure 5. Branches of the aorta and caudal vena cava in the abdomen.** Branches of the aorta supply blood to the stomach (the coeliac artery), the small intestine (the cranial mesenteric artery), the kidney (renal arteries), the hind limbs (iliac arteries), and the placenta (umbilical arteries). Branches of the caudal vena cava drain blood from the kidney (renal veins) and posterior limbs (common iliac veins).

You will observe the posterior branches of the aorta after the dissection of the reproductive system.

d. The dorsal aorta sends branches into the hind legs (the **external iliac arteries**) and to the placenta (the **umbilical arteries**) through the umbilical cord.

e. Separate the muscles of the leg to see that the external iliac artery divides into the **femoral artery** and the **deep femoral artery**. The femoral artery carries blood to the muscles of the lower leg, and the deep femoral artery carries blood to the thigh muscles.

2. Identify branches of the caudal vena cava.

   a. Using Figure 5 as a reference, push the digestive organs to the pigs left and trace the caudal vena cava into the abdominal cavity. It lies deep to the membrane lining the wall of the abdominal cavity, the **parietal peritoneum.** Peel off this membrane to see the vena cava, the dorsal aorta, and the kidneys.

   b. Identify **renal veins** carrying blood from the kidneys. **Common iliac veins** carry blood from the hind legs, and **hepatic veins** carry blood from the liver to the caudal vena cava. Hepatic veins are presented in Lab Study B.

## Lab Study B. The Hepatic Portal System

In the usual pathway of circulation, blood passes from the heart to arteries, to capillaries in an organ, and to veins leading from the organ back to the heart (Figure 6a). In a few rare instances, a second capillary bed is inserted in a second organ in the circulation pathway (Figure 6b). When this occurs,

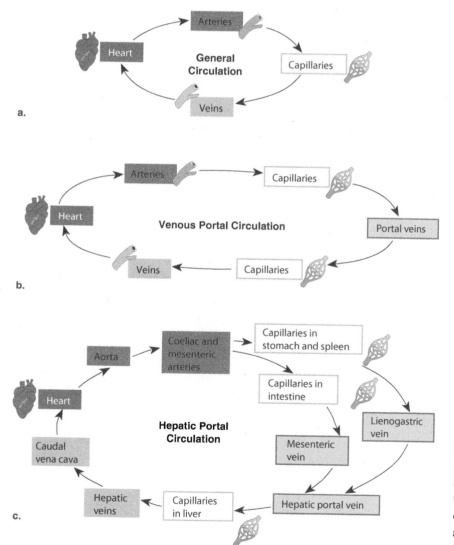

**Figure 6.**
**Circulatory pathways.** (a) General circulatory pathway; (b) circulation in a portal system; and (c) circulation in the hepatic portal system. Arteries are depicted in dark color, veins are gray, and portal veins are gray and outlined in color.

the circulatory circuit involved is called a **portal system.** Such a system of portal circulation exists in the digestive system (Figure 6c). An understanding of this circulation pathway will increase your understanding of the absorption and processing of nutrients.

You have previously exposed the coeliac and cranial mesenteric arteries, which send branches to the stomach, spleen, and small intestine. These arteries divide into smaller arteries, to arterioles, and, finally, to capillaries, thin-walled vessels that are the site of exchange between blood and the tissues of the organs. Arteries associated with the small intestine are called **mesenteric arteries;** veins leaving the small intestine are called **mesenteric veins,** and they unite to form one large **mesenteric vein.** Veins from the stomach and spleen unite to form the larger **lienogastric vein.** The mesenteric and lienogastric veins unite to form the **hepatic portal vein,** which enters the liver (Figure 7). In the fetal pig, small branches of the **umbilical vein** join the hepatic portal vein as it enters the liver. However, the greatest volume of blood in the umbilical vein passes directly through the liver into the caudal vena cava.

In the liver, the hepatic portal vein branches into a second capillary bed, where exchange takes place between blood and liver tissue. These capillaries reunite into **hepatic veins,** which join the caudal vena cava. To identify these vessels, begin by dissecting the veins.

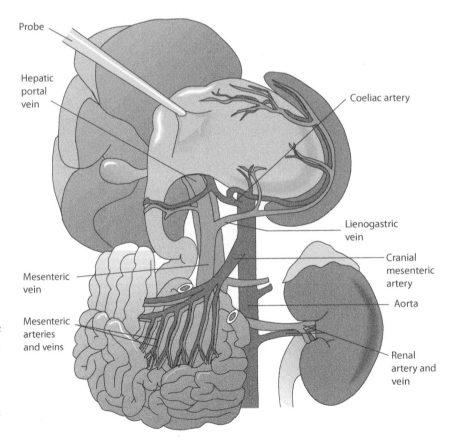

**Figure 7.**
**The hepatic portal system.** Blood from the small intestine passes into the mesenteric vein, which unites with the lienogastric vein to form the hepatic portal vein. This vessel leads to the liver, where it breaks into a capillary bed. Blood leaves the liver through the hepatic veins.

## Procedure

1. Push the stomach and spleen anteriorly and dissect away the pancreas.
2. Use the blunt probe to expose a vein (it will probably not be injected) leading from the mesenteries of the small intestine. This is the **mesenteric vein.** It is joined by a vein leading from the stomach and spleen, the **lienogastric vein.** The two fuse to form the **hepatic portal vein,** which continues to the liver.
3. Review the flow of blood from the mesenteric arteries to the liver.

## Results

Review the blood vessels and organs in the pathway of blood through the hepatic portal system of an adult pig with functioning digestive organs. Fill in the blanks in the next paragraph:

Blood that is poor in nutrients is carried from the aorta to the _____ _____ artery to smaller mesenteric arteries, which divide to a capillary bed in the wall of the _____, where, in the process of absorption, nutrients enter the blood. This nutrient-rich blood now flows into the _____ vein, which joins with the _____ vein from the spleen and stomach and becomes the _____ vein. This vein now carries blood to the liver, where it breaks into a second capillary bed. Capillaries in the liver converge into the _____ veins, which empty into the caudal vena cava for transport back to the heart.

## Discussion

Referring to your text, review the function of the liver in nutrient metabolism and relate this to the function of the hepatic portal system. Include information on digestive products, drugs, and toxins.

EXERCISE 5

# Fetal Pig Circulation

As you dissected the circulatory system in the fetal pig and observed the adult pig heart, you noted differences between the fetal heart and the adult heart, and you identified blood vessels found in the fetus but not in the adult. In this exercise you will review these vessels and structures, tracing blood flow through the fetal pig.

## Procedure

1. Return the umbilical cord to the position it occupied before you began your dissection. Locate again the umbilical vein as it passes from the umbilical cord toward the liver. You cut through this vein when you opened the abdominal cavity. The umbilical vein carries blood from the umbilical cord into the liver. In the liver, small branches of this vein join the hepatic portal vein, passing blood into the liver tissue. However, the majority of the blood passes through a channel in the liver called the **ductus venosus** into the caudal vena cava. Would blood be *high* or *low* in oxygen in the caudal vena cava?

2. Review the anatomy of the fetal pig heart, and retrace the flow of blood through the heart into the dorsal aorta by way of the **ductus arteriosus**. This represents one pathway of blood through the fetal heart.

3. A second pathway of blood through the heart is created by a structure in the fetal heart called the **foramen ovale.** To study this pathway, use your scalpel to open the pig heart by cutting it along a frontal plane, dividing it into dorsal and ventral portions. Begin at the caudal end of the heart and carefully slice along the frontal plane, cutting just through the ventricles, keeping the atria intact. Carefully lift the ventricles and look inside the heart for the wall between the two atria. Using your blunt probe, carefully feel along this wall for an opening between the two atria. This hole is the foramen ovale, which makes possible the second pathway of blood through the heart. How would this hole change the flow of blood through the heart?

In fact, most blood coming into the heart from the caudal vena cava passes from the right atrium through this hole into the left atrium. After leaving the left atrium, where would blood go next?

4. Follow the dorsal aorta into the abdominal cavity to the umbilical artery branches. These branches pass through the umbilical cord to the placenta. Would blood in these branches be *high* or *low* in oxygen?

## Results

Trace fetal blood circulation from the umbilical vein to the umbilical artery by filling in the blanks in the next paragraph.

Blood from the umbilical vein passes through the liver in a channel called the _____ and into the _____, which carries blood into the heart, specifically into the chamber called the _____. In one circuit of blood flow, blood goes from this chamber into the right ventricle and out the _____. A branch from this vessel, the _____ _____ (present only in fetal circulation), carries most of this blood into the dorsal aorta. The dorsal aorta passes through the body, giving off branches to all organs of the body. Two large branches located near the tail lead into the umbilical cord and are called the _____.

An alternate route carries blood from the right atrium through a fetal hole called the _____ into the heart chamber, the _____. From this chamber, blood next goes into the left ventricle and out the _____. Branches of this vessel lead to the head.

## Discussion

1. What is the advantage of the circuit of fetal blood flow through the ductus arteriosus?

2. What is the advantage of fetal blood flow through the foramen ovale?

---

# EXERCISE 6
# Details of the Respiratory System

---

You have previously located several of the major structures of the respiratory system (Exercise 1). Direct your attention again to the neck region of the pig and complete the study of the respiratory system.

## Procedure

1. Identify again the **larynx** and the **trachea** (Figure 8).
2. Follow the trachea caudally to the pleural cavities housing the lungs. The trachea branches into **bronchi** (sing., bronchus), which lead into

the lobes of the **lungs**. It will be necessary to push aside blood vessels to see this. *Take care not to destroy these vessels.*

3. Tease apart lung tissues to observe that the larger bronchi branch into smaller and smaller bronchi. When the tubes are about 1–2 mm in diameter, they are called **bronchioles.** Bronchioles continue to branch and ultimately lead to microscopic **alveoli** (not visible with the unaided eye), thin-walled, blind-ending sacs that are covered with capillaries. It is here that the exchange of oxygen and carbon dioxide takes place between the blood and the atmosphere.

4. Identify the epithelial lining of the pleural cavity. How would this epithelium be named?

5. After you complete this lab topic, return your pig to its plastic bag. Check that your labels are intact and that your name, lab room, and lab day are legible. Add preserving solution and securely close the bag.

## Results

List, in order, the structures, tubes, and cellular barriers through which air passes as it travels from outside the body to the circulatory system of a pig, a terrestrial vertebrate.

## Discussion

1. In terrestrial vertebrates, what is the advantage of having the surfaces for oxygen and carbon dioxide exchange embedded deep in lung tissue?

2. The capillaries that lie in close contact with alveoli are branches of what blood vessel?

3. The confluence of these capillaries forms what blood vessel?

4. Compare blood composition in adult circulation with reference to oxygen and carbon dioxide between capillaries approaching alveoli and capillaries leaving alveoli.

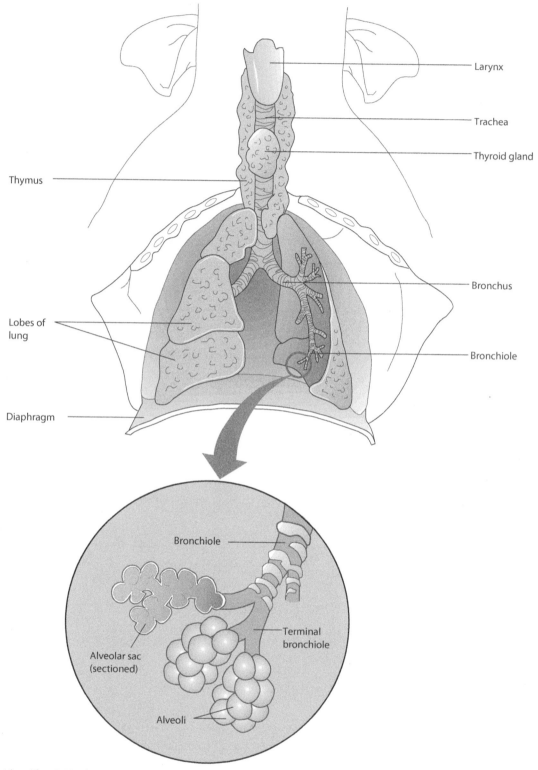

Larynx

Trachea

Thyroid gland

Thymus

Bronchus

Lobes of lung

Bronchiole

Diaphragm

Bronchiole

Alveolar sac (sectioned)

Terminal bronchiole

Alveoli

Adapted from E. Marieb, *Human Anatomy and Physiology Laboratory Manual*, Fetal Pig Version, 6th ed. (Menlo Park, CA: Benjamin/Cummings, 1999), © 1999 The Benjamin/Cummings Publishing Company.

**Figure 8.**

**The respiratory system of the fetal pig.** Air passes through a succession of smaller and more numerous tubes: the larynx, trachea, bronchi, bronchioles, and ultimately, microscopic alveoli (see enlarged area).

## Questions for Review

1. Review the coelomic cavities, the organs contained within them, and the associated coelomic membranes. Which two membranes fuse to form the pericardial sac?

2. Complete Table 1. List uniquely fetal circulatory structures and vessels, describe the position or location of each, and give the fate of each after birth.

**Table 1**
Names, Positions, and Fate of Uniquely Fetal Circulatory Structures

| Fetal Structure or Vessel | Location | Fate After Birth |
|---|---|---|
|  |  |  |
|  |  |  |
|  |  |  |
|  |  |  |
|  |  |  |

## Applying Your Knowledge

1. What differences would you expect to see in the appearance of lung tissue in adult and fetal pigs? Explain.

2. Using the Web, materials provided in the lab, your text, or library materials, answer the following questions related to the effects of smoking on the structure and function of the human respiratory system.

   a. Describe the effects and symptoms of each of the diseases linked to cigarette smoking listed in Table 2.

**Table 2**

Diseases Caused by Smoking: Their Effects and Symptoms

| Disease | Effects and Symptoms |
| --- | --- |
| Chronic bronchitis | |
| Emphysema | |
| Lung cancer | |

b. Describe smoking-induced changes in the cells and tissues of the lungs and describe the concomitant effects on function.

c. What effects does smoking during pregnancy have on the fetus?

3. The trachea is composed of rings of cartilage, while the nearby esophagus is composed of muscle and lacks cartilage. How are these structural differences related to the functions of each?

4. Scientists have concluded that a four-chambered heart is necessary to support the high metabolic rates seen in "warm-blooded" animals (endotherms)—that is, birds and mammals (see question 3, exercise 2). In 2000 scientists reported that a 66-million-year-old dinosaur found in South Dakota by an amateur fossil hunter in 1993 appeared to contain a fossilized heart with two ventricles, as one would find in a four-chambered heart. What does this discovery suggest about the metabolism of this dinosaur and the position of this species of dinosaur in the evolutionary tree?

## Case Studies

Extending their knowledge from this lab topic, students may investigate the following medical cases using various texts, the library, or Web resources. They may submit their findings in written or oral reports.

1. During cardiac development in an embryo or fetus, adequate flow of blood through the heart is necessary for normal development. Use your knowledge of blood flow through the fetal heart to predict which chambers and valves of the heart would not develop if the foramen ovale is absent or closes prematurely. Research identified syndromes that result from this condition.

2. Marilyn was admitted to the emergency room with pain in her chest and left shoulder, extending on to the pit of her stomach. After several tests to rule out other conditions, physicians administered nitroglycerin underneath her tongue and her pain subsided. Did this response give her physician any information to help determine if Marilyn suffered from *angina pectoris* or *myocardial infarction*? How do these two conditions differ? Which of these can be treated with *nitroglycerin*?

 ## Student Media Activities and Investigations

**Activities**—Ch. 42: Mammalian Cardiovascular System Structure; Path of Blood Flow in Mammals; Mammalian Cardiovascular System Function; The Human Respiratory System; The Transport of Respiratory Gases
**Investigations**—Ch.42: How Is Cardiovascular Fitness Measured? Biology Labs On-Line: CardioLab
www.masteringbio.com

## References

Burggren, W. "And the Beat Goes On—A Brief Guide to the Hearts of Vertebrates." *Natural History,* 2000, vol. 109, pp. 62–65.

Fisher, P. E., D. A. Russell, M. K. Stoskopf, R. E. Barrick, M. Hammer, and A. A. Kuzmitz. "Cardiovascular Evidence for an Intermediate or Higher Metabolic Rate in an Ornithischian Dinosaur." *Science,* 2000, vol. 288, pp. 503–505.

Marieb, E. N. *Human Anatomy and Physiology,* 6th ed. Menlo Park, CA: Benjamin Cummings, 2004.

"What You Need to Know about Cancer." *Scientific American,* Special Issue, vol. 275, 1996.

# Websites

Photographs of fetal pig anatomy:
http://www.biologycorner.com/pig/fetal.html

All About Smoking:
http://www.n/m.nih.gov/medlineplus/smoking.html
http://www.cde.gov/tobacco/quit_smoking/index.htm
http://www.americanheart.org/presenter.jhtml?identifer
=4545

Includes photographs of lungs of smokers and non-smokers and diagrams of microscopic changes in lungs of smokers:
http://whyquit.com/joel/Joel_02_17_smoke_in_lung
.html

For information on smoking and pregnancy:
http://www.lungusa.org/site/pp.asp?c=duLUK900E
+b=33573
http://www-med.stanford.edu/medicalreview/
smrp14-16.pdf

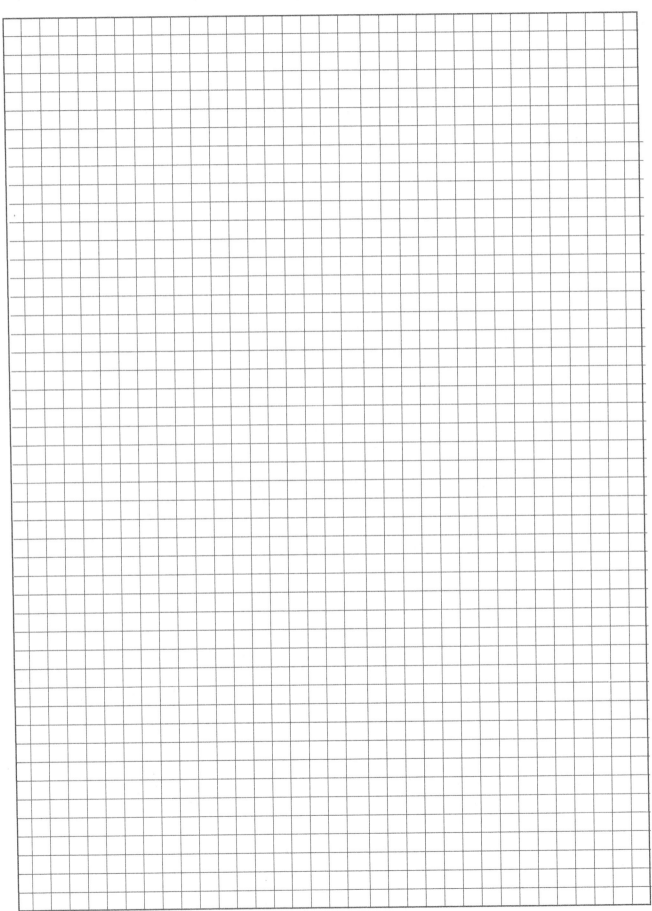

# Vertebrate Anatomy: The Excretory, Reproductive, and Nervous Systems

## Laboratory Objectives

After completing this lab topic, you should be able to:

1. Identify and describe the function of all parts of the excretory system of the fetal pig, noting differences between the sexes and noting structures shared with the reproductive system.
2. Identify and describe the function of all parts of the reproductive systems of male and female fetal pigs and trace the pathway of sperm and egg from their origin out of the body.
3. Compare reproductive systems in pigs and humans.
4. Describe the structure of a neuron.
5. Describe the pathway of a simple reflex, relating this to the structure of the spinal cord.
6. Describe the structure of a representative sensory receptor, the eye.
7. Discuss the role played by the nervous and endocrine systems in integrating all vertebrate systems into a functioning whole organism.

## Introduction

Functionally, the excretory system is closely related to the circulatory and respiratory systems. Developmentally, however, the excretory system shares many embryonic and some adult structures with the reproductive system. In the first two exercises of this lab topic, you will investigate form and functional relationships in the excretory and reproductive systems. In the last exercise of this lab topic, you will study the nervous system, which keeps all organ systems functioning appropriately and in harmony.

The action and interaction of organ systems must be precisely timed to meet specific needs within the animal. Two systems in the body, the nervous system and the endocrine system, coordinate the activities of all organ systems. The nervous system consists of a **sensory component**, made up of **sensory receptors** that detect such stimuli as light, sound, touch, and the concentration of oxygen in the blood, and **sensory nerves**, which carry the data to the **central nervous system**. The central nervous system consists of the brain and spinal cord. It integrates information from all stimuli, external and internal, and,

From *Investigating Biology Laboratory Manual,* Sixth Edition, Judith G. Morgan and M. Eloise Brown Carter. Copyright © 2008 by Pearson Education, Inc. Published by Benjamin Cummings, Inc. All rights reserved.

when appropriate, sends signals to the motor system. The **motor system** carries impulses along motor nerves to **effectors** such as glands, muscles, and other organs, bringing about the appropriate response. The nervous system provides rapid, precise, and complex control of body activities.

The endocrine system consists of endocrine glands, which respond to stimuli by secreting hormones into the blood to be transported to target tissues in the body. The target tissues then bring about the response. You have already observed several endocrine glands, including the thymus, thyroid, and pancreas. In this lab topic, you will study additional endocrine glands: ovaries and testes. Control mediated by hormones in the endocrine system is slower and less precise than nervous system control. The interaction of the nervous and endocrine systems brings about the coordination of physiological processes and the maintenance of internal **homeostasis,** the steady state condition in the vertebrate body.

## EXERCISE 1
# The Excretory System

### Materials

preserved fetal pig
dissecting instruments

dissecting pan
disposable gloves

### Introduction

Several important functions are performed by the vertebrate excretory system, including **osmoregulation,** the control of tissue water balance, and the elimination of excess salts and urea, a waste product of the metabolism of amino acids. In terrestrial animals, including most mammals, water conservation is an important function of the excretory system. Studying this system in the pig will reveal the organs and structures involved in producing and eliminating metabolic waste with minimal water loss.

 Wear disposable gloves when dissecting preserved animals.

### Procedure

1. Locate the blood vessels serving the kidneys, exposed in the dissection of the circulatory system. The arteries branch from the dorsal aorta caudal to the cranial mesenteric artery. Blood enters the kidney through the **renal artery** and exits through the **renal vein.** Identify these vessels and the **kidneys** lying deep to the **parietal peritoneum** lining the abdominal cavity.

2. Dissect the left kidney as follows. Leaving the kidney in the body and attached to all blood vessels and tubes, make a frontal section along the outer periphery, dividing it into dorsal and ventral portions (Figure 1a).

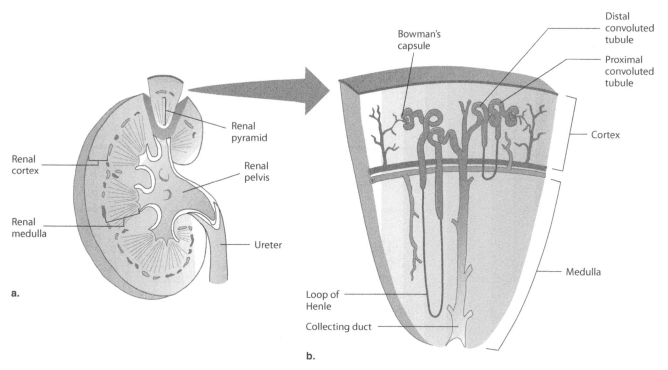

**Figure 1.**
**Structure of the kidney.** (a) The kidney consists of three major regions: the cortex, the medulla, and the pelvis. Renal pyramids make up the medulla, and the pelvis is continuous with the ureter. (b) An enlarged wedge of the kidney, including the cortical region over one pyramid. Nephrons—consisting of Bowman's capsule, a proximal convoluted tubule, the loop of Henle, a distal convoluted tubule, and a collecting duct—extend over the cortical and medullary regions. Waste carried in the collecting duct ultimately passes into the pelvis and ureter.

Observe the **renal cortex, renal medulla, renal pyramids, renal pelvis, and ureter.**

Each kidney is made up of microscopic tubules, blood vessels, and thousands of nephrons (over 1 million in humans). A nephron (not visible in your dissections) consists of Bowman's capsule, a proximal convoluted tubule, the loop of Henle, a distal convoluted tubule, and a collecting duct (Figure 1b). Cuboidal epithelial cells line most regions of the nephron. Bowman's capsule, a cup-shaped swelling at the end of the nephron, surrounds a ball of capillaries, the **glomerulus.** Blood is filtered as water and waste pass from the glomerulus into Bowman's capsule. (For details of nephron function, see your text.) Bowman's capsule, proximal and distal convoluted tubules, and associated blood vessels lie in the *renal cortex.* Loops of Henle and collecting ducts extend into *renal pyramids,* which make up the *renal medulla.* Both the loop of Henle and the collecting duct play a role in producing a concentrated urine, a significant adaptation for terrestrial vertebrates. The hypertonic urine passes into the collecting ducts, which ultimately empty into the renal pelvis, an expanded portion of the ureter into the kidney.

3. Using Figure 2 as a reference, follow the ureter as it exits the kidney at its medial border and turns to run caudally beside the dorsal aorta. The ureter then enters the **urinary bladder.** Also locate the ureter draining the right kidney and trace it to the urinary bladder. In the fetal pig, the urinary bladder is an elongate structure lying between the two **umbilical arteries**. It narrows into the small **allantoic stalk** identified in the study of the umbilical cord.

---

 Do not damage reproductive organs as you expose the structures of the excretory system.

---

4. Pull on the umbilical cord, extending the urinary bladder, and locate a single tube, the **urethra,** exiting the urinary bladder near the attachments of the ureters. At this stage, you will see only the end of the urethra near the entrance of the ureters. In male pigs (see Figure 2a), the urethra leads into the **penis.** This will be visible only after you have dissected the reproductive structures. In female pigs (Figure 3a), the urethra joins the **vagina,** forming a chamber, the **vaginal vestibule.** You will identify these structures after exposing the reproductive structures.

In male humans, the urethra is a tube in the penis. In female humans, the urethra does not join the vagina but empties to the outside of the body through a separate opening. The urethra becomes functional after birth when the umbilical cord and allantois wither and fall away. Waste stored in the bladder passes into the urethra, where it is carried to the outside of the body.

## Results

Describe the pathway of metabolic waste from the aorta to the outside of the body in the fetal pig.

## Discussion

How does the elimination of metabolic waste in the pig change after birth?

# EXERCISE 2
# The Reproductive System

## Materials

items from Exercise 1

## Introduction

Reproduction is perhaps the ultimate adaptive activity of all organisms. It is the means of transmitting genetic information from generation to generation. Less complex animals may reproduce sexually or asexually, but in general, vertebrates reproduce sexually. Sexual reproduction promotes genetic variation, which is important for species to adapt to changing environments. For evolution to occur, heritable variation must exist in populations. Although mutation is the source of variation, sexual reproduction promotes new and diverse combinations of genetic information. Ultimately, all sexual reproduction involves the production of gametes and the bringing together of gametes to enable fertilization to take place.

# Lab Study A. Male Reproductive System

The male reproductive system consists of gonads, ducts, and glands. Testes, the male gonads, produce sperm and secrete testosterone and other male sex hormones. Sperm pass from the testes into the epididymis, where they mature and are stored. When ejaculation takes place, sperm pass from the epididymis through the ductus deferens—also called the *vas deferens*—to the urethra. The urethra leads to the penis, which carries the sperm to the outside of the body. As sperm pass through the male tract, secretions from the seminal vesicles, the prostate gland, and the bulbourethral glands are added, producing semen, a fluid containing sperm, fructose, amino acids, mucus, and other substances that produce a favorable environment for sperm survival and motility.

## Procedure

 You will dissect the reproductive system of only one sex. However, you should observe the dissection of a pig of the opposite sex and be able to identify and describe various structures of both sexes.

1. Expose the structures of the male reproductive system (Figure 2a). The penis is located in the flap of ventral body wall caudal to the umbilical cord. To prevent damage to this structure, locate it before you make an incision. Hold the flap between your fingers and feel for the cordlike penis just below the skin. Once you locate the penis, using scissors, begin at the urogenital opening, the **preputial orifice**, and make a longitudinal incision, extending caudally, just through the skin. Push aside the

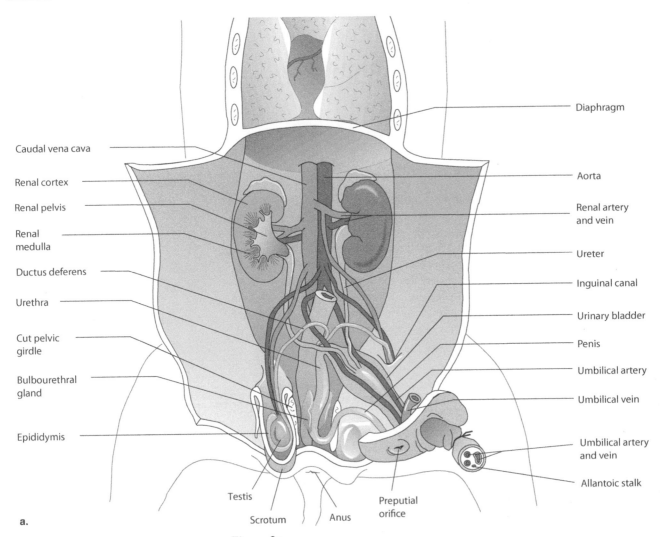

Caudal vena cava

Renal cortex

Renal pelvis

Renal medulla

Ductus deferens

Urethra

Cut pelvic girdle

Bulbourethral gland

Epididymis

Diaphragm

Aorta

Renal artery and vein

Ureter

Inguinal canal

Urinary bladder

Penis

Umbilical artery

Umbilical vein

Umbilical artery and vein

Allantoic stalk

Testis

Scrotum

Anus

Preputial orifice

a.

**Figure 2a.**
**Organs of the excretory and reproductive systems in the male fetal pig.** The ureters enter the urinary bladder between the umbilical arteries. The urethra exits the urinary bladder and leads to the penis. The penis leads to the preputial orifice. The testes lie in pouches in the scrotum. Sperm are produced in the testes, stored in the epididymis on the testis surface, and pass to the ductus deferens, which leads to the urethra.

skin and use the probe to locate and expose the long penis from the orifice caudally until it turns dorsally to meet the urethra (see Figure 2b).

2. Next, begin to expose the testis, epididymis, and ductus deferens. To do this, locate the **ureters** (identified in Exercise 1) and observe the right and left **ductus deferentia** (sing., deferens), which loop over the ureters. Follow a ductus deferens outward and caudally to the **inguinal canal** leading into the **scrotum.** Use scissors to cut carefully along the canal to expose the **testis** lying in a membranous sac. Remove this sac and identify the various structures.

   a. Identify the **testis,** a bean-shaped gonad. The testes first develop in the abdominal cavity and descend before birth into the scrotal sacs.

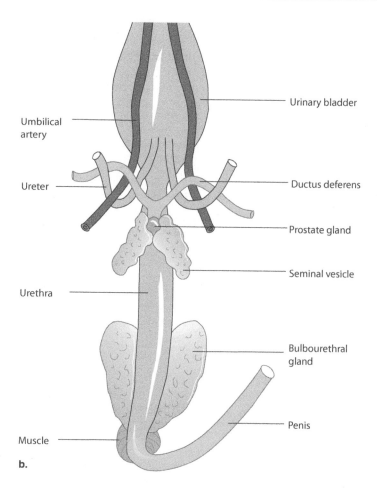

Umbilical artery

Ureter

Urethra

Muscle

Urinary bladder

Ductus deferens

Prostate gland

Seminal vesicle

Bulbourethral gland

Penis

b.

**Figure 2b.**
**Enlarged dorsal view** of male excretory and reproductive structures in the fetal pig. Seminal vesicles lie near the junction of the urethra and ductus deferens. Bulbourethral glands lie on either side of the urethra.

    b. Identify the **epididymis,** a convoluted duct that originates at the cranial end of the testis, extends caudally along one side, then turns and continues cranially as the ductus deferens.

    c. Identify the **ductus deferens,** a duct that leads away from the epididymis back into the abdominal cavity, where it loops over the ureter and enters the urethra. Also locate the ductus deferens from the other testis.

3. Turn your attention again to the area where the penis turns dorsally to meet the urethra. Push the penis to one side and probe through the muscle between the legs to locate the pubic symphysis, the portion of the pelvic girdle that fuses in a position ventral to several of the reproductive structures and the rectum. *Being careful not to go too deep or to cut the penis,* use heavy scissors to cut the pubic symphysis from posterior to anterior beginning at the bend in the penis. Press the hind limbs apart and trim the ends of the symphysis. Use the probe to remove connective tissue, and expose the **urethra,** which continues anteriorly from the bend of the penis. The urethra continues into the **urinary bladder** lying between the umbilical arteries. Identify the two large **bulbourethral glands** lying on either side of the urethra anterior to its junction with the penis (see Figure 2b).

4. Pull on the umbilical cord, reflecting the urethra, and locate a pair of glands, the **seminal vesicles,** that lie on the dorsal surface of the urethra near the junction of the ductus deferens and the urethra. The **prostate gland** lies between the lobes of the seminal vesicles, but because of its immature stage of development, it is difficult to identify.

At this time, complete the study of the branches of the dorsal aorta. Identify the **umbilical arteries** and the **external iliac arteries** to the legs and their branches, the **femoral** and **deep femoral arteries**. Also identify the **deep femoral, femoral,** and **common iliac veins,** which drain the legs and empty into the **caudal vena cava.**

5. After you conclude the study of the male pig, find someone with a female pig, and demonstrate the systems to each other.

6. Place your pig in its plastic bag, make sure the labels are legible, add preservative, secure the bag, and store it.

## Results

In Table 1, list the organs and ducts through which sperm pass from their origin to the outside of the body. Describe what takes place in each organ or duct, and note glandular secretions when appropriate. Refer to your text if needed.

## Discussion

1. Vasectomy is the most common form of human male sterilization used for birth control. Describe this process.

**Table 1**
Pathway of Sperm

| Organ/Duct | Activity and Glandular Secretion |
|---|---|
|  |  |
|  |  |
|  |  |
|  |  |
|  |  |

2. What structures identified are common to both reproductive and excretory systems?

3. The testes develop inside the abdominal cavity and descend through the inguinal canal into the scrotum before birth. Explain the significance of the external scrotum and external testes in mammals. Refer to your text if needed.

## Lab Study B. Female Reproductive System

The female reproductive system consists of the ovaries (female gonads), short uterine tubes (also called *fallopian tubes,* or *oviducts*), the uterus, the vagina, and the vaginal vestibule. The vaginal vestibule is present in the pig but not in the human. In the pig, the uterus consists of a uterine body and two uterine horns in which embryonic pigs develop. In the human female, the uterus does not have uterine horns but consists of a dome-shaped portion, the fundus, which protrudes above the entrance of the fallopian tubes, and an enlarged main portion, the body of the uterus, where embryos develop.

### Procedure

1. To study the female reproductive system (Figure 3a), use scissors and make a median longitudinal incision, cutting through the skin posterior to the umbilical cord. Push aside skin and muscles and probe in the midline to locate the pubic symphysis, the portion of the pelvic girdle that fuses in a position ventral to many of the female reproductive structures and the rectum. Being careful not to go too deep, use heavy scissors to cut through the muscles and the symphysis. Press apart the hind limbs and trim away the cut ends of the symphysis.

2. Begin observations by locating the **ovaries** in the abdominal cavity just caudal to the kidneys (Figure 3a). They are a pair of small, bean-shaped organs, one caudal to each kidney. (When the testes of the male first develop, they are located in approximately the same position in the abdominal cavity as the ovaries; however, the testes later descend, becoming supported in the scrotal sacs.) A small convoluted tube, the **uterine tube,** can be observed at the border of the ovary.

3. The reproductive structures form a long, continuous tract. Follow a uterine tube from one ovary into the associated **horn of the uterus.** Left and right horns join to form the **body of the uterus.** The body of the uterus lies dorsal to the urethra. Push the urethra aside and use the probe to separate the urethra from the uterus. Notice that the urethra and the reproductive structures meet.

4. The body of the uterus leads into the **cervix** of the uterus, which leads into the **vagina.** To conclusively identify these regions, you must open the uterus. Without disturbing the junction of the urethra and the

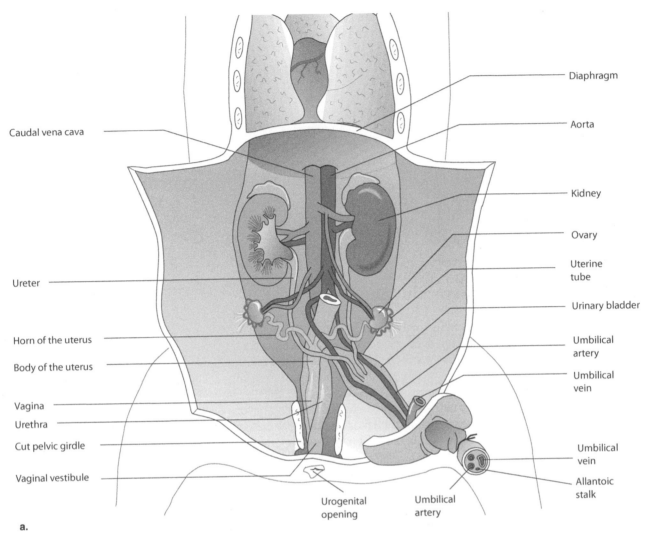

Caudal vena cava

Ureter

Horn of the uterus

Body of the uterus

Vagina

Urethra

Cut pelvic girdle

Vaginal vestibule

Diaphragm

Aorta

Kidney

Ovary

Uterine tube

Urinary bladder

Umbilical artery

Umbilical vein

Umbilical vein

Allantoic stalk

Urogenital opening

Umbilical artery

a.

**Figure 3a.**
**Organs of the excretory and reproductive systems in the female fetal pig.** The ureters enter the urinary bladder. The urethra exits the urinary bladder and joins the vagina, forming the vaginal vestibule.

reproductive structures, use scissors to make a longitudinal, lateral incision in the reproductive structures and push back the sides, exposing the interior. Your dissection should resemble Figure 3b. Now you should be able to identify all parts of the uterus, the vagina, and the opening of the urethra into the reproductive tract. Identify the cervix, easily identified by the presence of internal ridges. The vagina, which joins the cervix, does not have these ridges. The vagina joins the urethra to form a common chamber, the **vaginal vestibule**, leading to the outside of the body. The outer opening is the **urogenital opening**, ventral to the anus.

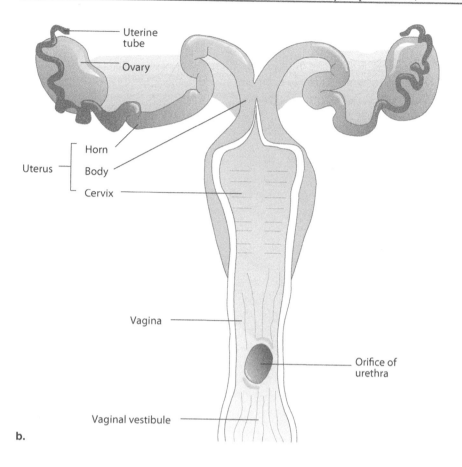

**b.**

Figure 3b.
**Enlarged view of the female reproductive system in a fetal pig.** The cervix and vagina have been opened to show the ridges in the cervix, which are absent in the vagina. The vaginal vestibule is the common chamber formed by the confluence of the vagina and the urethra.

 At this time, complete the study of the branches of the dorsal aorta. Identify the umbilical **arteries** and the **external iliac arteries** to the legs and their branches, the **femoral** and **deep femoral** arteries. Also identify the **deep femoral, femoral,** and **common iliac veins,** which drain the legs and empty into the **caudal vena cava.**

5. After you conclude your study of the female pig, find someone with a male pig, and demonstrate the systems to each other.
6. Place your pig in its plastic bag, make sure your labels are legible, add preservative, secure the bag, and store it.

## Results

Describe the pathway of an egg from the ovary to the outside of the body in a fetal pig, naming regions of organs when appropriate.

## Lab Study C. The Pregnant Pig Uterus

On demonstration is an isolated pregnant pig uterus, which should include uterine horns and the body of the uterus. Ovaries and uterine tubes may be attached. Fetal pigs are located in the uterine horns. Each fetal pig is attached to the mother pig by means of the **placenta,** a structure consisting of tissue from the inner lining of the uterus (maternal tissue) and the **chorionic vesicle** (embryonic tissue). These tissues are convoluted, creating interdigitating folds that increase the surfaces where the exchange of nutrients, oxygen, and wastes takes place between mother and fetus. Remember that blood does not flow directly between the mother and fetus, but the close proximity of the tissues allows diffusion across the placental membranes.

### Procedure

1. Observe the uterus with one uterine horn partially opened (Figure 4). Some fetal pigs should be visible.

2. If it is not already dissected, using scissors, carefully cut into the **chorionic vesicle,** a saclike structure surrounding each fetal pig. Note that the chorionic vesicle is composed of two fused membranes, the outer **chorion** and the inner **allantois.** Blood vessels are visible lying within the thin allantois. The allantoic stalk is a small tube in the umbilical cord extending between the fetal pig's urinary bladder and the allantois. Speculate about the function of the allantois. The blood vessels are branches of which vessels?

3. Observe the **amnion,** a very thin, fluid-filled sac around the fetus. What function do you think this membrane performs?

Figure 4.
**Section of uterine horn from an adult pig with two fetuses.** Two saclike structures, an amnion and a chorionic vesicle, surround the fetus on the left. The chorionic vesicle around the other fetus has been opened and the amnion removed.

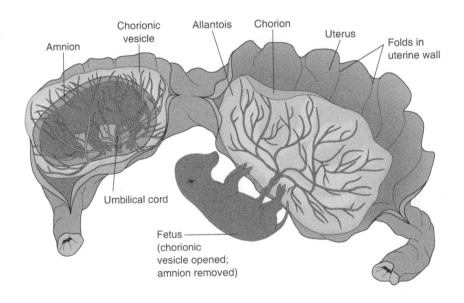

4. Open the amnion and see the **umbilical cord** attaching each fetus to the fetal membranes.

## Results

Beginning with those membranes closest to the fetal pig, list in order all embryonic and maternal membranes and tissues associated with the fetal pig.

## Discussion

1. Using your text if necessary, compare the female reproductive organs in a human and an adult pig with respect to the oviduct and uterus in the human and uterine tube, horns of the uterus, and body of the uterus in the pig. Speculate about the adaptive advantage of the differences.

2. Describe differences in the arrangement of the vagina and urethra in the fetal pig and human.

3. Tubal ligation is a common form of human female sterilization. Describe this process.

EXERCISE 3

# Nervous Tissue, the Reflex Arc, and the Vertebrate Eye

In this exercise, you will study several components of the nervous system: the structure of neurons, the pathway of a reflex arc as it relates to the structure of the spinal cord, and the structure of a sensory receptor, the vertebrate eye.

# Lab Study A. Nervous Tissue and the Structure of the Neuron

## Materials

compound microscope
prepared slide of nervous tissue

## Introduction

To understand the function of nervous tissue, review the structure of the **neuron**, the functional cell of nervous tissue. Neuron structure facilitates nervous impulse transmission. Each neuron has three parts: a **cell body**, which contains cytoplasm and the nucleus; **dendrites**, extensions from the cell body that transmit nervous impulses toward the cell body; and an **axon**, an extension that transmits nervous impulses away from the cell body to the next neuron or sometimes to a muscle fiber (Figure 5). Neurons are found in the brain and the spinal cord and in nervous tissue throughout the body. You will study the structure of nervous tissue and neurons in the spinal cord.

## Procedure

1. Using the intermediate objective on your compound microscope, scan the prepared slide of nervous tissue provided. This is a smear preparation of tissue taken from the spinal cord. You will see hundreds of small, dark dots, which are the nuclei of **glial cells.** Glial cells are nonconducting cells that support and protect neurons.

2. Look for large angular **cell bodies** of **motor neurons** scattered among the fibers and glial cells. Study one of these cell bodies on high power and locate the **nucleus**, usually with a prominent **nucleolus.** Try to identify the two types of **processes** extending from the cell body: the **axon** and **dendrites.** Although it is difficult to be certain, you may be able to differentiate between the single, broader axon and one or more slender dendrites extending from the cell body.

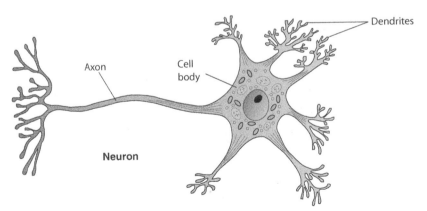

**Figure 5.**
**Structure of a neuron.** Dendrites and an axon, cytoplasmic processes, extend from the cell body.

E. Marieb, *Human Anatomy and Physiology Laboratory Manual*, Cat Version, 4th ed. (Menlo Park, CA: Benjamin/Cummings 1993), © The Benjamin/Cummings Publishing Company.

## Lab Study B. The Reflex Arc and Structure of the Spinal Cord

### Materials

stereoscopic microscope
compound microscope
prepared slide of a cross section of spinal cord

### Introduction

By studying the anatomy of the spinal cord, you will be able to better envision the interaction of the three components of the nervous system: the sensory component with sensory receptors and sensory nerves; the central nervous system, consisting of the brain and the spinal cord; and the motor system, consisting of motor nerves and effectors. Each of these components plays a role in a simple reflex such as the knee-jerk reflex.

### Procedure

1. Using the stereoscopic microscope, examine a prepared slide of a spinal cord cross section taken at a level that shows **dorsal** and **ventral roots.** The roots are collections of processes of neurons in spinal nerves.

2. Identify the dorsal and ventral surfaces of the spinal cord by locating the **ventral fissure** (Figure 6). Vertebrates have a tubular nervous system. Show this by locating the **central canal**, a small channel in the center of the cord.

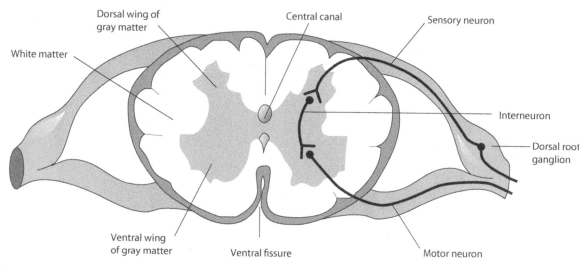

**Figure 6.**
**Cross section of the spinal cord at the level of dorsal and ventral roots.** Sensory neurons enter the dorsal wing of the gray matter, and the cell bodies of motor neurons lie in the ventral portion of the gray matter. Interneurons may be present in simple reflex arcs. A simple reflex arc may include two neurons—one motor neuron and one sensory neuron—or three neurons if an interneuron is present.

3. Locate **gray** and **white matter.** In the spinal cord, white matter lies outside the butterfly-shaped gray matter. In sections through the spinal cord at the level where dorsal and ventral roots enter and exit the cord, you will be able to identify the **dorsal root ganglion,** in which cell bodies of sensory neurons lie. Look for the neuronal processes from these cell bodies. These processes continue into the tip of the dorsal "wing" of the gray matter. Sensory neurons receive impulses directly from the environment or from a specific sensory receptor.

4. Locate cell bodies of **motor neurons** in the ventral "wing" of the gray matter. These are best studied using lower powers on the compound microscope. Many of these cell bodies contain conspicuous nuclei and nucleoli. Whereas the simplest reflex involves only one sensory and one motor neuron, most reflexes involve many **interneurons,** lying between sensory and motor neurons. Motor neurons carry impulses to muscles or glands and bring about a **response.**

5. Careful observations may reveal axons from motor neuron cell bodies coursing through the white matter and into the ventral root of the spinal nerve.

### Results

Using information from the study of the spinal cord, list in sequence the structures or neurons involved in the simplest reflex.

### Discussion

Most reflexes involve a specific sensory receptor (such as the eye, ear, or pain or touch receptors), several sensory neurons, several interneurons, several motor neurons, and effectors (muscles or glands). Propose a reflex arc that would result from your touching a hot plate in the lab.

## Lab Study C. Dissection of a Sensory Receptor, the Eye

### Materials

| | |
|---|---|
| preserved cow or sheep eye | dissecting pan |
| dissecting instruments | disposable gloves |

### Introduction

The goal of this study is not to perform a comprehensive study of eye structure but rather to identify those structures in the eye that enable it to receive stimuli and transmit the signals in sensory nerves to the central nervous system for processing. After processing, the signals are sent through motor nerves to the effector, bringing about the response.

The vertebrate eye is a complex sensory organ containing nervous tissue capable of being stimulated by light to produce nervous impulses. Sensory neurons carry these impulses to the brain, where they are interpreted, resulting in the perception of sight. The light-sensitive, or photoreceptor, cells in the eye are called *rods* and *cones*. They are the sensory part of a multilayered tissue, the retina. Other structures in the eye protect the retina and regulate the amount and quality of light stimulating the photoreceptor cells.

As you dissect an isolated eyeball from a cow or sheep, determine the contribution of each structure to the production of sight.

## Procedure

1. Examine the isolated eye and notice that it is covered with fatty tissue and muscle bands except in the region of the **cornea**, a tough, transparent layer that allows light to enter the eye (Figure 7a).

2. Search through the fatty tissue on the eye sphere approximately opposite the cornea and locate the round stub of the **optic nerve** exiting the eyeball (Figure 7b).

3. Use forceps and scissors to trim away all fat and muscle on the eye surface, taking care to leave the optic nerve undisturbed.

4. Once the fat is removed, you will see that the cornea is the anterior portion of the tough, outer layer of the eyeball, the **fibrous tunic.** The posterior portion of this layer is the white **sclera** (Figure 7b). The fibrous tunic protects the internal eye structures.

5. Use scissors to cut the eye in half, making an equatorial incision and separating the anterior hemisphere (with the cornea) from the posterior hemisphere (bearing the optic nerve). Open the eye by placing it, nerve down, in the dissecting tray and lifting off the front hemisphere. Place this hemisphere in the tray with the cornea down. Your dissection should look like Figure 7c.

6. Identify the various structures in the anterior hemisphere.

   a. Identify the **lens,** a hard, oval-shaped structure that focuses the light on the retina (Figure 7c). In life, this is transparent. Surrounding and

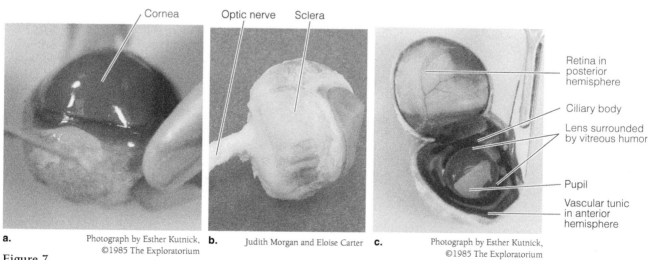

**a.** Photograph by Esther Kutnick, ©1985 The Exploratorium  **b.** Judith Morgan and Eloise Carter  **c.** Photograph by Esther Kutnick, ©1985 The Exploratorium

**Figure 7.**
(a) Isolated cow eye, (b) sheep eye with fatty tissue removed, and (c) cow eye opened to show internal structures.

attached to the lens may be a jellylike clear substance, the vitreous humor, described in step 8.

    b. Identify the **ciliary body,** a dark, ridged, muscular structure surrounding and attached to the lens by thin ligaments. The ciliary body is a component of the second tunic of the eye, the darkly pigmented **vascular tunic.** Contraction of muscle fibers in the ciliary body changes the shape of the lens. What role does this process play in eye function?

7. Carefully remove the lens (and vitreous humor, if attached) and observe that the ciliary body merges anteriorly into another component of the vascular tunic, the **iris.** The iris surrounds an opening, the **pupil.** In the cow or sheep eye, the pupil is more irregular in shape than in the human eye. The pupil allows light to pass through the vascular tunic to the lens. The iris is a sphincter muscle. What is its function?

8. Turn your attention to the posterior hemisphere of the eye. If dissected as described, this hemisphere should hold the **vitreous humor,** which holds the retina in place and is the major internal support of the eye.

9. Using forceps, carefully remove the vitreous humor and identify the pale, delicate **retina,** the third tunic of the eye. The retina contains microscopic rods and cones. What is the function of the retina?

10. The retina lies on the inside surface of the pigmented **choroid layer,** another component of the vascular tunic. The choroid layer absorbs extraneous light rays passing through the retina. Gently push the retina aside and notice that it appears to be attached to the choroid layer in only one spot. This point of attachment is actually where processes from sensory neurons exit the retina as fibers of the **optic nerve.** You may notice a semicircular area of rainbow-colored tissue in the choroid layer. This is the **tapetum lucidum,** a tissue found in the choroid of some animals (but not humans) that enhances vision in limited light.

## Results

Examining your dissected eye, list in sequence all tissues and structures in the eye through which light passes to create an image, beginning outside the eye through to the brain.

## Discussion

1. Using your text or library sources, describe each listed functional impairment of the eye.

myopia (nearsightedness):

hyperopia (farsightedness):

astigmatism:

cataracts:

Which of the above impairments is (are) most likely to occur as a result of aging?

## Questions for Review

Complete Table 2, naming the three tunics of the eye and their subdivisions, if appropriate. Give the function of each subdivision.

**Table 2**
Eye Tunics and Their Functions

| Tunic | Subdivision | Function |
|-------|-------------|----------|
|       |             |          |
|       |             |          |
|       |             |          |

## Applying Your Knowledge

1. Normally a fatty encasement surrounds the kidney helping to maintain its normal position in the body. In cases of extreme emaciation in humans—for example, as in anorexia—the kidneys may drop to a lower position. Consider the ducts associated with the kidney and propose one side effect to the kidney that could result from severe weight loss.

2. A person who has lost a limb may experience phantom pain, feeling pain in the part of the body that is gone. Suggest an explanation for this phenomenon.

3. Both the eye and a camera focus an image using a lens, but the mechanisms differ. How does the eye lens focus light on the retina? How is this different in a camera?

4. As humans age, the lens loses its elasticity. How would this affect its ability to focus light on the retina?

5. How would hypertrophy (swelling) of the prostate gland (often a symptom of prostate cancer) affect functioning of the excretory system?

## Case Studies

Extending their knowledge from this lab topic, students may investigate the following medical cases using various texts, the library, or Web resources. They may submit their finding in written or oral reports.

1. Kim and Joseph Lang have been married 5 years. Two years ago they decided to have a baby, but have been unable to conceive. Laboratory tests show that Kim is ovulating normally and has normal hormone cycles. Now that you know more about male and female reproduction systems, use the Web and other resources to investigate possible causes for their infertility. Consider potential obstructions in structures of both male and female systems, the effects of sexually transmitted diseases, and causes of abnormal pregnancies.

2. Victoria has peritonitis, which she was told resulted from a urinary tract infection. What is peritonitis? Why would this result from a urinary tract infection in females but not males? Discuss the occurrence of this disease in relation to the anatomy of female and male reproductive tracts.

3. Consult a text and write a definition of *homeostasis*. It is said that disease is the failure to maintain homeostatic conditions in the body. Investigate disorders or diseases that may result when homeostasis is disrupted owing to problems in the respiratory, digestive, circulatory, nervous, or excretory systems.

 ## Student Media Activities and Investigations

**Activities**—Ch. 44: Structure of the Human Excretory System; Nephron Structure; Ch. 46: Reproductive System of the Human Female; Reproductive System of the Human Male
**Investigation**—Ch. 46: What Might Obstruct the Male Urethra?
www.masteringbio.com

## References

Fawcett, D. W., and W. Bloom. *A Textbook of Histology*, 11th ed. Philadelphia, PA: Saunders College Publishing, 1986.

Marieb, E. N. *Human Anatomy and Physiology*, 6th ed. Menlo Park, CA: Benjamin Cummings, 2004.

Rust, T. G. *A Guide to Biology Lab*. San Antonio, TX: Southwest Educational Enterprises, 1983.

Werbin, F. and B. Rosha. "The Movies In Our Eyes." *Scientific American*, April, 2007.

## Websites

Photographs of fetal pig anatomy:
http://www.biologycorner.com/pig/fetal.html

Vertebrate eye anatomy:
http://www.stlukeseye.com/anatomy.htm
http://www.discoveryfund.org/anatomyoftheeye.html

A Google search for "reflex arc" will yield many informative websites:
http://www.google.com

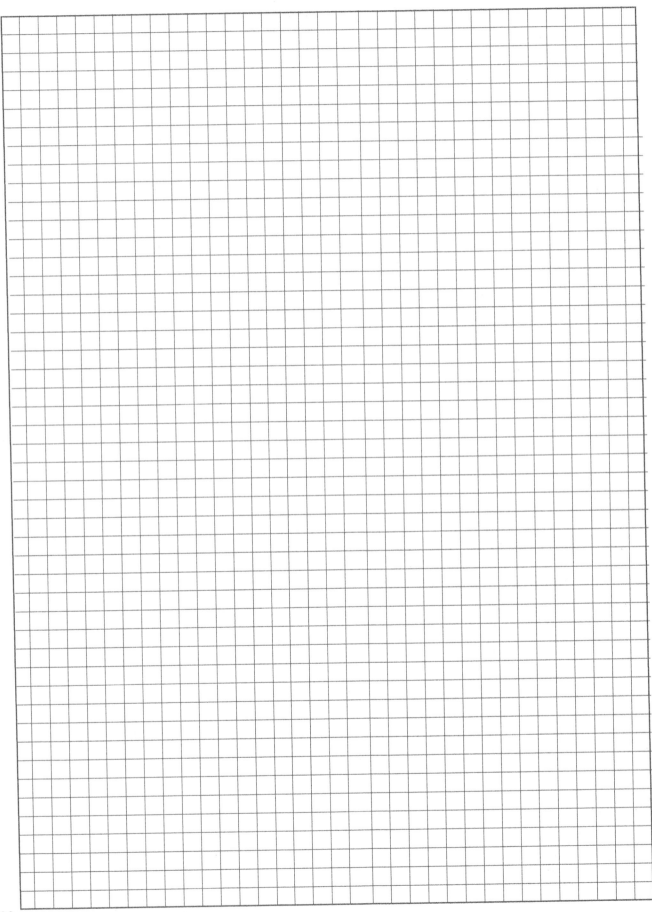

# Animal Development

## Laboratory Objectives

After completing this lab topic, you should be able to:

1. Describe early development in echinoderms (sea urchin and sea star), amphibian (frog or salamander), fish (zebrafish), and bird (chicken).

2. List the events in early development that are common to all organisms.

3. Compare early development in the organisms studied, speculating about factors causing differences.

4. Relate the events of early development in vertebrates to the formation of a dorsal nerve cord.

5. Discuss the effects of large amounts of yolk on the events of early development.

## Introduction

The development of a multicellular organism involves many stages in a long process beginning with the production and fusion of male and female gametes, continuing with the development of a multicellular embryo, the emergence of larval or juvenile stages, growth and maturation to sexual maturity, and the process of aging, and eventually ending with the death of the organism. A range of biological processes functions in development, including **cell division; differentiation,** where cells, tissues, and organs become specialized for a particular function; and **morphogenesis,** the development of the animal's shape, or body form, and organization.

Fifty years ago, developmental biologists primarily studied **morphology,** or form, to describe the process of development, asking questions about the forces involved in morphogenesis. Model organisms used in these studies included the sea urchin and sea star (echinoderms), frogs and salamanders (amphibians), and the chick. More recently, the zebrafish and other organisms have become important subjects for developmental studies. Currently, developmental biologists use these same animals to ask questions about the genetic control of development and the processes involved in activating different genes in different cells. Before these questions can be pursued, however, it is important to have a basic understanding of early development.

In this lab topic, you will use several of the model organisms of classical and current research to investigate major early developmental events common to most animals. These events include **gametogenesis,** the production of gametes; **fertilization,** the union of male and female gametes; **cleavage** and **blastulation,** the production of a multicellular blastula; **gastrulation,** the formation of three primary germ layers—ectoderm,

From *Investigating Biology Laboratory Manual,* Sixth Edition, Judith G. Morgan and M. Eloise Brown Carter. Copyright © 2008 by Pearson Education, Inc. Published by Benjamin Cummings, Inc. All rights reserved.

**Figure 1.**

**Egg types based on amount and distribution of yolk.** (a) Isolecithal eggs have small amounts of evenly distributed yolk. (b) Telolecithal eggs have large amounts of yolk concentrated at one end.

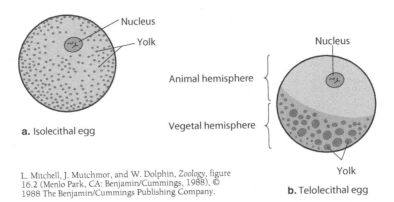

L. Mitchell, J. Mutchmor, and W. Dolphin, *Zoology*, figure 16.2 (Menlo Park, CA: Benjamin/Cummings, 1988), © 1988 The Benjamin/Cummings Publishing Company.

mesoderm, and endoderm; **neurulation,** the formation of the nervous system in chordates; and **organogenesis,** the development of organs from the three primary germ layers. Although you may observe all of these developmental stages, you will study primarily cleavage and blastulation, gastrulation, neurulation, and organogenesis.

## Overview of Stages in Early Development

### Stage 1: Preparation of the Egg, Fertilization, and Cleavage

Development begins as sperm and egg prepare for fertilization. Sperm develop a flagellum, which propels the cell containing the haploid genetic complement of the paternal parent to the egg, which contains the haploid maternal genetic complement. The egg builds up food reserves called **yolk,** which is composed of protein and fat, to be utilized by the early embryo.

When egg and sperm come into contact, their nuclei, each containing a haploid set of chromosomes, combine to form one diploid cell, the **zygote.** The mitotic cell divisions of cleavage rapidly convert the zygote to a multicellular ball, or disc, called the **blastula.** The cells of the blastula are called **blastomeres.** A cavity, the **blastocoel,** forms within the ball of cells. The blastocoel is centrally located in embryos developing from isolecithal eggs. In embryos developing from telolecithal eggs, the blastocoel is associated with the dividing cells in the animal hemisphere.

### Egg Types

Because early events in development are affected by the amount of yolk present in the egg, the classification of eggs is based on the amount and distribution of yolk. Eggs with small amounts of evenly distributed yolk are called **isolecithal** eggs (Figure 1a). Eggs containing large amounts of yolk

**Figure 2. (☞)**

**Cleavage types based on amount and distribution of yolk.** (a) In isolecithal eggs, cleavage is holoblastic, and the blastocoel is centrally located. (b) In moderately telolecithal eggs, cleavage is holoblastic, and the blastocoel develops in the animal hemisphere. (c) In strongly telolecithal eggs, cleavage is meroblastic. Only the active cytoplasm divides, producing a cap of cells, the blastoderm. The blastocoel forms within the blastoderm.

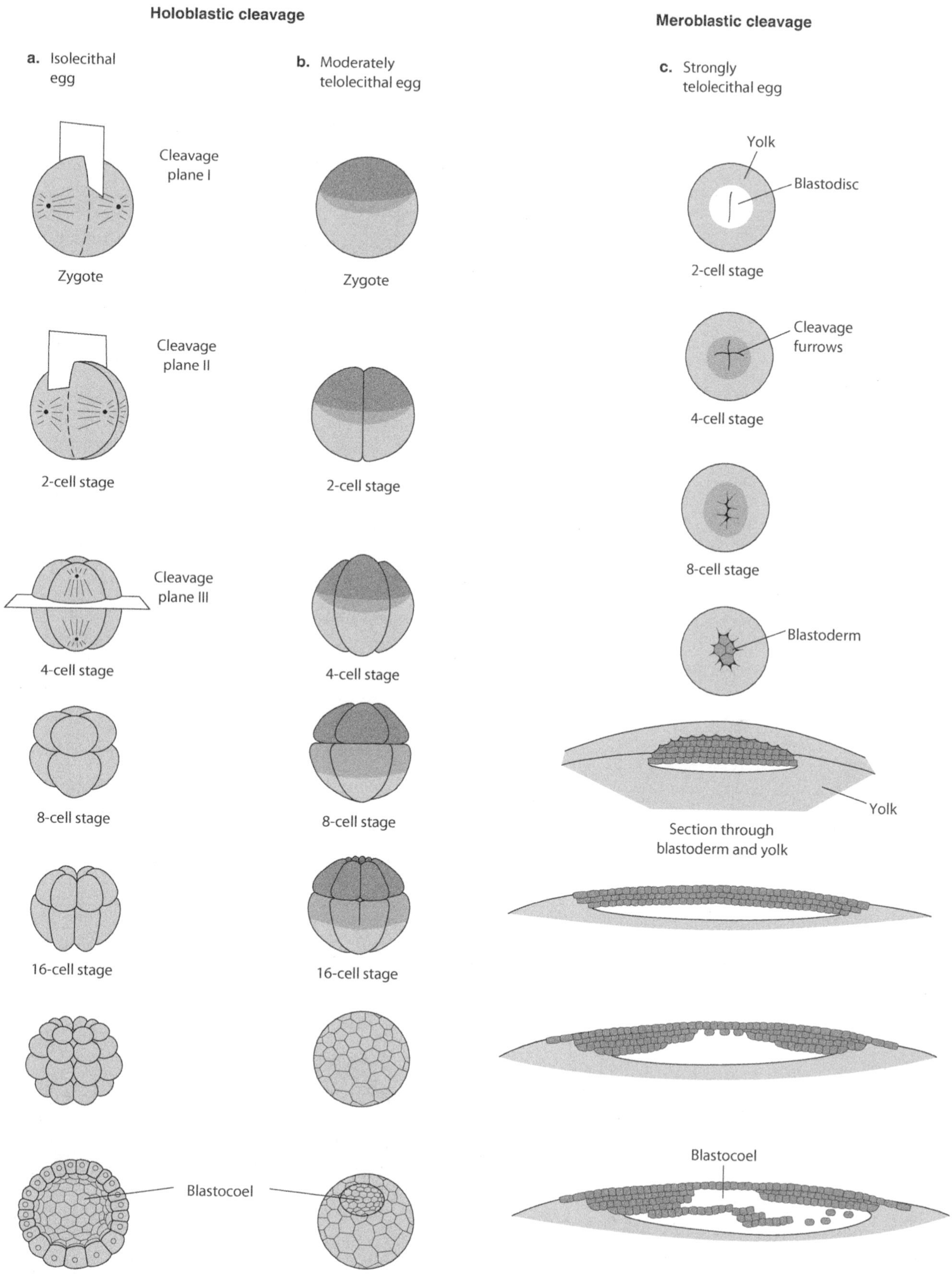

## Holoblastic cleavage

**a.** Isolecithal egg

**b.** Moderately telolecithal egg

## Meroblastic cleavage

**c.** Strongly telolecithal egg

Cleavage plane I

Zygote

Zygote

Yolk

Blastodisc

2-cell stage

Cleavage plane II

2-cell stage

2-cell stage

Cleavage furrows

4-cell stage

Cleavage plane III

4-cell stage

8-cell stage

4-cell stage

8-cell stage

8-cell stage

Blastoderm

16-cell stage

16-cell stage

Yolk

Section through blastoderm and yolk

Blastocoel

Blastocoel

L. Mitchell, J. Mutchmor, and W. Dolphin, *Zoology*, figure 16.2 (Menlo Park, CA: Benjamin/Cummings, 1988), © 1988 The Benjamin/Cummings Publishing Company.

concentrated at one end are called **telolecithal** eggs (Figure 1b). Some species are moderately telolecithal, whereas others are strongly telolecithal. Eggs may also be classified as **centrolecithal** (yolk in the center of the egg) or **alecithal** (no significant yolk reserves). Neither of these conditions will be studied in this lab topic.

In strongly telolecithal eggs, the nucleus is surrounded by **active cytoplasm,** which is relatively devoid of yolk. This nuclear-cytoplasmic region is called the **blastodisc.** The blastodisc is displaced toward the pole of the egg where polar bodies budded from the cell in meiosis. This pole is designated the **animal pole.** The half of the egg associated with the animal pole is the **animal hemisphere.** In these eggs, the yolk is concentrated in the other half of the egg, designated the **vegetal hemisphere.** The pole of this hemisphere is the **vegetal pole.**

## Cleavage Types

Although the end result of cleavage, the formation of the blastula, is the same in all organisms, the pattern of cleavage can differ. One factor that influences the pattern of cleavage is the amount of yolk present. In total, or **holoblastic,** cleavage, cell divisions pass through the entire fertilized egg. This type of cleavage takes place in isolecithal eggs, where the impact of yolk is minimal (Figure 2a). In these eggs, the blastocoel forms in the center of the blastula. In moderately telolecithal eggs, the yolk will retard cytoplasmic divisions and affect the size of cells. However, if the entire egg is cleaved, cleavage is considered holoblastic (Figure 2b). In this case, the blastocoel develops in the animal hemisphere. Cells in this hemisphere will be smaller and have less yolk than cells in the vegetal hemisphere.

In a strongly telolecithal egg, only the active cytoplasm is divided during cleavage. This process is called **meroblastic** cleavage, and it produces a cap of cells called a **blastoderm** (Figure 2c). In meroblastic embryos, the blastocoel forms between two layers of cells within the blastoderm.

## Stage 2: Gastrulation

Gastrulation transforms the blastula, the hollow ball of cells (in holoblastic cleavage) or cap of cells (in meroblastic cleavage), into a **gastrula** made up of three embryonic, or germ, layers: endoderm, ectoderm, and mesoderm (Figure 3). Whereas cleavage is characterized by cell division, gastrulation is characterized by cell movement. Surface cells migrate into the interior of

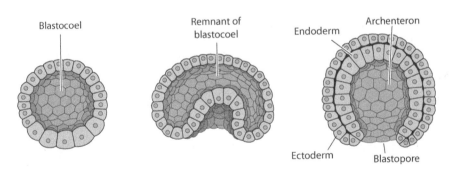

**Figure 3.**
**Gastrulation.** The blastula is converted to a three-layer embryo. Ectoderm and endoderm germ layers form first. Mesoderm forms later between the ectoderm and endoderm.

**a.** Blastula    **b.** Early gastrula    **c.** Late gastrula

L. Mitchell, J. Mutchmor, and W. Dolphin, *Zoology,* figure 16.2 (Menlo Park, CA: Benjamin/Cummings, 1988), © 1988 The Benjamin/Cummings Publishing Company.

the embryo in a process called **involution.** The involuted cells form a new internal cavity, the **archenteron,** lined by the **endoderm,** the embryonic germ layer that ultimately forms the digestive tract. The archenteron opens to the outside through the **blastopore,** which in deuterostomes becomes the anus. In protostomes, the blastopore becomes the mouth. The cells that remain on the surface of the embryo become the **ectoderm.** A third layer of cells, the **mesoderm,** develops between ectoderm and endoderm.

## Stage 3: Neurulation

Late in gastrulation, neurulation, the formation of a dorsal, hollow neural tube, begins (Figure 4). In this strictly chordate process, certain ectodermal cells flatten into an elongated **neural plate** extending from the dorsal edge of the blastopore to the anterior end of the embryo. The center of the plate sinks, forming a **neural groove.** The edges of the plate become elevated to form **neural folds,** which approach each other, touch, and eventually fuse, forming the hollow **neural tube.** The anterior end of the tube develops into the brain, while the posterior end develops into the nerve (spinal) cord.

## Stage 4: Organogenesis

After the germ layers and nervous system have been established, organogenesis, the formation of rudimentary organs and organ systems, takes place. Ectoderm, the source of the neural tube in chordates, also forms skin and associated glands. In chordates, somites and the notochord develop early from mesodermal cells. Later, muscles, the skeleton, gonads, the excretory system, and the circulatory system develop from mesoderm. Nonchordate animals lack somites and the notochord, but their muscles and organs of the excretory, circulatory, and reproductive systems develop from mesoderm. The endoderm develops into the lining of the digestive tract and such associated organs as the liver, pancreas, and lungs.

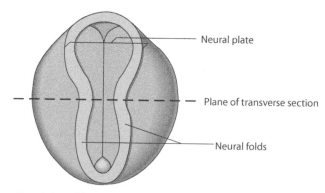

Neural plate

Plane of transverse section

Neural folds

**a.** Dorsal view of frog embryo

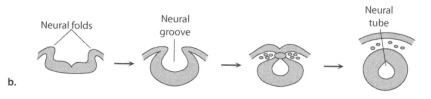

Neural folds

Neural groove

Neural tube

**b.**

**Figure 4.**

**Neurulation.** (a) Dorsal view of the entire frog embryo, showing the ectodermal neural plate with edges elevated, forming the neural folds. (b) Seen in transverse section, the neural folds meet and fuse, forming the neural tube.

Today's lab will be a comparative study of early development in five organisms including the sea urchin and the sea star, both echinoderm invertebrates; the salamander, an amphibious vertebrate; the fish, an aquatic vertebrate; and the chick, a terrestrial vertebrate.

EXERCISE 1

# Development in Echinoderms: Sea Urchin and Sea Star

Sea urchins and sea stars (starfish) are classified in the phylum Echinodermata, the invertebrate group that is phylogenetically closer to chordates than any other. Echinoderms release large numbers of gametes into the sea, and fertilization is external. Early development leads to a larval stage that is free-swimming and free-feeding. In this exercise, you will observe fertilization and early development in living sea urchins, and then you will observe a prepared slide of sea star development.

## Lab Study A: Fertilization in Living Sea Urchins

### Materials

clean slides and coverslips
sand or glass chips in a small petri dish
transfer pipettes, one labeled "egg," the other labeled "sperm," cut to
   make a slightly larger bore
small clean test tube labeled "egg" containing a suspension of living eggs
   from a sea urchin, e.g., *Lytechinus* sp. or *Arbacia* sp.
small clean test tube labeled "sperm" containing a suspension of living
   sperm from a sea urchin, e.g., *Lytechinus* sp. or *Arbacia* sp.
moisture chamber made from a petri dish containing a piece of moist (not
   wet) filter paper

### Introduction

Before your laboratory began, your instructor collected sperm and eggs from living sea urchins by injecting a KCl solution into the body cavity of the urchin. An injection of this solution causes the urchin to extrude gametes from its genital pore located on its upper (aboral—opposite the mouth) surface. It is not possible to determine the sex of a sea urchin from its external anatomy. However, it is possible to determine its sex once it begins to extrude its gametes. Whereas eggs are colored (e.g., light orange in *Lytechinus*), sperm in all species are whitish. Each female sea urchin can spawn over a million eggs and each male a billion sperm. Your instructor collected living eggs and sperm in sea water.

An unfertilized echinoderm egg is surrounded by a jelly coat that slowly dissolves in sea water. When eggs and sperm come into contact, fertilization takes place and a halo—the **fertilization envelope**—forms around the fertilized egg. This envelope helps prevent multiple fertilizations, or *polyspermy*. Two sequential processes prevent polyspermy, the *fast block* and the *slow block*. When a sperm first fuses with an egg, the permeability of the egg plasma membrane immediately changes, allowing an influx of sodium ions. The sodium ions change the electric potential across the cell membrane and, within a second or so, create a *fast block to polyspermy*. A second block to multiple fertilization takes about 20 to 30 seconds. This *slow block to polyspermy* involves the fusion of egg cytoplasmic vesicles with the egg plasma membrane. These vesicles lie in the cortex, or outer portion of the egg cytoplasm, and are called *cortical vesicles*. When they fuse with the egg membrane, their contents are expelled to the egg surface. Enzymes from the vesicles break bonds between the vitelline layer and the egg plasma membrane, and water flows between the two layers. The vitelline layer rises up from the egg membrane and becomes the fertilization envelope. Some time after the egg and sperm cells fuse, the egg and sperm nuclei, called **pronuclei,** move toward the center of the egg, where they fuse and almost immediately begin to prepare for the first mitotic division of cleavage.

In this lab study you will observe fertilization and early development. In Lab Study B, you will learn more details about the process and early stages of development in the sea star.

## Procedure

1. Place a generous drop of egg suspension on a clean microscope slide. Add a few grains of sand or glass chips and cover with a coverslip. Place the slide on your compound microscope stage and observe the eggs using first 4 × and then 10 × objectives.

2. Take a drop of sperm suspension and add this to the edge of the coverslip.

3. Working quickly, note the time and immediately begin observing the slide using first the 10 × and then the high power objectives. Use phase-contrast microscopy on both powers if your microscope has this capability. Look for sperm swimming toward the eggs.

4. Carefully observe the eggs watching for the formation of fertilization envelopes (a clear halo surrounding the egg), indicating that fertilization has taken place.

5. After observing fertilization for several minutes, place your slide in a moisture chamber made from a petri dish.

6. At 30-minute intervals until the end of lab, remove your slide from the petri dish, carefully dry off the bottom of the slide, and use the compound microscope to observe developing embryos. After you complete your observations, return the slide to the moisture chamber each time.

## Results

1. Describe the events that take place as sperm and eggs are mixed. How long did it take for fertilization envelopes to become visible?

2. Are membranes present around all eggs? If not, can you estimate the percent of eggs that have been fertilized?

3. Describe the activity of the sperm. Do active sperm bounce off the egg, or do they become stuck to the jelly coat?

4. Did you observe cleavage? How long after you first observed fertilization? Was the cleavage pattern *holoblastic* or *meroblastic* (Figure 2)?

### Discussion

1. What role might the jelly coat surrounding the egg perform in the process of fertilization?

2. What would you predict would happen if sperm were exposed to a solution containing only egg jelly coat? Would these sperm still be capable of fertilization?

**Student Media Video—Ch. 47: Sea Urchin Embryonic Development**

## Lab Study B: Development in the Sea Star

### Materials

compound microscope
prepared slide of whole sea star embryos in different stages of development

### Introduction

In this lab study, you will observe a prepared slide containing an assortment of whole sea star embryos in various stages of development. You will identify each developmental stage and determine the type of egg and cleavage pattern of the sea star.

### Procedure

1. View the prepared slide of sea star embryos using low and intermediate powers on the compound microscope.

Use only low and intermediate powers. Using the high power objective to view this slide will destroy the slide!

2. Find examples of all stages of development. When you find a good example of each of the stages described, make a careful drawing of that stage in the appropriate square in Figure 5.

## Unfertilized Egg

By the time sea star eggs leave the body of the female, meiosis I and II are completed. The nucleus, called the *germinal vesicle,* is conspicuous because the nuclear envelope is intact. A nucleolus is usually distinct. The plasma membrane surrounding the egg cytoplasm closely adheres to a thin external layer known as the **vitelline layer.** The vitelline layer contains species-specific sperm receptors.

## Fertilized Egg

The fertilized egg, or zygote, has no visible nuclear envelope giving this cell a uniform appearance. Look on the zygote surface for a **fertilization envelope,** most easily seen using phase-contrast microscopy. In Lab Study A you learned that this envelope forms as a result of sperm–egg fusion. The presence of the fertilization envelope and the absence of the visible nuclear envelope will help distinguish fertilized and unfertilized eggs.

## Early Cleavage

Cleavage begins with the zygote and converts this single cell into a multicellular embryo. Find two-, four-, and eight-cell stages. Is the entire zygote involved in early cleavage?

The fertilization envelope remains intact around the embryo until the gastrula stage. What is happening to the size of the cells as cleavage takes place and cell numbers increase?

## Late Cleavage

As cleavage continues, a cavity, the **blastocoel,** forms in the center of the cell cluster. The end product of cleavage will be a hollow ball of cells, the **blastula.** Locate and study a blastula. How does the size of individual cells compare with the size of the fertilized egg?

How does the overall size of the blastula compare with that of the fertilized egg?

## Early Gastrulation

Gastrulation converts the blastula into the gastrula, an embryo composed of three primary germ layers. The early gastrula can be recognized by a small bubble of cells protruding into the blastocoel. These cells push into the blastocoel through a region on the embryo surface called the **blastopore.** As cells continue to invaginate, or move inward, a tube called the archenteron forms. The archenteron eventually becomes the adult gut. Which embryonic germ layer lines the archenteron?

## Middle Gastrulation

The archenteron continues to grow across the blastocoel. It takes on a bulb-like appearance as the advancing portion swells.

## Late Gastrulation

Cells at the leading edge of the advancing archenteron extend pseudopodia that attach to a specific region across the blastocoel. These cells continue to pull the archenteron across the blastocoel. As the tip of the archenteron approaches the opposite wall of the embryo, it bends to one side and fuses with surface cells. The site of fusion will eventually become the mouth of the embryo. What will be formed from the blastopore at the opposite end of the archenteron?

What is the germ layer of cells on the surface of the embryo called?

The amoeboid cells that attach the archenteron to the embryo wall are called *mesenchyme cells*. These cells later detach from the archenteron, proliferate, and form a layer of cells lining the old blastocoel, now divided by the archenteron. This layer of cells will become the mesodermal germ layer.

## Bipinnaria Larval Stage

The archenteron of the gastrula differentiates into a broad **esophagus** leading from the **mouth** to a large oval **stomach** and on to a small, tubular **intestine.** All these structures will be visible in the bilaterally symmetric bipinnaria larva. Locate these structures in larvae on your slide. The larva is now self-feeding and begins to grow. It will later be transformed into the radially symmetric adult sea star.

## Results

Draw stages of sea star development in the appropriate boxes in Figure 5.

a. Unfertilized egg

b. Fertilized egg

c. Early cleavage

d. Late cleavage

e. Early gastrulation

f. Middle gastrulation

g. Late gastrulation

h. Bipinnaria larva

**Figure 5.**
**Early stages of development in the sea star.**

## Discussion

1. What is the advantage of species-specific sperm receptors in the vitelline layer of the egg?

2. What type of egg does the sea star have? What evidence have you observed that supports your answer?

3. Describe the pattern of cleavage seen in the sea star and give the name for this type of cleavage.

---

# EXERCISE 2
# Development in an Amphibian

## Materials

video or film of early development in a salamander or some other amphibian

## Introduction

Amphibians are vertebrates that lay jelly-coated eggs in water or in moist areas on land. Common examples include frogs and salamanders. For most species, fertilization is external, with the male depositing sperm over the eggs after the female releases them. Internal fertilization takes place in some amphibians, however, in which cases the young are born in advanced developmental stages. Early development is similar in all species. After fertilization, the zygote begins cleavage followed by gastrulation, neurulation, and organogenesis.

In this exercise, you will study early development in an amphibian by observing a video or film presentation of some species such as the salamander *Triturus alpestris*. The film or video shows dramatic time-lapse photography of cleavage, gastrulation, and neurulation.

## Procedure

1. Before viewing the film or video, complete Table 1 by defining terms commonly used when describing early embryos. (You may need to refer to your text.)

### Table 1
Common Terms Used in Embryology

| Term | Definition |
|------|------------|
| Animal pole | |
| Animal hemisphere | |
| Equator | |
| Vegetal hemisphere | |
| Vegetal pole | |

2. Read the questions in the Results section, view the film or video, and then answer the questions.

## Results

1. Would you describe the amphibian egg as isolecithal, moderately telolecithal, strongly telolecithal, or alecithal?

2. Describe the cleavage pattern. Is it holoblastic or meroblastic? Are cleavages synchronous or irregular? Can you detect any particular pattern in the cleavage? Where is the second cleavage plane in relation to the first?

3. Does the size of the embryo change as cleavage progresses?

4. Visually follow surface cells during gastrulation. Do they all move at the same rate? Describe gastrulation, comparing the process with that in the sea star. Notice the position of the blastopore and the yolk plug located in the blastopore.

5. During neurulation, do the neural ridges (folds) meet and fuse simultaneously along the entire length of the neural tube or do they close like a zipper?

## Discussion

1. Name at least two major differences in early development between the salamander and the sea star and describe factors responsible for these differences.

2. Compare the video of amphibian development with Figure 6. Label the following in the appropriate figure: **animal pole, vegetal pole, blastocoel, archenteron, yolk plug, neural plate,** and **neural folds.**

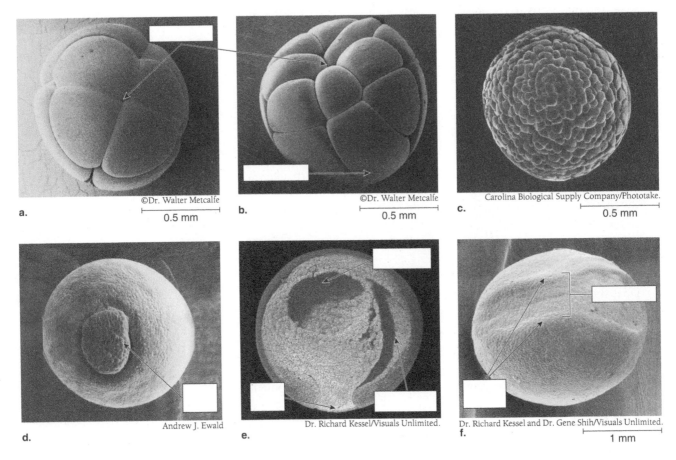

a. ©Dr. Walter Metcalfe    0.5 mm
b. ©Dr. Walter Metcalfe    0.5 mm
c. Carolina Biological Supply Company/Phototake.    0.5 mm
d. Andrew J. Ewald
e. Dr. Richard Kessel/Visuals Unlimited.
f. Dr. Richard Kessel and Dr. Gene Shih/Visuals Unlimited.    1 mm

**Figure 6.**
**Early amphibian development.** (a) and (b) Early cleavage. (c) Surface view of the hollow blastula in late cleavage. (d) Surface view of a gastrula. (e) Cross section of a gastrula. (f) Surface view of a neurula.

Student Media Video—Ch. 47: Frog Embryo Development

# EXERCISE 3
# Development in the Zebrafish

## Materials

small petri dishes
depression slides
embryo-rearing solution
clean toothpicks
fish embryos in various developmental stages (some on ice)
stereoscopic microscope
compound microscope

## Introduction

In this portion of the laboratory, you will observe living embryos in early developmental stages using a freshwater fish commonly known as the zebrafish, or zebra danio (*Brachydanio rerio*). This fish is a native of streams in India. Male and female fish are similar in appearance, but the male is generally smaller, with a streamlined body shape. The female is larger and broader than the male, especially when carrying eggs.

In nature, zebrafish are stimulated to reproduce when days consist of approximately 16 hours of light and 8 hours of dark. This photoperiod corresponds to favorable weather and food supplies for developing embryos. By artificially creating this photoperiod in the laboratory, we can produce conditions that stimulate the zebrafish to spawn. After only 2 or 3 days on a cycle of 16 hours of light and 8 hours of dark, female fish will lay eggs, and male fish will deposit sperm for external fertilization.

The embryos you will observe today were collected from zebrafish on the artificial schedule. Newly spawned embryos were placed in embryo-rearing solution in petri dishes. Some embryos were maintained at room temperature, while others were placed on ice to retard development. The petri dishes were labeled to indicate the approximate stage of development. Because some embryos have been kept on ice, and because not all female fish lay their eggs at exactly the same time, a variety of early developmental stages should be available for your study. Neurulation and organogenesis stages are available from yesterday's spawning.

The approximate schedule of development at 25°C is described in Table 2. Use this schedule to predict the approximate stage of development for eggs collected at 8 A.M. and maintained at room temperature (approximately 23°C).

**Table 2**
Developmental Schedule for Zebrafish at 25°C

| Hour | Time | Comments |
|------|------|----------|
| 0 | 8 A.M. | Lights on. Fish stimulated to spawn. Fish begin to dart back and forth, depositing eggs and sperm (spawning) close to the bottom of the aquarium. Fertilization takes place, forming the zygote. Cleavage begins in 35 minutes. |
| 1 | 9 A.M. | Cleavage continues. Some embryos are collected and placed on ice to slow development. |
| 2 | 10 A.M. | Embryos are in midblastula stage (approximately 64 cells). |
| 4 | 12 noon | Late blastula. |
| 5 | 1 P.M. | Early gastrula. |
| 6 | 2 P.M. | Midgastrula. |
| 12 | 8 P.M. | Gastrulation completed; neurulation taking place. |
| 18 | 2 A.M. | Neurulation completed; organogenesis beginning. |
| 24 | 8 A.M. | Second day begins; organogenesis continues. |
| 96 | 8 A.M. | Day 4 begins; embryos hatch. |

## Procedure

1. Obtain a petri dish with an embryo in embryo-rearing solution from the lab supply. View it using the stereoscopic microscope. Gently roll the embryo using a toothpick to see the embryo from several angles.

2. Read the description (following) of each stage of development, and determine the stage of the embryo. Remember that these are living embryos, and the stage of development may have changed from that indicated on the petri dish label.

3. Using a pipette, carefully transfer the embryo and rearing solution to a depression slide and view it on the lowest power of the compound microscope.

4. Remembering that these are living embryos, watch carefully to observe cells dividing. You may observe a two-cell embryo changing to a four-cell embryo or a late blastula beginning gastrulation. With careful and patient observations, you may be fortunate enough to see the developmental stages unfolding.

5. Make drawings in the margin of your lab manual so that you will be able to refer to them later.

6. Using the pipette, return the embryo to the petri dish. Then return the petri dish to the lab supply.

7. Obtain a petri dish with an embryo in a different stage of development and repeat steps 1 to 6. Continue your observations until you have seen all listed stages of development.

## Unfertilized Egg

Because most eggs are immediately fertilized after spawning, you may not find any unfertilized eggs. The unfertilized egg is about 0.5 mm in diameter. It is spherical, with yolk granules evenly distributed. There is a membrane, the **chorion,** around the egg.

## Fertilized Egg (Zygote)

A thin **fertilization membrane** forms after fertilization. The yolk granules condense, and the active cytoplasm migrates to the **animal pole,** where it becomes the **blastodisc,** or germinal disc. The blastodisc is visible as a bulge in the otherwise spherical cell. The future embryo will develop from the blastodisc, and the yolk will serve as the nutrient supply.

## Cleavage

Cleavage takes place in the blastodisc. Cells resulting from cleavage are called **blastomeres.** The blastodisc divides into 2, then 4, 8, and 16 cells of equal size.

## Blastula

By the 64-cell stage, the blastula appears as a high dome of cells at the animal pole (Figure 7a). This dome of cells is called the **blastoderm.** As cleavage continues, the cells become more compact, and the interface between the blastoderm and the yolk flattens out (Figure 7b).

## Gastrula

Gastrulation in the zebrafish is strikingly different from the process in the sea star and the salamander, because cleavage is restricted to the blastodisc. The surface cells of the blastula spread over the entire yolk mass toward the vegetal pole in a process called **epiboly.** The surface cells produce the ectoderm. When the advancing blastoderm cells have covered approximately one-half of the yolk, a type of cell movement called **involution** begins when cells move into the interior of the embryo in a ring at the edge of the advancing blastoderm. These involuting cells will eventually form mesoderm and endoderm. Figure 7c and d illustrate early and late gastrulation.

## Neurulation

The antero/posterior, dorso/ventral embryonic axes are first obvious during neurulation. As neurulation takes place, ectodermal cells form the neural plate and eventually the neural tube. In the whole embryo, the region of the neural tube appears as a ridge on the dorsal surface. With careful investigation, you can discern that one end of the neural tube is enlarged. This enlarged portion is the **brain** developing at the anterior end of the embryo. The posterior end of the neural tube develops into the **nerve** (spinal) **cord.** As development progresses, a supportive rod, the **notochord,** forms from mesoderm beneath the neural tube. The notochord is later replaced by vertebrae. Blocks of tissue called **somites** form from mesoderm along each side of the nerve cord (Figure 7e).

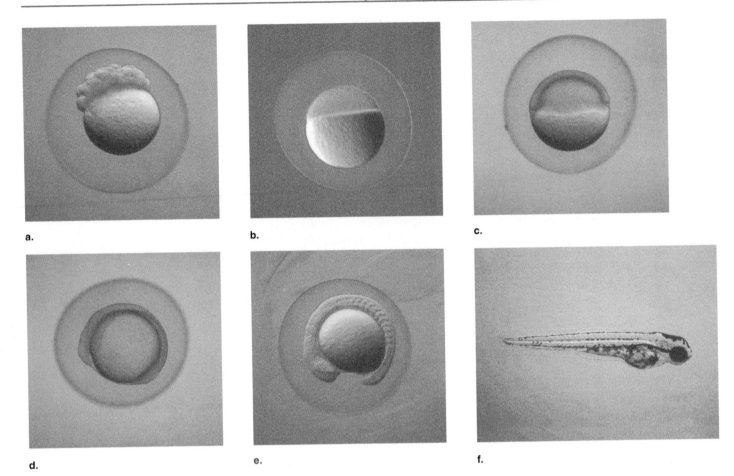

**Figure 7.**
**Development in the zebrafish.** (a) The 64-cell blastula. (b) Late blastula in side view. (c) The early gastrula. Surface cells move over the yolk mass. When they cover approximately one-half of the yolk, they begin to involute at the blastopore. (d) The late gastrula and early neurulation. (e) Neurulation and organogenesis. Ectodermal cells form the neural tube, which eventually develops into the anterior brain and posterior spinal cord. (f) Newly hatched embryo.

## Organogenesis

In organogenesis, formation of rudimentary organs and organ systems takes place. In the fish, the brain, eyes, somites, spinal cord, and tail bud are visible. The rhythmic beating of the heart and circulating blood are seen.

Among other things, somites develop into skeletal muscles, and older embryos will be actively twisting and turning in the fertilization membrane. Developing **pigmentation** will be visible in the skin and eye.

## Hatching

As organogenesis continues, embryos grow and develop, and after 4 days, the eggs hatch (Figure 7f).

## Results

In the margin of your lab manual, draw the stages of development. Include at least two stages in early cleavage (2-cell, 4-cell, 8-cell, 16-cell) and label the animal pole, vegetal pole, blastomere, and fertilization membrane.

## Discussion

1. What type of egg does the zebrafish have (Figure 2)?

2. Is cleavage in the zebrafish holoblastic or meroblastic?

3. Compare the size of the blastodisc and the size of cells before and after cleavage.

---

EXERCISE 4

# Development in a Bird: The Chicken

## Materials

compound microscope
stereoscopic microscope
unincubated egg (demonstration)
prepared slide of 16-hour chick
prepared slide of 24-hour chick
living egg incubated 48 hours
living egg incubated 96 hours

finger bowl
warm 0.9% NaCl
flat-tipped forceps
sharp-pointed scissors
watch glass
disposable pipette
pipette bulb

## Introduction

Immature eggs, or **oocytes**, develop within follicles in the single ovary of the adult female bird. (Two ovaries begin to develop in birds, but the second ovary degenerates.) In the sexually mature bird, hormonal stimulation brings about **ovulation**, the release of oocytes into a single oviduct. An oocyte consists of active cytoplasm, called the **blastodisc**, or germinal disc, floating on a huge amount of food reserve, the yolk, surrounded by a plasma membrane. At the time of ovulation, chromosomes in the large oocyte nucleus have just completed the first maturation division of meiosis (meiosis I). At ovulation in chickens, the oocyte nucleus measures approximately 0.5 mm and the oocyte measures approximately 35 mm in diameter.

Fertilization is internal in birds. If sperm are present in the oviduct at ovulation, they will penetrate each oocyte (one per oocyte), stimulating the completion of meiosis in the oocyte nucleus. The sperm nucleus and the now mature egg nucleus fuse, producing the zygote nucleus, which begins to divide by mitosis followed by cytoplasmic cleavage. As this developing embryo continues its passage down the oviduct, albumin, shell membranes, and finally a calcareous shell are deposited on its surface. In chickens, passage down the oviduct takes about 25 hours. This means that a freshly laid chicken egg, if it has been fertilized, has completed about 25 hours of development. The cleaved blastodisc is now called the **blastoderm,** or **blastula.** Development continues in the blastoderm, giving rise to all parts of the embryo, with yolk containing carbohydrates, proteins, lipids, and vitamins serving as the food reserves.

In this exercise, you will observe an unincubated egg and incubated eggs in several stages of development. As you study the embryos, identify developing structures and compare bird development with that of the sea star, salamander, and zebrafish.

## Procedure

1. Refer to Figure 8 and observe the unincubated chicken egg on demonstration.

   Most eggs sold for human consumption are purchased from commercial egg farms where hens are not allowed contact with roosters. The egg you are studying may or may not have been fertilized.

   a. Observe the broken calcareous **shell** with outer and inner **shell membranes** just inside. The shell and membranes are porous, allowing air to pass through to the embryo inside. You have probably noticed an air chamber at one end of a hard-boiled egg, between the two membranes.

   b. Observe the watery, proteinaceous **egg albumin** (egg white) and the yellow yolk. The layers of albumin closest to the yolk are more viscous and stringy than the outer albumin. As the yolky egg passes down the oviduct, it rotates, twisting the stringy albumin into two whitish strands on either end of the yolk. Called **chalaza,** these strands suspend the yolk in the albumin.

   c. Locate the **cytoplasmic island,** a small whitish disc lying on top of the yolk. This is larger in a fertilized egg because of the development that has taken place. Remember that this island is called the *blastodisc* before cleavage begins and the *blastoderm* after cleavage

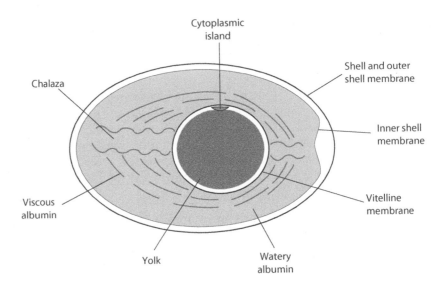

**Figure 8.**
**The unincubated chicken egg.** The chalaza suspends the yolk in the albumin.

has begun. If you are studying a fertilized egg, cleavage is completed. Cleavage is restricted to the blastoderm; the yolk does not divide.

As cleavage takes place, the blastoderm, now a mass of cells, becomes elevated above the yolk. Subsequent horizontal cleavages create three or four cell layers in the blastoderm, and a space, the blastocoel, forms within these layers.

2. Study the prepared slide of the 16-hour egg (the **gastrula**). Refer to Figure 9a, a surface view of the embryo.

 Use only low and intermediate powers when viewing this slide. The high power objective will break the slide!

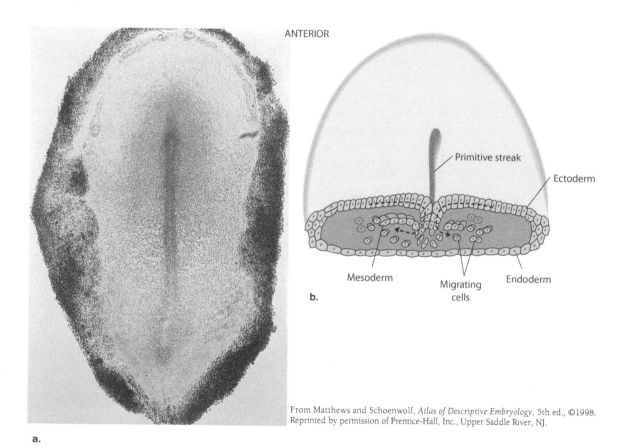

b.

ANTERIOR

Primitive streak

Ectoderm

Mesoderm

Migrating cells

Endoderm

From Matthews and Schoenwolf, *Atlas of Descriptive Embryology*, 5th ed., ©1998. Reprinted by permission of Prentice-Hall, Inc., Upper Saddle River, NJ.

a.

**Figure 9.**
**Chick gastrulation.** (a) Surface view of chick blastoderm after 16 hours of incubation, the gastrula stage. The primitive streak is visible. (b) Cross section of blastoderm after 16 hours of incubation. Cells turn in at the primitive streak, initiating the formation of mesodermal tissues.

a. Using low and then intermediate powers on the compound microscope, view a prepared slide of the whole chick embryo after about 16 hours of incubation. At this stage, cells in the blastoderm have separated into an upper layer forming ectoderm and an inner layer forming endoderm. These layers are visible only in sections of the embryo.

b. Locate a dark, longitudinal thickening, the **primitive streak.** Surface cells migrate toward the primitive streak and then turn under, through the primitive streak. By 18 hours, they have spread out and initiated the formation of mesodermal tissues (Figure 9b). The notochord is one of the first structures to develop in the mesodermal layer.

3. Study the prepared slide of the 24-hour chick (**neurulation**). Refer to Figure 10.

 Use only low and intermediate powers to view this slide. The high power objective will break the slide!

a. Use the low and then intermediate powers on the compound microscope to view the prepared slide of a chick after 24 hours of incubation. At this stage, the neural tube is forming anterior to the primitive streak in a process similar to neurulation in fish.

b. Look for the developing longitudinal ectodermal **neural tube** with elevated edges called **neural folds** and a depressed center called the **neural groove.** The margins of the neural folds, which appear as a pair of dark longitudinal bands, become elevated and approach each other until they touch and eventually fuse. This fusion of the

**Figure 10.**
**The chick after 24 hours of incubation (neurulation).** Edges of the ectodermal neural plate elevate, forming neural folds. The depressed center is the neural groove. The neural folds eventually fuse, forming the neural tube.

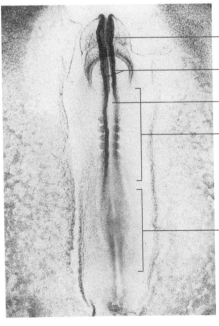
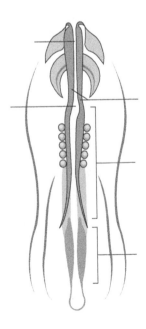

folds completes the formation of the neural tube. The anterior end of the neural tube becomes the brain; the posterior end becomes the spinal, or nerve, cord.

c. Label the following on the photo and diagram of Figure 10: *neural folds, neural groove, developing brain, spinal cord region* of the *neural tube,* and *primitive streak.*

---

 Study the next two stages of development using living chick embryos and the materials listed at the beginning of the exercise. Work in pairs. One student will open the 48-hour chick; the other will open the 96-hour chick. Collaborate as you observe both eggs.

---

4. Prepare each egg to study the 48- and 96-hour chicks (**organogenesis**).

   a. Pour warm (heated to about 38°C) 0.9% NaCl solution into a clean finger bowl.

   b. Obtain an egg and carry it to your desk, keeping it oriented with the "top" up as it has been in the incubator. Crack the "down" side of the egg on the edge of the finger bowl. Hold the egg, cracked side down, in the NaCl solution, and carefully open the shell, allowing the egg to slide out of the shell.

   c. Using the stereoscopic microscope, observe the embryo on the surface of the yolk. The embryo should either be on top of the yolk or it should float to the top. The embryo is in the center of the vascularized blastoderm.

   d. Remove the finger bowl from the microscope and, using broad-tipped forceps and sharp scissors, remove the embryo from the yolk surface by carefully snipping outside the vascularized region of the embryo. Use the forceps to hold the blastoderm as you cut. Do not let go or you may lose the embryo in the mass of yolk.

   e. Hold a watch glass under the NaCl solution and carefully pull the blastoderm away from the surface of the yolk into the watch glass. Carefully lift the watch glass and embryo out of the solution and pipette away excess solution until only a small amount remains.

   f. Wipe the bottom of the watch glass, place on the stereoscopic microscope, and observe.

5. Study the 48-hour chick (early organogenesis). Refer to Figure 11a.

   a. Identify structures in the circulatory system. In the living embryo, the **heart** is already beating at this stage, pumping blood through the **vitelline blood vessels,** which emerge from the embryo and carry food materials from the yolk mass to the embryo. If the heart is still beating, you should be able to see blood passing from the **atrium** into the **ventricle.** The atrium lies behind the ventricle, which is a larger, U-shaped chamber.

   b. Identify structures in the nervous system. The anterior part of the neural tube has formed the **brain. Eyes** are already partially formed. You may be able to locate the developing ear. Follow the tube posteriorly to the **spinal cord.**

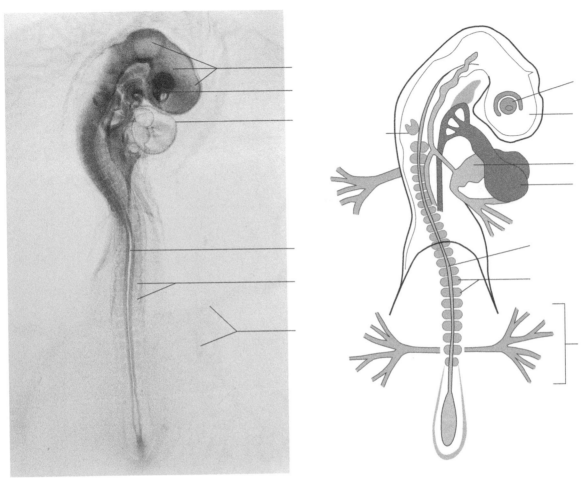

From Matthews and Schoenwolf, *Atlas of Descriptive Embryology*, 5th ed., ©1998. Reprinted by permission of Prentice-Hall, Inc., Upper Saddle River, NJ.

**Figure 11.**
**The chick after 48 hours of incubation.** Identify the heart (atrium and ventricle), vitelline blood vessels, the brain, an eye, the spinal cord, and somites.

    c. Observe **somites,** blocks of tissue lying on either side of the **spinal cord.** Somites develop into body musculature and several other mesodermal organs.

    d. Label Figure 11.

    e. Swap chick embryos with your lab partner.

6. Study the 96-hour chick (later organogenesis). Refer to Figure 12.

    a. Notice that the 96-hour chick has a strong **cervical flexure,** bending the body into a C configuration. Several organs are noticeably larger than in the 48-hour chick.

    b. Locate the developing **brain, eyes,** and **ears.**

    c. Identify the conspicuous **heart.**

    d. Locate one of the two **anterior limb buds** just behind the heart. Anterior limb buds develop into wings.

    e. Locate the **posterior limb buds** near the tail. These limb buds grow into legs.

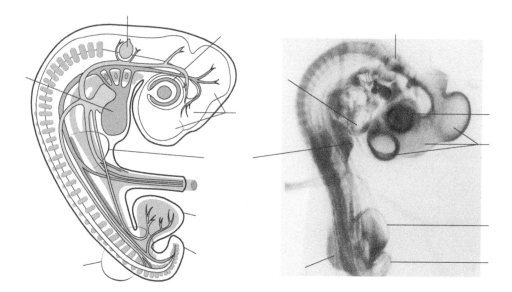

**Figure 12.**
**The chick after 96 hours of incubation.** A strong cervical flexure has developed. Limb buds, allantois, ears, and tail are visible.

  f. Identify one of four **extraembryonic membranes,** the **allantois,** which protrudes outward from the hindgut near the posterior limb bud (see Figure 12 and Figure 13). Be sure you can distinguish between limb bud and allantois. Extraembryonic membranes are derived from embryonic tissue, but are found outside the embryo proper. These membranes are important adaptations for land-dwelling organisms like reptiles, birds, and mammals. They help solve problems such as desiccation, gas exchange, and waste removal in the embryo. The large saclike allantois will continue to grow until it lies close inside the porous shell. It functions to bring oxygen to the embryo, carry away carbon dioxide, and store liquid wastes.

  g. Look for a second extraembryonic membrane, the **amnion,** a thin, transparent membrane that encloses the embryo in a fluid-filled sac.

  h. Using the broad-tipped forceps, carefully lift the embryo to observe the yolk stalk and **yolk sac,** a third extraembryonic membrane that surrounds the yolk. The fourth extraembryonic membrane, the **chorion,** is not easily observed.

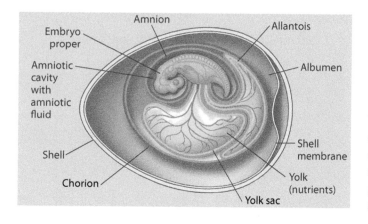

**Figure 13.**
**Extraembryonic membranes in a chick between 96 and 120 hours of incubation.** The allantois protrudes from the gut near the posterior limb bud. The amnion surrounds the embryo proper, creating a fluid-filled amniotic cavity; the yolk sac surrounds the yolk; and the chorion grows until it eventually fuses with the shell membrane.

    i. Label Figure 12.

    j. Swap chick embryos with your lab partner.

## Results

Label Figures 10, 11, and 12 and make additional sketches in the margin of your lab manual for future reference.

## Discussion

1. What type of egg is the chicken egg (Figure 2)?

2. This egg undergoes what type of cleavage?

3. Collaborating with your lab partner, describe major differences between the 48-hour and 96-hour chicken embryos.

# Questions for Review

1. Having completed this lab topic, define and describe the following terms, giving examples when appropriate: *cleavage, blastula, gastrula, involution, archenteron, blastocoel, blastopore, isolecithal, telolecithal, alecithal, meroblastic, holoblastic, bipinnaria, epiboly, neurulation, organogenesis, animal pole, vegetal pole, blastodisc, blastoderm, ectoderm, mesoderm, endoderm, neural tube, neural groove,* and *neural fold.*

2. List the embryonic germ layers and the organs derived from each.

3. Differentiate between epiboly and involution.

# Applying Your Knowledge

1. Review the stages of early development in animals. How are these stages similar in the animals you have studied? How do they differ? Complete Table 3.

**Table 3**
Comparison of Stages of Early Development in the Sea Urchin, Sea Star, Salamander, Fish, and Chick

| Organism | Cleavage | Gastrulation | Neurulation | Organogenesis |
|---|---|---|---|---|
| Sea urchin and sea star | | | | |
| Salamander | | | | |
| Fish | | | | |
| Chick | | | | |

2. What is yolk? What is its function in development? Do mammals have yolk? Explain.

3. Giving examples from organisms studied, explain how the amount of yolk affects cleavage and gastrulation.

4. How do the differences in development lead to adaptations to the particular lifestyles of these organisms? (Some are aquatic, others terrestrial, and so on.)

5. Sea urchins live in marine communities that include a variety of species living in close proximity. Most of these species, including sea urchins, have external fertilization, a reproductive strategy that potentially has a low probability of sperm and egg contact. List several adaptations of sea urchins that help insure successful reproduction.

6. Eggs of reptiles, birds, and a few primitive mammals are laid on land, usually away from water and independent sources of food. What features of the land egg (chick) allow this type of early development?

7. The extraembryonic membranes in mammals (including humans) are homologous to those of birds and develop in a similar way. In what ways are their functions the same, and how are they different? Use your text, if needed.

   **Chorion**

   **Amnion**

   **Yolk sac**

   **Allantois**

8. Using your text or other resources, describe possible differences in the arrangement of the chorion and amnion in the formation of identical twins in humans.

# Investigative Extensions

Sea urchin, fish, and chicken eggs collected for this lab topic provide an opportunity for student independent projects. Living amphibian eggs also may be available from colleagues or, in season, from streams or ponds in your area. Recent concern about declining populations of sea urchins (for example, *Diadema antillarum,* the black sea urchin once abundant throughout the Caribbean) and the decline of healthy populations of amphibians in North America are just two examples where environmental factors may be having an impact on animal development.

Suggestions follow for possible questions to investigate:

1. What effects do specific pollutants—pesticides, herbicides, fertilizers—have on fertilization rates in sea urchins, amphibians, or fish?
2. What effect does acid rain-induced pH change have on fertilization rates?
3. Does a change in pH have an impact on the jelly coat of sea urchin eggs?
4. Is sperm motility affected by specific pollutants? At what concentration?
5. Which common pesticides or herbicides have an impact on amphibian development, perhaps contributing to the decline in numbers and increase in abnormalities of this group of animals?
6. Does UV radiation cause limb deformities in amphibians or fish?
7. Does UV radiation change the rate of fertilization in sea urchins?

 **Student Media Activities and Investigations**

**Activities**—Ch. 47: Sea Urchin Development; Frog Development
www.masteringbio.com

## References

Beams, H. W., and R. G. Kessel. "Cytokinesis: A Comparative Study of Cytoplasmic Division in Animal Cells." *American Scientist,* 1976, vol. 64, pp. 279–290. Scanning electron micrographs of development in zebrafish.

Campbell, N., and J. Reece. *Biology,* 8th ed. San Francisco, CA: Benjamin Cummings, 2008.

Gilbert, S. F. *Developmental Biology,* 5th ed. Sunderland, MA: Sinauer Associates, 1997.

Hisaoka, K. K., and C. F. Firlit. "Further Studies on the Embryonic Development of the Zebra Fish, *Brachydanio rerio* (Hamilton-Buchanan)." *Journal of Morphology,* 1960, vol. 107, pp. 205–226.

Patten, B. M. *Early Embryology of the Chick,* 5th ed. New York, NY: McGraw-Hill, 1971.

Westerfield, M. (ed.). *The Zebrafish Book; A Guide for the Laboratory Use of Zebrafish (Brachydanio rerio).* Eugene, OR: University of Oregon Press, 1989.

Exercise 3, Development in the Zebrafish, is based on an exercise by John Pilger, Professor of Biology, Agnes Scott College, Decatur, GA, and a workshop presented by Robert R. Cohen, Professor of Biology, Metropolitan State College, Denver, at a meeting of the American Society of Zoologists. Used by permission.

## Websites

The Fish Net-Zebrafish Information Network:
http://zfin.org/index.html

Sea urchin fertilization animations developed by teachers and Stanford University researchers. Includes instructions on injecting sea urchins to stimulate egg and sperm release:
http://www.stanford.edu/group/Urchin

Video of sea urchin development from fertilization through gastrulation:
www.masteringbio.com (Ch.47)

Developmental biology web links:
http://www.uoguelph.ca/zoology/devobio/wwwlinks.htm

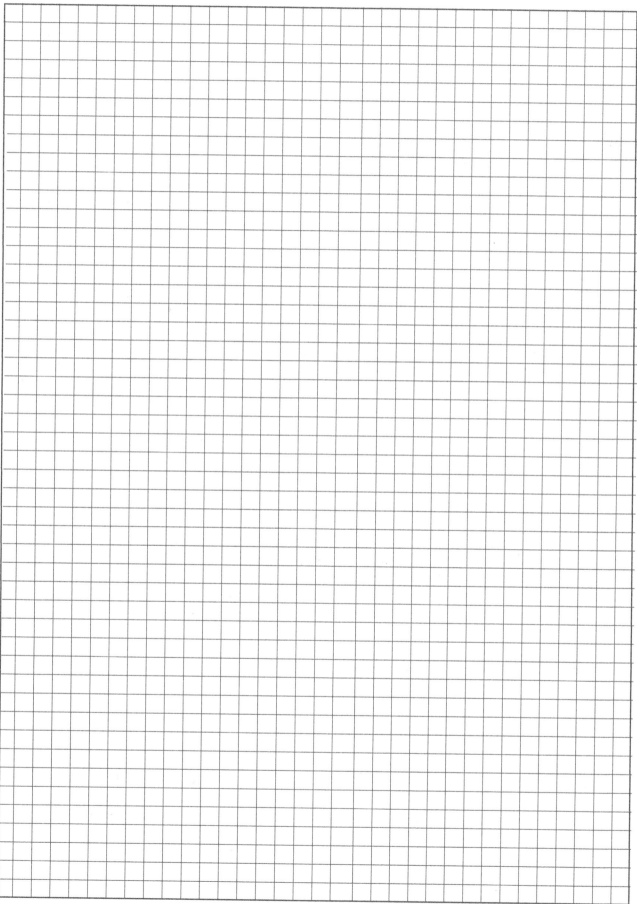

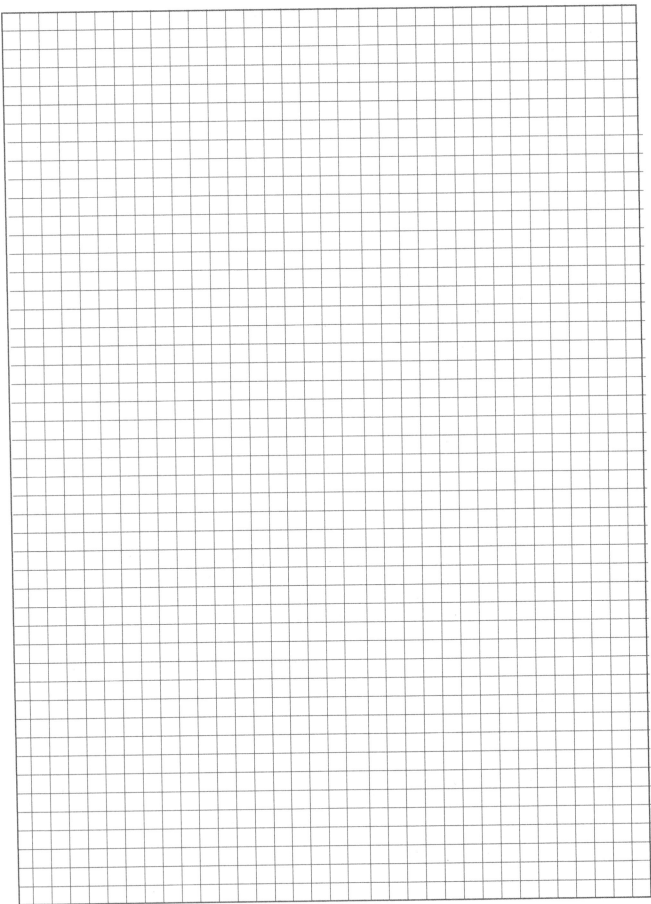

# Animal Behavior

## Laboratory Objectives

After completing this lab topic, you should be able to:

1. Define *ethology.*
2. Define and give an example of *taxis, kinesis, agonistic behavior,* and *reproductive behavior.*
3. State the possible adaptive significance of each of these behaviors.
4. Propose hypotheses, make predictions, design experiments to test hypotheses, collect and process data, and discuss results.
5. Present the results of your experiments in a scientific paper.

## Introduction

**Behavior,** broadly defined, is the sum of the responses of an organism to stimuli in its environment. In other words, behavior is what organisms do. **Ethology** is the study of animal behavior in the context of the evolution, ecology, social organization, and sensory abilities of an animal (Gould, 1982). Ethologists concentrate on developing accurate descriptions of animal behavior by carefully observing and experimentally analyzing overt behavior patterns and by studying the physiology of behavior.

Explaining a particular behavior in the broad, multivariable context of evolution or ecology can become a complex undertaking. It is often necessary, therefore, to study behavior in animals that have a limited range of behaviors and for which more is known about their evolution, ecology, and sensory abilities. Understanding simple and isolated behaviors is important in unraveling more complex behaviors.

There are two basic categories of behavior—**learned** (depends on experiences) and **innate** (inherited—exhibited by nearly all individuals of a species). Experimental evidence suggests that the basis of both lies in the animal's genes. As with all genetically controlled features of an organism, behavior is subject to evolutionary adaptation. As you study animal behavioral activities in this lab topic, think in terms of both **proximate causes,** the immediate physiological events that led to the behavior, and **ultimate causes,** the adaptive value and evolutionary origin of the behavior. To illustrate, a fiddler crab will respond to human intrusion into its feeding area by running into its burrow. The proximate cause of this behavior might be the vibration caused by footsteps stimulating sensory receptors and triggering nervous impulses. The nervous impulses control muscle contractions in the crab's legs. Ultimate causes are the adaptive value of retreating from predators to avoid being eaten.

From Chapter 26 of *Investigating Biology Laboratory Manual*, Seventh Edition. Judith Giles Morgan, M. Eloise Brown Carter.

Note that you will be asking **causal** questions in your investigations. It is inappropriate to ask **anthropomorphic** questions—that is, questions that ascribe human attributes to the animal. Consider, for example, a behavior that places an animal in its best environment. An anthropomorphic explanation for this behavior would be that the animal makes a conscious choice of its environment. There is no way for us to come to this conclusion scientifically. The causal explanation would be that the animal is equipped with a sensory system that responds to environmental stimuli until the favorable environment is reached.

Ethologists have categorized behavioral patterns based on the particular consequence of that behavior for the organism. **Orientation behaviors** place the animal in its most favorable environment. Two categories of orientation behaviors are **taxis** (plural, **taxes**) and **kinesis.** *A taxis is movement directly toward or away from a stimulus.* When the response is toward a stimulus, it is said to be *positive;* when it is away from the stimulus, it is *negative.* Prefixes such as *photo, chemo,* and *thermo* can be added to the term to describe the nature of the stimulus. For example, an animal that responds to light may demonstrate positive phototaxis and is described as being *positively phototactic.*

*A kinesis differs from a taxis in that it is undirected, or random, movement.* A stimulus initiates the movement but does not necessarily orient the movement. The intensity of the stimulus determines the rate, or velocity, of movement in response to that stimulus. If a bright light is shined on an animal and the animal responds by moving directly away from it, the behavior is a taxis. But if the bright light initiates random movement or stimulates an increase in the rate of turning with no particular orientation involved, the behavior is a kinesis. The terms *positive* and *negative* and the prefixes mentioned earlier are also appropriately used with *kinesis.* An increase in activity is a positive response; a decrease in activity is a negative response.

Another complex of behaviors observed in some animals is **agonistic behavior.** In this case, the animal is in a conflict situation where there may be a threat or approach, then an attack or withdrawal. Agonistic behaviors in the form of force are called **aggression;** those of retreat or avoidance are called **submission.** Often the agonistic behavior is simply a display that makes the organism look big or threatening. It rarely leads to death and is thought to help maintain territory so that the dominant organism has greater access to resources such as space, food, and mates.

**Reproductive behavior** can involve a complex sequence of activities, sometimes spectacular, that facilitate *finding, courting,* and *mating* with a member of the same species. It is an adaptive advantage that reproductive behaviors are species-specific. Can you suggest reasons why?

For the first hour of lab, you will perform Experiment A in each of the exercises that follow, briefly investigating the four behaviors just discussed: *taxis in brine shrimp, kinesis in pill bugs, agonistic behavior in Siamese fighting fish,* and *reproductive behavior (courting and mating) in fruit flies.* After completing every Experiment A, your team will choose one of the systems discussed and perform Experiment B in that exercise. *In Experiment B, you will propose one or more testable hypotheses and design a simple experiment to test your hypotheses.* Then you will spend the remainder of the laboratory period carrying out your experiments.

Near the end of the laboratory period, several of you may be asked to present your team's results to the class for discussion. One part of the scientific process involves persuading your colleagues that your experimental design is sound and that your results support your conclusions (either negating or supporting your hypothesis). Be prepared to describe your results in a brief presentation in which you will use your experimental evidence to persuade the other students in your class.

You may be required to submit a laboratory report describing your experiment and results in the format of a scientific paper (see Appendix entitled "Scientific Writing and Communication"). You should discuss results and come to conclusions with your team members; however, you must turn in an originally written lab report. Your Materials and Methods section and your tables and figures may be similar, but your Introduction, Results, and Discussion sections must be the product of your own library and online research, creative thinking, evaluating, and writing.

Remember, first complete Experiment A in each exercise. Then discuss with your research team a possible question for your original experiment, choosing one of the animals investigated in Experiment A as your experimental organism. Be certain you can pose an interesting question from which you can develop a testable hypothesis. Then turn to Experiment B in the exercise for your chosen organism and design and execute an experiment.

# EXERCISE 1
# Taxis in Brine Shrimp

Brine shrimp (*Artemia salina*) are small crustaceans that live in salt lakes and swim upside down using 11 pairs of appendages. Their sensory structures include two large compound eyes and two pairs of short antennae (Figure 1). They are a favorite fish food and can be purchased in pet stores.

**Figure 1.**
**Brine shrimp (*Artemia salina*) magnified about 20×.** A type of fairy shrimp, brine shrimp live in inland salt lakes such as the Great Salt Lake in Utah. Bruce Taylor/Bruce Coleman/Photoshot

# Experiment A. Brine Shrimp Behavior in Environments with Few Stimuli

## Materials

brine shrimp
2 large test tubes
black construction paper

1 small finger bowl
salt water
dropper

## Introduction

In this experiment, you will place brine shrimp in a test tube of salt water similar to the water of their normal environment. You will not feed them or disturb them in any way. You will observe their behavior in this relatively stimulus-free environment. Notice their positions in the test tube. Are they in groups, or are they solitary? Are they near the top or near the bottom? You should make careful observations of their behavior, asking questions about possible stimuli that might initiate taxes in these animals.

## Hypothesis

Hypothesize about the behavior of brine shrimp in an environment with few stimuli.

## Prediction

Predict the result of your experiment based on the hypothesis (if/then).

## Procedure

1. Place six brine shrimp in a test tube filled two-thirds with salt water. Rest the test tube in the finger bowl in such a way that you can easily see all six shrimp. You may need to use black construction paper as a background.

2. Describe the behavior of the brine shrimp in the Results section; for example, are they randomly distributed throughout the test tube or do they collect in one area?

3. Record your observations in the Results section.

## Results

1. By describing the behavior of brine shrimp in an environment with relatively few stimuli, which component of experimental design are you establishing?

2. Describe the behavior of the brine shrimp.

## Discussion

On separate paper, list four stimuli that might initiate taxes in brine shrimp and predict the response of the animal to each. What possible adaptive advantage could this behavior provide?

# Experiment B. Student-Designed Investigation of Brine Shrimp Behavior

## Materials

supplies from Experiment A
piece of black cloth
lamp

dropper bottles—solutions
of sugar, egg albumin, acid,
and base

## Introduction

If your team chooses to perform your original experiment investigating taxes in brine shrimp, return to this experiment after you have completed all the introductory investigations (Experiment A of each exercise). Using the materials available and collaborating with other members of your research team, design a simple experiment to investigate taxes in brine shrimp.

## Hypothesis

State the hypothesis that you will investigate.

## Prediction

Predict the results of your experiment based on your hypothesis (if/then).

## Procedure

 Allow a conditioning period of several minutes after the shrimp have been disturbed or stimulated. If you add something to the water in one experiment, begin additional experiments with fresh water and shrimp.

1. On separate paper, list in numerical order each step of your procedure. Remember to include the number of repetitions, levels of treatment, the duration of each stimulus, and other time intervals when appropriate.

2. If you have an idea for an experiment that requires materials other than those available, ask your laboratory instructor. If possible, additional supplies will be made available.

3. Quantify your data whenever possible (count, weigh, measure, time).

## Results

On separate paper, record your data and describe your results. You should design at least one table and figure.

## Discussion

1. Among members of your team, discuss your results in light of your hypothesis. If possible, come to conclusions about the behaviors you have been investigating. Record your conclusions on a separate paper.

2. You may be asked to report the results of your experiments to the class.

## EXERCISE 2
# Kinesis in Pill Bugs

Kinesis can be studied using a crustacean in the order Isopoda (called *isopods*). These animals are called by many common names, including *pill bugs, sow bugs, wood lice,* and *roly-polies* (Figure 2). Although most crustaceans are aquatic, pill bugs are truly terrestrial, and much of their behavior is involved with their need to avoid desiccation. They are easily collected in warm weather under flowerpots, in leaf litter, or in woodpiles. Some species respond to mechanical stimuli by rolling up into a ball.

## Experiment A. Pill Bug Behavior in Moist and Dry Environments

### Materials

pill bugs
2 large petri dishes

filter paper
squirt bottle of water

**Figure 2.**
**Pill bugs measure up to about 15 mm in length.** These terrestrial isopods are also called *sow bugs, wood lice,* and *roly-polies.* Veer Marketplace

## Introduction

In this experiment, you will investigate pill bug behavior in moist and dry environments by observing the degree of their activity, that is, the number of times they circle and turn. As you observe their behavior, ask questions about possible stimuli that might modify this behavior.

## Hypothesis

Hypothesize about the degree of activity of pill bugs in moist and dry environments.

## Prediction

Predict the results of the experiment based on your hypothesis (if/then).

## Procedure

1. Prepare two large petri dishes, one with wet filter paper, the other with dry filter paper.
2. Place five pill bugs in each dish.
3. Place the dishes in a dark spot, such as a drawer, for 5 minutes.
4. After 5 minutes, carefully observe the pill bugs in the petri dishes. Before you open the drawer or uncover the petri dishes, assign each of the following procedures to a member of your team.

   a. Count the number of pill bugs moving in each dish.

   b. Choose one moving pill bug in each dish and determine the rate of locomotion by counting revolutions per minute (rpm) around the petri dish.

c. Determine the rate of turning by counting turns (reversal of direction) per minute for one pill bug in each dish.

## Results

Record your results in Table 1.

### Table 1
Kinesis in Pill Bugs: Response to Wet and Dry Environments

| Environmental Condition | Number Moving | Rate of Locomotion (rpm) | Rate of Turning (turns/min) |
|---|---|---|---|
| Moist | | | |
| Dry | | | |

## Discussion

1. Kinetic response to varying moisture in the environment is called *hygrokinesis*. What other environmental factors might influence the behavior of pill bugs?

2. On separate paper, list four factors that might initiate kineses in pill bugs and predict their response to each. What possible adaptive advantage could this behavior provide?

3. Some terrestrial arthropods display a behavior where they avoid decaying organisms of their own species, but not other species. Can you suggest an adaptive advantage for this behavior? How would you design an experiment to test this?

# Experiment B. Student-Designed Investigation of Pill Bug Behavior

## Materials

supplies from Experiment A
white enamel pan
wax pencils
beaker of water

construction paper
manila folder
large pieces of black cloth

## Introduction

If your team chooses to perform your original experiment investigating kineses in pill bugs, return to this experiment after you have completed all the introductory investigations (Experiment A of each exercise). Using the materials available and collaborating with other members of your research team, design a simple experiment to investigate kineses in pill bugs.

## Hypothesis

State the hypothesis that you will investigate.

## Prediction

Predict the results of the experiment based on your hypothesis (if/then).

## Procedure

1. On separate paper, list in numerical order each step of your procedure. Remember to include the number of repetitions, the levels of treatment, the duration of stimulus, and other time intervals where appropriate.
2. If you have an idea for an experiment that requires materials other than those available, ask your laboratory instructor. If possible, additional supplies will be made available.
3. Quantify your data whenever possible (count, weigh, measure, time).

## Results

On separate paper, record your data and describe your results. You should design at least one table and figure.

## Discussion

1. Among members of your team, discuss your results in light of your hypothesis. If possible, come to conclusions about the behaviors you have been investigating. Record your conclusions on a separate paper.
2. You may be asked to report the results of your experiments to the class.

---

EXERCISE 3

# Agonistic Display in Male Siamese Fighting Fish

---

The innate agonistic behavior of the male Siamese fighting fish (*Betta splendens*) has been widely studied (Simpson, 1968; Thompson, 1969). The sight of another male *Betta* or even its own reflection in a mirror will stimulate a ritualized series of responses toward the intruder. If two fish are placed in the same aquarium, their agonistic behavior usually continues until one fish is defeated or subordinated (see Color Plate 70).

# Experiment A. Display Behavior in Male Siamese Fighting Fish

## Materials

male Siamese fighting fish in a 1- to 2-L flat-sided fishbowl
mirror
watch (must record seconds, one per student)

## Introduction

The purpose of this experiment is to describe the ritualized agonistic display of a male Siamese fighting fish after being stimulated by its own reflection in a mirror. Before you begin the experiment, become familiar with the fish's anatomy, identifying its dorsal, caudal (tail), anal, pectoral, and ventral (pelvic) fins, and its gill cover (Figure 3 and Color Plate 70).

When you begin the experiment, you will be looking for several possible responses: frontal approach (facing intruder), broadside display, undulating movements, increased swimming speed, and enhanced coloration in tail, fin, or body. You should note the duration and intensity of elevation for each fin and changes in the gill cover.

## Hypothesis

Hypothesize about the response of the fish to its image in the mirror.

## Prediction

Predict the result of the experiment based on your hypothesis (if/then).

## Procedure

1. Plan your strategy.

   a. Be ready with your pencil and paper to record your observations. Behaviors can happen very quickly. Your entire team should observe and record them.

**Figure 3.**
**Male Siamese fighting fish (*Betta splendens*).** Thinkstock

b. Each team member should be responsible for timing the beginning and duration of particular responses (listed in the Introduction). For example, one or two team members will observe the response in one or two specific fins and record their results in Table 2 of the Results section. Another team member will observe more general responses, such as "increased swimming speed" or "broadside display for 60 seconds."

2. Place the mirror against the fishbowl.

3. As the fish reacts to its reflection, record your observations in the table or on separate paper.

4. Compare collective results.

5. In the Results section, using the time you present the mirror as time zero, make a *sequential* list of the recognizable responses involved in the display. Be as quantitative as possible; for example, you might record "gill cover extended 90° for 30 seconds," or "broadside display for 60 seconds."

6. Note in the Results section those responses that take place simultaneously.

## Results

1. Record your data for each response in Table 2. Consider the time when you place the mirror next to the fishbowl as time zero. Then note how many seconds lapse before the specific response and its intensity. Use these symbols as estimates of response intensity: - (none), + (slight response), + + (moderate response), + + + (intense response).

### Table 2
Behaviors, Response Times, and Response Intensity for Siamese Fighting Fish Presented with a Mirror Stimulus

| Response | Time Before Response (seconds) | Intensity - (none), + (slight), + + (moderate), + + + (intense) |
|---|---|---|
| Fish notices mirror | | |
| Approaches mirror | | |
| Dorsal fin flare | | |
| Caudal fin (tail) flare | | |
| Anal fin flare | | |
| Ventral fin flare | | |
| Pectoral fin flare | | |
| Gill cover flare | | |

2. Record your sequential list.

3. Record the responses that take place simultaneously.

## Discussion

1. Collaborating with your teammates, write a descriptive paragraph, as quantitative and detailed as possible, describing the agonistic display elicited in the Siamese fighting fish in response to its reflection.

2. Consult your text for the definition of the behavior called *fixed action pattern*. Do you conclude that agonistic behavior in Siamese fighting fish is an example of this type of behavior? Why or why not?

3. What is the obvious adaptive advantage of complex agonistic displays that are not followed by damaging fights? Are there advantages that are not so obvious?

4. Name several other animals that demonstrate a strong display that is seldom followed by a damaging fight.

5. Name several animals that do engage in damaging fights.

## Experiment B. Student-Designed Investigation of Siamese Fighting Fish Behavior

### Materials

| | |
|---|---|
| supplies from Experiment A | wooden applicator sticks |
| colored pencils and index cards or | transparent tape |
| brightly colored paper | fish of different species in fishbowls |
| scissors | female Siamese fighting fish |

### Introduction

If your team chooses to perform your original experiment investigating agonistic behavior in Siamese fighting fish, return to this experiment after you have completed all the introductory investigations (Experiment A of each exercise). Using the materials available and collaborating among your research team, design a simple experiment to investigate this behavior.

Discuss with your team members possible investigations that might be carried out. Several questions follow that might give you ideas.

1. What is the simplest stimulus that will initiate the response? Is color important? Size? Movement?

2. Is the behavior "released" by a specific stimulus or by a complex of all the stimuli?

3. Will another species of fish initiate the response?

4. Will a female *Betta* fish initiate the response, and, if so, how does the response compare with the response to a fish of a different species?

5. Is the response all or none—that is, are there partial displays with different stimuli?

6. Does the fish become "conditioned"—that is, after repeated identical stimuli, does the duration of the display change, or does the display cease?

7. Could chemical stimulation contribute to the response? (Transfer water from one fishbowl to another.)

## Hypothesis

After your team has decided on one or more questions to investigate, formulate a testable hypothesis.

## Prediction

Predict the results of the experiment based on your hypothesis (if/then).

## Procedure

1. On separate paper, list in numerical order each step of your procedure. Remember to include the number of repetitions, the levels of treatment, the duration of a stimulus, and other time intervals where appropriate.
2. If you have an idea for an experiment that requires materials other than those available, ask your laboratory instructor. If possible, additional supplies will be made available.
3. Quantify your data whenever possible (count, weigh, measure, time).

## Results

On separate paper, design a table and then record your data. Describe your results. Create a figure to illustrate some aspect of your results. Your Results section should include at least one table and one figure.

## Discussion

1. Among members of your team, discuss your results in light of your hypothesis. If possible, come to conclusions about the behaviors you have been investigating. Record your conclusions on a separate paper.
2. You may be asked to report the results of your experiments to the class.

EXERCISE 4

# Reproductive Behavior in Fruit Flies

Reproductive behavior in some animals involves a complex sequence of activities that may include courtship and mating. Spieth (1952, described in Marler, 1968) has classified courtship and mating behavior of the fruit fly *Drosophila melanogaster* as being a complex of at least 14 behaviors.

Courtship behavior in these animals is an example of a *stimulus-response chain*. The response to a stimulus becomes the stimulus for the next behavior. If there is no response, then the behavior changes. Described below are 10 of the most common and easily recognized of these behaviors. Read the list carefully and become familiar with the behaviors you will be required to recognize. Six of the behaviors are seen in males, four in females. The behavior sequence begins as the male orients his body toward the female (Figure 4a).

## Male Behaviors

1. *Tapping.* The forelegs are extended to strike or tap the female (tactile communication) (Figure 4b).

2. *Waving.* The wing is extended and held 90° from the body, then relaxed without vibration (Figure 4c).

3. *Wing vibration.* The male extends one or both wings from the resting position and moves them rapidly up and down (producing a courtship song—auditory communication) (Figure 4c).

4. *Licking.* The male licks the female's genitalia (on the rear of her abdomen) (Figure 4d).

5. *Circling.* The male postures and then circles the female, usually when she is nonreceptive.

6. *Stamping.* The male stamps forefeet as in tapping but does not strike the female.

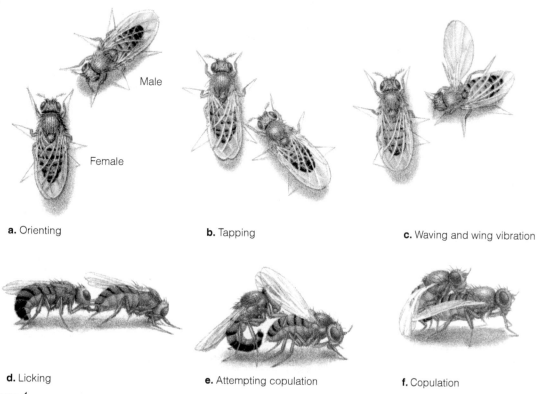

**a.** Orienting    **b.** Tapping    **c.** Waving and wing vibration

**d.** Licking    **e.** Attempting copulation    **f.** Copulation

**Figure 4.**

**Mating behavior in fruit fly, *Drosophila melanogaster*.** From R. J. Greenspan. 1995. Understanding the genetic construction of behavior. *Scientific American*, April 1995, pp. 72-73, figures 1-6. Illustrations copyright © by Suzanne Barnes

## Female Behaviors

1. *Extruding.* A temporary, tubelike structure is extended from the female's genitalia.
2. *Decamping.* A nonreceptive female runs, jumps, or flies away from the courting male.
3. *Depressing.* A nonreceptive female prevents access to her genitalia by depressing her wings and curling the tip of her abdomen down.
4. *Ignoring.* A nonreceptive female ignores the male.

If the behavior display is successful, the flies will copulate (Figure 4e, f).

# Experiment A. Reproductive Behavior in *Drosophila melanogaster*

## Materials

stereoscopic microscope
fly vials with 2 or 3 virgin female *D. melanogaster* flies
fly vials with 2 or 3 male *D. melanogaster* flies

## Introduction

In this experiment, you will place virgin female *D. melanogaster* flies in the same vial with male flies and observe the behavior of each sex. Working with another student, discuss the behaviors described in the introduction to this exercise and plan the strategy for your experiment. Identify mating behaviors of *D. melanogaster* and record their sequence and duration (when appropriate). As you observe the behavior of the flies, discuss possible original experiments investigating courtship and mating behavior in flies.

## Hypothesis

Hypothesize about the presence of flies of the opposite sex in the same vial.

## Prediction

Predict the results of the experiment based on your hypothesis (if/then).

## Procedure

1. Set up the stereoscopic microscope.
2. Have paper and pencil ready. The behaviors can happen very rapidly. One person should call out observations while the other person records.

3. Obtain one vial containing virgin females and one vial containing males, and gently tap the male flies into the vial containing females.

4. Observe first with the naked eye. Once flies have encountered each other, use the stereoscopic microscope to make observations.

### Results

1. Describe, in sequence, the response of the male to the female and the female to the male. Quantify your observations. To do this, you may consider counting the number of times a behavior takes place and timing the duration of behaviors.

2. Describe rejection if this takes place.

3. In the margin of your lab manual, note any behaviors that can be analyzed quantitatively.

### Discussion

Speculate about the adaptive advantage of elaborate courtship behaviors in animals.

## Experiment B. Student-Designed Investigation of Reproductive Behavior in Fruit Flies

### Materials

supplies from Experiment A
fly vials with 2 or 3 virgin females of an alternate fly species (other than *D. melanogaster*)

fly vials with 2 or 3 males of the alternate species (other

### Introduction

If your team chooses to perform your original experiment investigating courtship and mating behavior in fruit flies, continue with this experiment after you have completed all the introductory investigations (Experiment A of each exercise). Using the materials available and collaborating with your research partner, design a simple experiment to investigate this behavior. Several questions follow that might provide ideas.

1. Will courtship and mating in another species be identical to that in *D. melanogaster*?
2. Will males placed in the same vial demonstrate courtship behaviors?
3. Will males respond to dead females?
4. What is the response of a male *D. melanogaster* to females of a different species?
5. Do males compete?

Quantify your observations. To do this, you may consider counting the number of times a behavior takes place or timing the duration of behaviors.

## Hypothesis

After your team has decided on one or more questions to investigate, formulate a testable hypothesis.

## Prediction

Predict the results of your experiment based on your hypothesis (if/then).

## Procedure

1. On a separate paper, list in numerical order each step of your procedure. Remember to include the number of repetitions, the levels of treatment, the duration of stimulus, and other time intervals where appropriate.
2. If you have an idea for an experiment that requires materials other than those available, ask your laboratory instructor. If possible, additional supplies will be made available.
3. Quantify your data whenever possible (count, weigh, measure, time).

## Results

On a separate paper, record your data and describe your results. You should design at least one table and figure.

## Discussion

1. Within your team, discuss your results in light of your hypothesis. If possible, come to conclusions about the behaviors you have been investigating. Record your conclusions on a separate paper.
2. You may be asked to report the results of your experiments to the class.

# Reviewing Your Knowledge

Define, compare, and give examples for each item in the following pairs.

1. Learned behavior—innate behavior
2. Proximate cause of behavior—ultimate cause of behavior

3. Causal explanation for a behavior—anthropomorphic explanation for a behavior

4. Taxis—kinesis

Define the following terms.

1. Fixed action pattern

2. Stimulus-response chain

# Applying Your Knowledge

1. Adult male European robins have red feathers on their breasts. A male robin will display aggressive behavior and attack another male robin that invades his territory during mating season. Immature male robins with all brown feathers do not elicit this behavior in the adult robin. How could you explain this behavior? Design an experiment to test your explanation (hypothesis).

2. Bees, ants, and other social insects are able to detect and will remove dead organisms from their colony. Scientists have analyzed decaying insects and found they give off compounds—mostly oleic acid and linoleic acid—as they decay. You know that social insects display some of the most complex behaviors in response to environmental stimuli of any other animal groups. In lab today, you learned that it is possible to explain behaviors based on anthropomorphic causes, but that scientists base explanations on proximate and ultimate causes (see Lab Topic Introduction). Using bees as the experimental animals, in the space below, propose explanations (hypotheses) based on these three perspectives—anthropomorphic, proximate, and ultimate—and then propose a research project for those hypotheses that can be tested scientifically.

a. Anthropomorphic causes:

Possible research project:

b. Proximate causes:

Possible research project:

c. Ultimate causes:

Could an experiment similar to this be used to investigate ancestors of insects and isopods and to answer questions about when these groups diverged?

 **Student Media: BioFlix, Activities, Investigations, and Videos**
www.masteringbiology.com (select Study Area)

**Activities**—Ch. 51: Honeybee Waggle Dance Video
**Investigations**—Ch. 51: How Can Pillbug Responses to Environments Be Tested?
   LabBench: Animal Behavior
**Videos**—Ch. 51: Ducklings; Chimp Cracking Nut; Snake Ritual Wrestling; Albatross Courtship Ritual; Blue-footed Boobies Courtship Ritual; Chimp Agonistic Behavior; Wolves Agonistic Behavior; Giraffe Courtship Ritual

# References

Alcock, J. *Animal Behavior: An Evolutionary Approach,* 9th ed. Sunderland, MA: Sinauer Associates, 2009.

Gould, J. L. *Ethology: The Mechanisms and Evolution of Behavior.* New York, NY: W. W. Norton & Company, 1982.

Greenspan, R. J. "Understanding the Genetic Construction of Behavior." *Scientific American,* 1995, vol. 272(4) p. 72.

Johnson, R. N. *Aggression in Man and Animals.* Philadelphia, PA: Saunders College Publishing, 1972.

Marler, P. "Mating Behavior of *Drosophila*." In *Animal Behavior in Laboratory and Field,* editor A. W. Stokes. San Francisco, CA: Freeman, 1968.

Reebs, S. "Death Whiff." *Natural History,* October 2009. (pill bugs' response to their dead)

Raham, G. "Pill Bug Biology." *The American Biology Teacher,* 1986, vol. 48(1).

Reece, J. et al. *Campbell Biology,* 9th ed. San Francisco, CA: Pearson Education, 2011.

Simpson, M. J. A. "The Threat Display of the Siamese Fighting Fish, *Betta splendens*." *Animal Behavior Monograph,* 1968, vol. 1, p. 1.

Thompson, T. "Aggressive Behavior of Siamese Fighting Fish," in *Aggressive Behavior,* editors S. Garattini and E. B. Sigg. Proceedings of the International Symposium on the Biology of Aggressive Behavior. New York, NY: Wiley, 1969.

Waterman, M., and E. Stanley. *Biological Inquiry: A Workbook of Investigative Cases.* San Francisco, CA:

Pearson Benjamin Cummings, 2011. In this supplement to Campbell Biology, 9th ed., see "Back to the Bay," a case study applying principles of animal behavior to an environmental problem.

## Websites

Animal Behavior Society Website. The education section describes experiments submitted by college professors suitable for independent projects. Select Education and Behavior.
http://animalbehaviorsociety.org/

J. Kimball's online discussion of innate behavior: http://users.rcn.com/jkimball.ma.ultranet/BiologyPages/I/InnateBehavior.html

Overview of topics in animal behavior: http://cas.bellarmine.edu/tietjen/animal_behavior_and_ethology.htm

# Appendix
# Scientific Writing and Communication

For the scientific enterprise to be successful, scientists must clearly communicate their work. Scientific findings are never kept secret. Instead, scientists share their ideas and results with other scientists, encouraging critical review and alternative interpretations from colleagues and the entire scientific community. Communication, both oral and written, occurs at every step along the research path. While working on projects, scientists present their preliminary results for comments from their co-workers at laboratory group meetings and in written research reports. At a later stage, scientists report the results of their research activities as a poster or oral presentation at a scientific meeting. Then the final report is prepared in a rather standard scientific paper format and submitted for publication in an appropriate scientific journal. At each stage in this process, scientists encourage and require critical review of their work and ideas by their peers. The final publication in a peer-reviewed journal generally promotes additional research and establishes this contribution to current knowledge.

One of the objectives of every lab topic is to develop your writing skills. You will generate and write hypotheses, observations, answers to questions, and more, as one way of learning biology. Also, you will practice writing in a scientific paper format and style to communicate the results of your investigations. The scientific process is reflected in the design of a scientific paper and the format you will use for your laboratory papers.

A scientific paper usually includes the following parts: a **Title** (statement of the question or problem), an **Abstract** (short summary of the paper), an **Introduction** (background and significance of the problem), a **Materials and Methods** section (report of exactly what you did), a **Results** section (presentation of data), a **Discussion** section (interpretation and discussion of results), and **References Cited** (books and periodicals used). A **Conclusion** (concise restatement of conclusions) and **Acknowledgments** (recognition of assistance) may also be included.

We propose that you practice writing throughout the biology laboratory program by submitting individual sections of a scientific paper. Your instructor will determine which sections you will write for a given lab topic and will evaluate each of these sections, pointing out areas of weakness and suggesting improvements. By the time you have completed these assignments, you will have submitted the equivalent of one scientific paper. Having practiced writing each section of a scientific paper in the first half of the laboratory program, you will then write one or two complete laboratory papers in scientific paper format during the second half of the laboratory program, reporting the results of experiments, preferably those that you and your research team have designed and performed.

# Successful Scientific Writing

The following notes for success apply to writing throughout all sections of a scientific paper.

- Your writing should be clear and concise. Delete unnecessary words—for example, adjectives and adverbs have limited use in describing your work. Write clearly in short and logical, but not choppy, sentences. Avoid run-on sentences and use grammatically correct English. Avoid long introductions. (See Appendix 4, "Sentences Requiring Revision," in Knisely [2005] for basic rules of writing and practice in editing for common errors.)

- Your audience is your peers, other student-scientists. Write as though they are scientists: professional and knowledgeable.

- Use the past tense in the Abstract, Materials and Methods, and Results sections. Also use the past tense in the Introduction and Discussion sections when referring to *your* work. Use the present tense when relating the background information as you refer to other investigator's published work. Previously published research is considered established in the present body of knowledge.

- Use the active voice whenever possible. Doing so makes the paper easier to read and more understandable. However, in the Materials and Methods section you may use the passive voice so that the focus of your writing is the methodology, rather than the investigator.

- When referring to the scientific name of an organism, the genus and species should be in italics or underlined. The first letter of the genus is capitalized, but the species is written in lowercase letters, for example, *Drosophila melanogaster.*

- Use metric units for all measurements. Use numerals when reporting measurements, percentages, decimals, and magnifications. When beginning a sentence, write the number as a word. Numbers of ten or less that are not measurements are written out. Numbers greater than ten are given as numerals. Decimal numbers less than one should have a zero in the one position (e.g., 0.153; not .153).

- Clearly label each section (except the title page), placing the title of the section against the left margin on a separate line. Each section does not begin a new page but continues in order.

- Begin writing early to allow time for researching your topic, analyzing your results, and revising your writing. Revise, revise, and then revise! For suggestions and examples of how to revise your work, see Chapter 5, "Revision," in Knisely (2005) and Chapter 5, "Revising," in Pechenik (2007).

- Note the word "data" is plural.

- Remember the results cannot "prove" the hypothesis, but rather they may "support" or "falsify" the hypothesis.

- Carefully proofread your work even if your word processor has checked for grammatical and spelling errors. These programs cannot distinguish between "your" and "you're," for example.

- Save a copy of your work on a disk or USB flash drive, and print a copy of your paper before turning in the original.

## Plagiarism

Students will write their papers independently. Because performing the experiment will be a collaborative effort, you and your teammates will share the results of your investigation. The Introduction, Discussion, and References Cited (or References) sections must be the product of your own personal library research and creative thinking. If you are not certain about the level of independence and what constitutes plagiarism in this laboratory program, ask your instructor to clarify the class policy. *In the most extreme case of plagiarism, a student presents another student's report as his or her own. However, representing another person's ideas as your own without giving that person credit is also plagiarism and is a serious offense.*

## Plan for Writing a Scientific Paper

The sections of a scientific paper and particular material to be covered in each section are described in this appendix in order of appearance in the paper. However, most scientists do not follow that sequence in the actual writing of the paper, but rather begin with the methodology. A typical plan for writing a scientific paper follows.

- Begin writing the Materials and Methods section. The first draft of this section can be written before all the results are completed. Remember to review and carefully edit after completing all work. (See Materials and Methods)

- Construct the tables and figures. Compose the text for the Results section based on the tables and figures. (See Results)

- Consult references for background information and interpretation of results. Locate and review primary and secondary references for use in the Discussion and Introduction sections. (See References Cited)

- Develop the Introduction section and begin the References Cited section. (See Introduction and References Cited) Most scientists prefer to write the Introduction before the Discussion. Both sections require background information and a clear understanding of the results of the work. Remember to carefully check and revise your Introduction if you write it first.

- Write the Discussion section and complete the References Cited section. (See Discussion)

- Write the Title and Abstract.

- Review checklist, if available, before preparing final version of the paper. (Remember to leave time for revisions.)

## Title Page and Title

The title page is the first page of the paper and includes the title of the paper, your name, the course title, your lab time or section, your instructor's name, and the due date for the paper. *The title should be as short as possible and as long as necessary to communicate to the reader the question being answered in the paper.* For example, if you are asking a question about the inheritance patterns of the gene for aldehyde oxidase production in *Drosophila melanogaster,* a possible title might be "Inheritance of the Gene for Aldehyde Oxidase in *Drosophila melanogaster.*" Something like "Inheritance in Fruit Flies" is too general, and "A Study of the Inheritance of the Enzyme Aldehyde Oxidase in the Fruit Fly

*Drosophila melanogaster*" is too wordy. The words "A Study of the" are superfluous, and "Enzyme" and "Fruit Fly" are redundant. The suffix *-ase* indicates that aldehyde oxidase is an enzyme, and most scientists know that *Drosophila melanogaster* is the scientific name of a common fruit fly species. However, it is appropriate to include in the title both common and scientific names of lesser known species.

Place the title about 7 cm from the top of the title page. Place "by" and your name in the center of the page, and place the course name, lab section, instructor's name, and due date, each on a separate centered line, at the bottom of the page. Leave about 5 cm below this information.

## Abstract

The abstract, if one is requested by the instructor, is placed at the beginning of the second page of the paper, after the title page. *The abstract concisely summarizes the question being investigated in the paper, the methods used in the experiment, the results, and the conclusions drawn.* The reader should be able to determine the major topics in the paper without reading the entire paper. The abstract should be no more than 250 words, and fewer if possible. Compose the abstract after the paper is completed.

## Introduction

*The introduction has two functions: (1) to provide the context for your investigation and (2) to state the question asked and the hypothesis tested in the study.* Begin the introduction by reviewing background information that will enable the reader to understand the objective of the study and the significance of the problem, relating the problem to the larger issues in the field. Include only information that directly prepares the reader to understand the question investigated. Most ideas in the introduction will come from outside sources, such as scientific journals or books dealing with the topic you are investigating. All sources of information must be referenced and included in the References Cited (or References) section of the paper, but the introduction must be in your own words. Refer to the references when appropriate. Unless otherwise instructed, place the author of the reference cited and the year of publication in parentheses at the end of the sentence or paragraph relating the idea; for example, (Finnerty, 1992). Additional information on citing references is provided in the section References Cited. Do not use citation forms utilized in other disciplines. Do not use footnotes and avoid the use of direct quotes.

As you describe your investigation, include only the question and hypothesis that you finally investigated. Briefly describe the experiment performed and the outcome predicted for the experiment. Although these items are usually presented after the background information near the end of the introduction, you should have each clearly in mind before you begin writing the introduction. It is a good idea to write down each item (question, hypothesis, prediction) before you begin to write your introduction.

# Materials and Methods

*The Materials and Methods section describes your experiment in such a way that it can be repeated. This section should be a narrative description that integrates the materials with the procedures used in the investigation.* Do not list the materials and do not list the steps of the procedure. Rather, write the Materials and Methods section concisely in paragraph form in the past tense. Be sure to include levels of treatment, numbers of replications, and controls. If you are working with living organisms, include the scientific name and the sex of the organism if that information is relevant to the experiment. If you used computer software or any statistical analyses, include these in the Materials and Methods section.

The difficulty in writing this section comes as you decide the level of detail to include in your paragraphs. You must determine which details are essential for another investigator to repeat the experiment. For example, if in your experiment you incubated potato pieces in different concentrations of sucrose solution, it would not be necessary to explain that the pieces were incubated in plastic cups labeled with a wax marking pencil or to provide the numbers of the cups. In this case, the molarity of the sucrose solutions, the size of the potato pieces and how they were obtained, and the amount of incubation solution are the important items to include. Do not include failed attempts unless the technique used may be tried by other investigators. Do not try to justify your procedures in this section.

The Materials and Methods section is often the best place to begin writing your paper. The writing is straightforward and concise, and you will be reminded of the details of the work.

# Results

The Results section consists of at least four components: (1) one or two sentences reminding the reader about the nature of the research, (2) one or more paragraphs that describe the results, (3) figures (graphs, diagrams, pictures), and (4) tables. *The Results section is the central section of a scientific paper.* Therefore, you should think carefully about the best way to present your results to the reader. The data included in tables and graphs should be summarized and emphasized in the narrative paragraph. Draw the reader's attention to the results that are important. Describe trends in your data and provide evidence to support your claims. This section also is written in the past tense.

Before writing the Results section, prepare the tables and figures. Remember to number figures and tables consecutively throughout the paper. Refer to figures and tables within the paragraph as you describe your results, using the word Figure or Table, followed by its number; for example, (Figure 1). If possible, place each figure or table at the end of the paragraph in which it is cited.

If you have performed a statistical analysis of your data, such as chi-square, include the results in this section.

Report your data as accurately as possible. Do not report what you expected to happen in the experiment nor whether your data supported your hypothesis. Do not discuss the meaning of your results in this section. Do not critique the results. Any data you plan to include in the Discussion section must be presented in the Results. Conversely, do not include data in the Results that you do not mention in the Discussion.

Write the Results section before attempting the Discussion section. This will ensure that the results of your investigation are clearly organized, logically presented, and thoroughly understood before they are discussed. For this reason, some scientists begin with the Results section when writing a paper.

## Discussion

*In the Discussion section, you will analyze and interpret the results of your experiment.* Simply restating the results is not interpretation. The Discussion must provide a context for understanding the significance of the results. Explain why you observed these results and how these results contribute to our knowledge. Your results either will support or confirm your hypothesis or will negate, refute, or contradict your hypothesis; but the word *prove* is not appropriate in scientific writing. If your results do not support your hypothesis, you must still state why you think this occurred. Support your ideas from other work (books, lectures or outside reading of scientific literature). State your conclusions in this section.

Complete your Introduction and Results sections before you begin writing the Discussion. The figures and tables in the Results section will be particularly important as you begin to think about your discussion. The tables allow you to present your results clearly to the reader, and graphs allow you to visualize the effects that the independent variable has had on the dependent variables in your experiment. Studying these data will be one of the first steps in interpreting your results. As you study the information in the Introduction section and your data in the Results section, write down relationships and integrate these relationships into a rough draft of your discussion.

The following steps may be helpful as you begin to outline your discussion and before you write the narrative:

- Restate your question, hypothesis, and prediction.
- Write down the specific data, including results of statistical tests.
- State whether your results did or did not confirm your prediction and support or negate your hypothesis.
- Write down what you know about the biology involved in your experiment. How do your results fit in with what you know? What is the significance of your results?
- How do your results support or conflict with previous work? Include references to this work.
- Clearly state your conclusions.
- List weaknesses you have identified in your experimental design that affected your results. The weaknesses of the experiment should not, however, dominate the Discussion. *Include one or two sentences only if these problems affected the results.* Remember the focus of the Discussion is to convey the significance of the results.
- You are now ready to write the narrative for the Discussion. Integrate all of the above information into several simple, clear, concise paragraphs. Discuss the results; do not simply restate the data. Refer to other work to support your ideas.

# References Cited (or References)

A References Cited section lists only those references cited in the paper. A References section (bibliography), on the other hand, is a more inclusive list of all references used in producing the paper, including books and papers used to obtain background knowledge that may not be cited in the paper. Most references will be cited in the Introduction and Discussion sections of your paper. For your paper you should have a References Cited section that includes only those references cited in the paper.

## Locating Appropriate References

Textbooks and review articles are an excellent starting place for developing background information for your independent investigations. Consult texts and books that are more specific than your general biology textbook. For example, if your project is on plant hormones, you might consult a plant physiology textbook to provide foundational information. Books will often have lists of articles and other references that may be helpful. (Also see the References section for each Lab Topic in this manual.) Textbooks, review articles, and articles from popular science magazines are **secondary references,** which generally provide a summary and interpretation of research (for example, *Annual Review of Genetics, Science News,* and *Scientific American*).

Scientific papers in general rely on **primary references,** reports of original research that present the work of scientists in such a way that it can be repeated. Primary references are journal articles that have been reviewed by other scientists and the journal editor. In addition to articles in journals (e.g., *American Journal of Botany, Cell, Ecology,* and *Science*), primary references include conference papers, dissertations, and technical reports. Many scientific journals are available in a full-text version online; these are still primary references. However, websites are not primary references, because they are not required to participate in the peer review process. Your instructor will indicate the number of primary references required for your paper. Gillen (2007) provides useful suggestions for how to read and evaluate scientific papers.

Record the citation information for any references, including online sources, at the time you read the information. Refer to the citation format to record the complete citation.

## Examples of Reference Citations

The format for the References Cited section differs slightly from one scientific journal to the next. How does an author know which format to use? Every scientific journal provides "Instructions to Authors" that describe specific requirements for this important section and all other aspects of the paper. You may use the format used in this lab manual and provided in the examples below, select the format in a scientific journal provided by your instructor, or use another accepted format for listing your references. Your instructor may provide additional instructions. Be sure to read the references that you cite in your paper.

Journal article, one author:

> Whittaker, R. H. "New Concepts of Kingdoms of Organisms." *Science,* 1969, vol. 163, pp. 150–160.

Journal article, two or more authors:

> Watson, J. D., and F. H. Crick. "Molecular Structure of Nucleic Acids: A Structure for Deoxyribose Nucleic Acid." *Nature,* 1953, vol. 171, pp. 737–738.

Book:

> Darwin, C. R. *On the Origin of Species.* London: John Murray, 1859.

Chapter or article in an edited book:

> Baker, H. G. "Characteristics and Modes of Origin of Weeds," in *Genetics and Colonizing Species,* eds. H. G. Baker and G. L. Stebbins. New York: Academic Press, 1965, pp. 147–152.

Government publication:

> Office of Technology Assessment. *Harmful Non-indigenous Species in the United States.* Publication no. OTA-F-565. Washington, D.C.: U.S. Government Printing Office, 1993.

### Citing References in Text

In the text of the paper, cite the references using the author's name and the year. For example: "The innate agonistic behavior of the male Siamese fighting fish has been widely studied (Simpson, 1968)." "Simpson (1968) has described the agonistic behavior of the male Siamese fighting fish." *If there are more than two authors,* use the first author's name followed by *et al.* (and others). For example: (Simpson *et al.,* 1968).

## Using Information Sources from the Internet

The Internet can provide access to online reference resources and databases including *Biological Abstracts, Current Contents, Medline,* and *Annual Reviews* among many others. These search tools provide access to a wide range of published papers, some of which may be available online as full text journals. For suggestions and examples of how to locate sources using the Internet, see Harnack and Kleppinger (2003) and Knisely (2005). Scientific papers published in professional journals have gone through an extensive review process by other scientists in the same field. Most scientific articles have been revised based on comments by the reviewers and the editors. Sources of information that lack this critical review process do not have the same validity and authority.

The Internet is an exciting, immediate, and easily accessible source of information. However, unlike traditional bibliographic resources in the sciences, the Internet includes websites with material that has not been critically reviewed. Your instructor may prefer that you use the Internet only for locating peer-reviewed primary references or as a starting point to promote your interest and ideas. You may not be allowed to use Internet sources at all. Consult your instructor concerning use of Internet information.

If you do use the Internet to locate information, you should be prepared to evaluate these sites critically. Remember always to record the online address for any site you use as a reference. Tate and Alexander (1996) suggest the following five criteria for evaluating Internet sources:

1. **Authority.** Determine the author and sponsor for the Internet site. What is the professional affiliation of the author? Are phone numbers and addresses included? Is there a link to the sponsor's home page? Does the author list his or her qualifications? If the material is copyrighted, who owns the copyright?

2. **Accuracy.** Look for indications of professional standards for writing, citations, figures, and tables. Are there typographical, spelling, and grammatical errors? Are sources of information cited? Are the data presented or simply summarized?

3. **Objectivity.** Is the site provided as a public service, free of advertising? If advertising is present, is it clearly separate from the information? Does the site present only the view of the sponsor or advertiser?

4. **Currency.** Determine the date of the site and whether it is regularly revised. How long has the site existed? When was it last updated? Are figures and tables dated? Some Internet sites disappear overnight. Always record the date that you visited the site and retrieved information.

5. **Coverage.** Is the information offered in a complete form or as an abstract or summary of information published elsewhere? Is the site under construction? When was the site last revised?

Below find a model format and examples for citing Internet sources in the References Cited section of your paper. Other formats may be suggested by your instructor or librarian.

**Model:**

Author's last name and initials. Date of Internet publication. Document title. <URL> or other retrieval information. Date of access.

**Examples:**

(Professional site)

[CBE] Council of Biology Editors. 1999, Oct. 5. CBE home page. <http://www.councilscienceeditors.org>. Accessed Oct. 7, 1999.

(e-journal)

Browning T. 1997. Embedded visuals: Student design in Web spaces. *Kairos: A Journal for Teachers of Writing in Webbed Environments* 3(1). <http://english.ttu.edu/kairos/2.1/features/browning/bridge.html>. Accessed Oct. 4, 1999.

(Government publication)

Food and Drug Administration, 1996, Sep. "Outsmarting Poison Ivy and Its Cousins." *FDA Consumer Magazine*. <http://www.fda.gov/fdac/features/796_ivy.html>. Accessed Aug. 9, 2004.

# Oral and Poster Presentations

## Oral Presentations

In this laboratory program you may be asked to give an oral report on your experiments in laboratory or in a research symposium. Following are suggestions to help you prepare and present oral reports.

Oral reports should include all the components of a scientific paper, with an Introduction, Procedures, Results, Discussion, and Conclusions. In your introduction, provide background information, state your hypothesis, give a brief description of your experiment, and state your predicted results. Briefly discuss the procedures, and then use clear figures and tables to present your results. Follow this with your discussion and conclusions. You may suggest ideas for the next step—further experiments that should be performed. Be prepared to answer questions.

For your 10–15-minute presentation, you need to capture the interest of your audience and make a convincing presentation of your results and conclusions. Pay attention to your presentation delivery. Use simple, bold visual aids that are easily visible from the back of the room. These may be overhead transparencies or slides prepared using PowerPoint. For information on preparing PowerPoint slides, see Knisley (2005) and www.Dartmouth.edu/~biomed/new.htmld/ppt_resources.shtml. As you speak, look at your audience, speaking slowly and clearly, projecting your voice so all members of the audience can hear you. Keep your objective in mind—to clearly communicate your ideas. A checklist and other suggestions for preparing successful oral presentations may be found in McMillan, 2006.

## Poster Presentations

Another form of scientific communication that has become popular in recent years is the scientific poster, a large document usually created on a single, large sheet. If a large printer is not available, a poster may be created on a multiple-paneled mat board. Most scientific societies are now organizing poster sessions at their annual meetings, often featuring undergraduate and graduate student research. Your instructor may ask you to model this form of communication by preparing a poster about your student-designed investigations or extended research projects as part of a poster symposium.

In many situations, posters may be a more effective method of presentation than writing a scientific paper or giving an oral report. While a scientific paper may be read only by the instructor, a poster may be prominently displayed for a wider audience for an extended period. The presenters are then available at designated times to explain the research and engage in meaningful discussion. A poster presents the essentials of a research project in a format with minimal text. Creating a poster that will immediately attract interested persons should be your first objective, since studies show that you have only 11 seconds to grab their attention. In the same way that a scientific paper has a specific format and organization, a scientific poster must also follow several basic rules of organization and presentation. Include the sections of a scientific paper—Title, Introduction, Experiment Summary, Results, Discussion, and References. Present the main sections in large typeface headings and the content in abbreviated format under each, in fonts that are readable from 6–10 feet away. Include simple figures and tables.

Your instructor may give specific guidelines for your poster, or you may follow guidelines from other sources. There are several excellent websites with instructions for preparing posters. One of the most complete and well-designed sites is http://www.Swarthmore.edu/NatSci/cpurrin1/poster. This website includes links to many of the computer programs that are available to help with poster design, and also includes a poster template, suggested layouts, and examples of good and mediocre posters.

# References

The following sources are recommended to give additional help and examples in scientific writing:

Gillen, C. *Reading Primary Literature: A Practical Guide to Evaluating Research Articles in Biology.* San Francisco, CA: Benjamin/Cummings, 2007.

Harnack, A. and E. Kleppinger. *Online! A Reference Guide to Using Internet Sources,* 3rd ed. Boston: Bedford/St. Martin's, 2003.

Knisely, K. *A Student Handbook for Writing in Biology,* 2nd ed. Sunderland, MA: Sinauer Associates, 2005.

McMillan, V. E. *Writing Papers in the Biological Sciences,* 4th ed. Boston: Bedford/St.Martin's, 2006.

Pechenik, J. A. *A Short Guide to Writing about Biology,* 6th ed., New York, NY: Addison Wesley, 2007.

Style Manual Committee, Council of Biology Editors. *Scientific Style and Format: The CBE Manual for Authors, Editors and Publishers,* 6th ed. Cambridge, MA: Cambridge Univ. Press, 1994.

Tate, M., and J. Alexander. "Teaching Critical Evaluation Skills for World Wide Web Resources." *Computers in Libraries,* Nov/Dec 1996, pp. 49–55.

# Websites

How to cite Internet sources:
http://www.bedfordstmartins.com/online/cite8.html

How to evaluate Web sources:
http://lib.nmsu.edu/instruction/eval/bib.htm.

Purrington, C.B. 2006. Advice on designing scientific posters:
http://www.swathmore.edu/NatSci/cpurrin1/poster

How to prepare and present effective PowerPoint presentations:
www.dartmouth.edu/~biomed/new.htmld/ppt_resources.shtml

# Appendix
# Terminology and Techniques for Dissection

## Orientation Terminology

The terms defined below are used with bilaterally symmetrical animals, both invertebrates and vertebrates (Figures 1 and 2). Use these terms as you describe animals studied in this laboratory manual. Note that texts may use different terminology for those animals called bipeds (for example, humans) and those called quadrupeds (for example, the fetal pig). Terminology used exclusively with bipeds is not included in this appendix.

**Right/left:** always refer to the animal's right or left, not yours.

**Anterior, cranial:** toward the head.

**Posterior, caudal:** toward the tail.

**Dorsal:** backside; from the Latin *dorsum,* meaning "back."

**Ventral:** bellyside; from the Latin *venter,* meaning "belly."

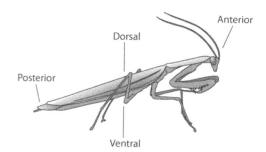

**Figure 1.**
Orientation terminology in a bilaterally symmetrical invertebrate, the praying mantis.

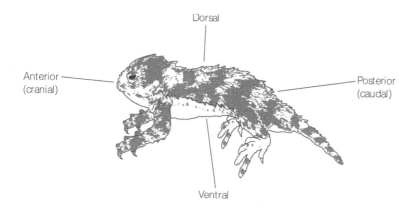

**Figure 2.**
Orientation terminology in a quadruped vertebrate, a horned lizard.

## Terms Relating to Position in the Body

**Proximal:** near the trunk, attached portion, or point of reference, for example: "The pig's elbow is *proximal* to its wrist."

**Distal:** farther from the trunk, attached portion, or point of reference, for example: "The toes are *distal* to the ankle."

**Superficial:** lying on top or near the body surface.

**Deep:** lying under or below.

## Planes and Sections

A **section** is a cut through a structure. A **plane** is an imaginary line through which a section can be cut. Anatomists generally refer to three planes or sections (Figure 3).

- **Sagittal section:** divides the body into left and right portions or halves. This is a longitudinal or lengthwise section from anterior to posterior.

- **Frontal section:** A longitudinal or lengthwise section from anterior to posterior, this divides the body into dorsal and ventral portions or halves.

- **Transverse section:** Also called a **cross section**, this divides the body into anterior and posterior portions or cuts a structure across its smallest diameter.

## Dissection Techniques

When studying the anatomy of an organism, the term **dissection** is perhaps a misnomer. *Dissection* literally means to cut apart piece by piece. In lab, however, it is usually more appropriate to expose structures rather than dissect them. Initial incisions do require that you cut into the body, but after body cavities are opened, you will usually only separate and expose body parts, using dissection rarely. Accordingly, you will use the scalpel when you make initial incisions into the body wall of large animals, but seldom when studying small animals or organs of large animals.

Scissors are used to deepen initial cuts made by the scalpel in large animals and to cut into the bodies of smaller animals. When using scissors, direct the tips upward to prevent gouging deeper organs. Once the animal's body is open, use forceps and the blunt probe to carefully separate organs and to pick away connective tissue obstructing and binding organs and ducts. Needle probes are only minimally useful. Never cut away an organ or cut through a blood vessel, nerve, or duct unless given specific instructions to do so.

Producing a good dissection takes time and cannot be rushed. As you study the anatomy of animals, your goal should be to expose all parts so that they can be easily studied and demonstrated to your lab partner or instructor.

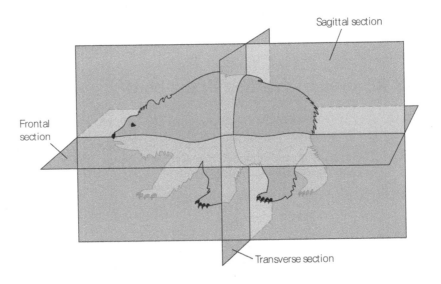

**Figure 3.**
Sections of a bilaterally symmetrical animal.

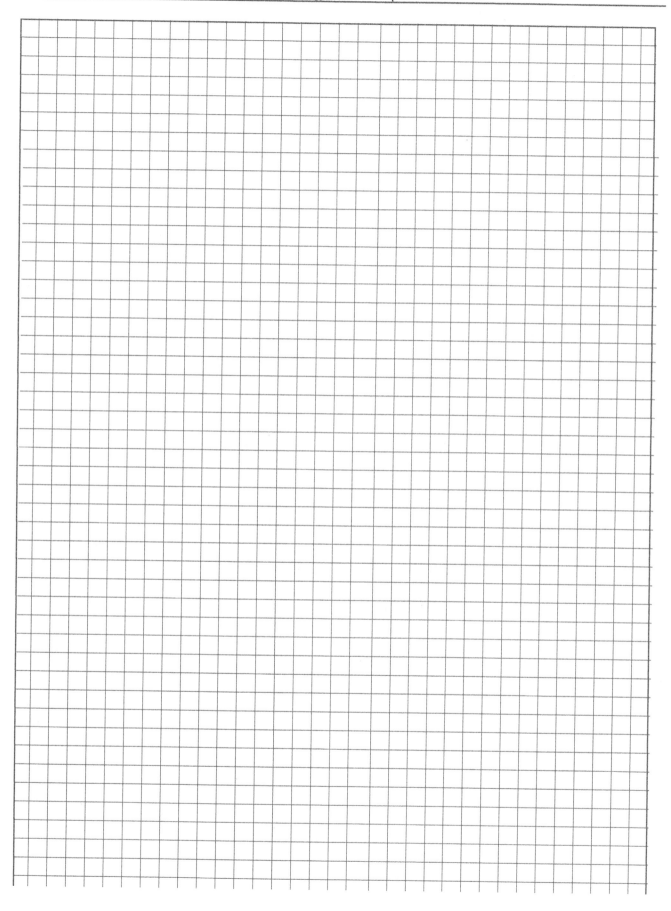

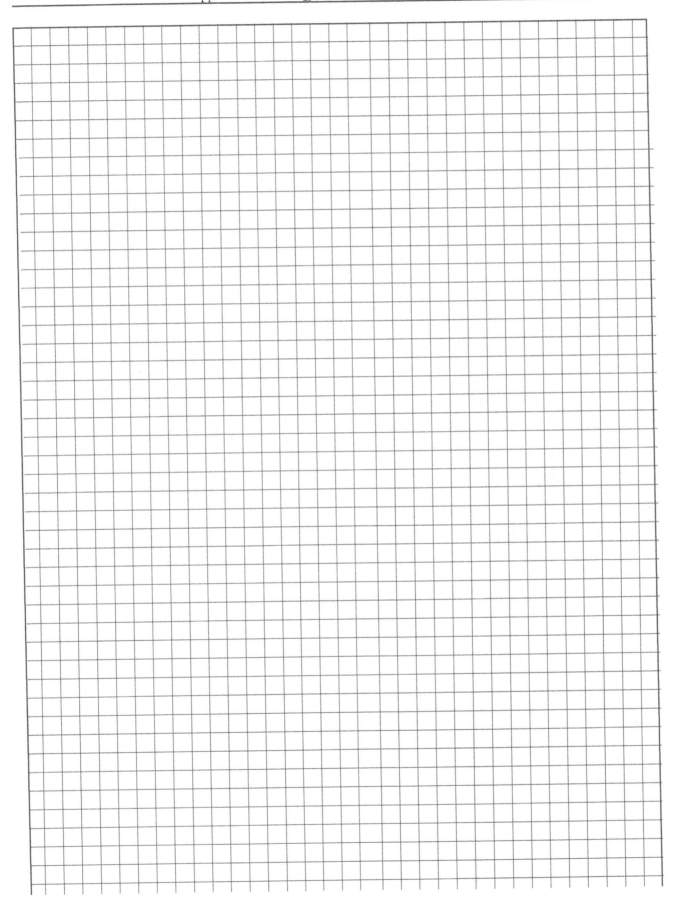

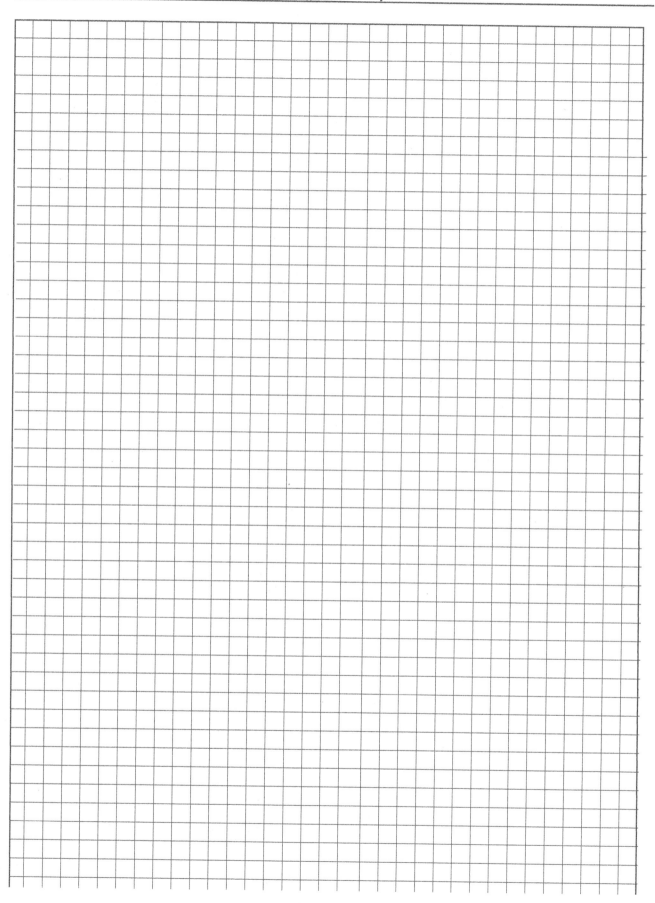

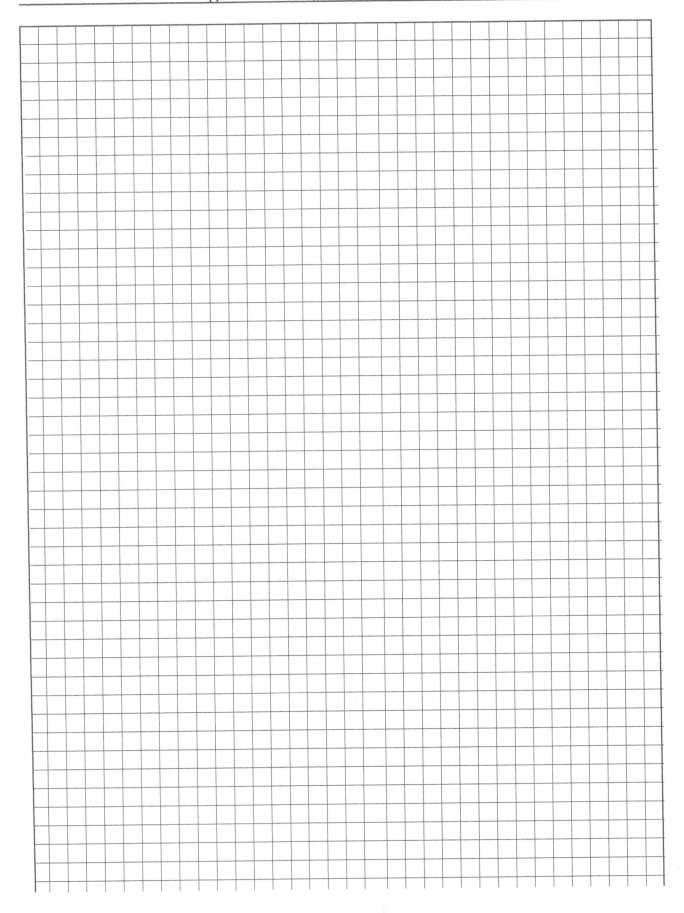

# COLOR PLATES

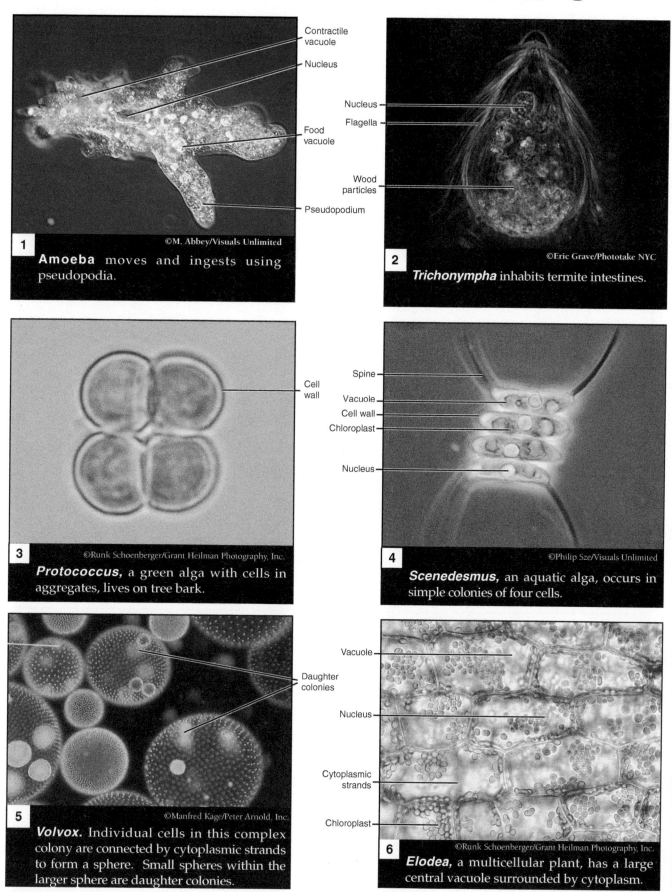

**Contractile vacuole**

**Nucleus**

**Food vacuole**

**Pseudopodium**

**1** ©M. Abbey/Visuals Unlimited

**Amoeba** moves and ingests using pseudopodia.

**Nucleus**

**Flagella**

**Wood particles**

**2** ©Eric Grave/Phototake NYC

**Trichonympha** inhabits termite intestines.

**Cell wall**

**3** ©Runk Schoenberger/Grant Heilman Photography, Inc.

**Protococcus,** a green alga with cells in aggregates, lives on tree bark.

**Spine**

**Vacuole**

**Cell wall**

**Chloroplast**

**Nucleus**

**4** ©Philip Sze/Visuals Unlimited

**Scenedesmus,** an aquatic alga, occurs in simple colonies of four cells.

**Daughter colonies**

**5** ©Manfred Kage/Peter Arnold, Inc.

**Volvox.** Individual cells in this complex colony are connected by cytoplasmic strands to form a sphere. Small spheres within the larger sphere are daughter colonies.

**Vacuole**

**Nucleus**

**Cytoplasmic strands**

**Chloroplast**

**6** ©Runk Schoenberger/Grant Heilman Photography, Inc.

**Elodea,** a multicellular plant, has a large central vacuole surrounded by cytoplasm.

From *Investigating Biology Laboratory Manual*, Sixth Edition, Judith G. Morgan and M. Eloise Brown Carter. Copyright © 2008 by Pearson Education, Inc. Published by Benjamin Cummings, Inc. All rights reserved.

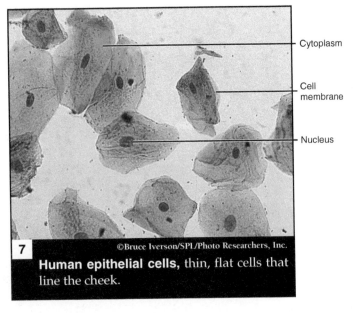
Cytoplasm

Cell
membrane

Nucleus

©Bruce Iverson/SPL/Photo Researchers, Inc.

**7 Human epithelial cells,** thin, flat cells that line the cheek.

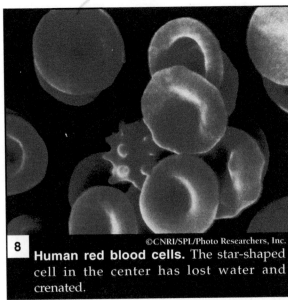
©CNRI/SPL/Photo Researchers, Inc.

**8 Human red blood cells.** The star-shaped cell in the center has lost water and crenated.

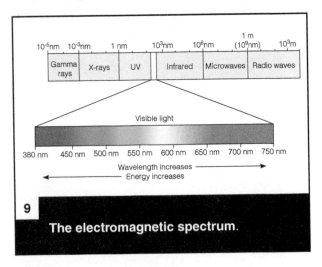

$10^{-5}$nm  $10^{-3}$nm  1 nm  $10^{3}$nm  $10^{6}$nm  1 m ($10^{9}$nm)  $10^{3}$m

| Gamma rays | X-rays | UV | Infrared | Microwaves | Radio waves |

Visible light

380 nm  450 nm  500 nm  550 nm  600 nm  650 nm  700 nm  750 nm

← Wavelength increases →
← Energy increases →

**9 The electromagnetic spectrum.**

 **See color plates 11 and 12 on next page**

Judith Morgan

**10** *Coleus* **leaves with green and pink pigments.**

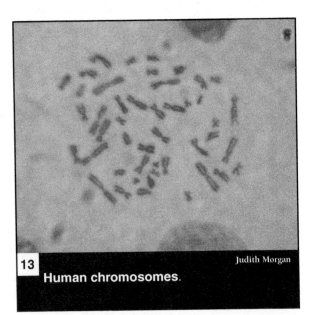
Judith Morgan

**13 Human chromosomes.**

©Phototake

**14** Two mating types of *Sordaria fimicola* growing on agar.

370

## 11a–e Mitosis in plant cells, onion root tip.

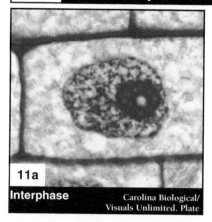

**11a**

**Interphase**
Carolina Biological/
Visuals Unlimited. Plate

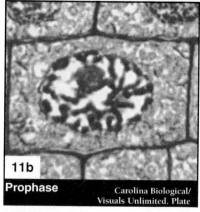

**11b**

**Prophase**
Carolina Biological/
Visuals Unlimited. Plate

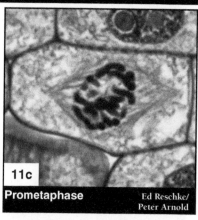

**11c**

**Prometaphase**
Ed Reschke/
Peter Arnold

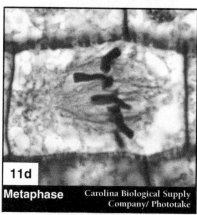

**11d**

**Metaphase**
Carolina Biological Supply
Company/ Phototake

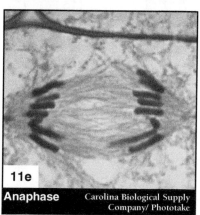

**11e**

**Anaphase**
Carolina Biological Supply
Company/ Phototake

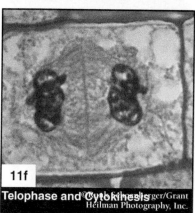

**11f**

**Telophase and Cytokinesis**
©C. Winberger/Grant
Heilman Photography, Inc.

## 12a–e Mitosis in animal cells, whitefish blastula.

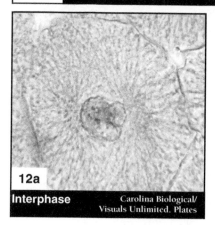

**12a**

**Interphase**
Carolina Biological/
Visuals Unlimited. Plates

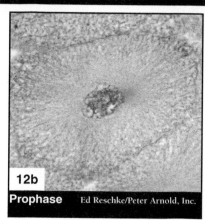

**12b**

**Prophase**
Ed Reschke/Peter Arnold, Inc.

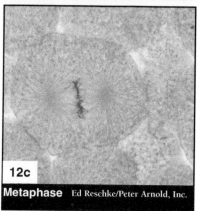

**12c**

**Metaphase**
Ed Reschke/Peter Arnold, Inc.

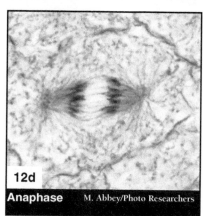

**12d**

**Anaphase**
M. Abbey/Photo Researchers

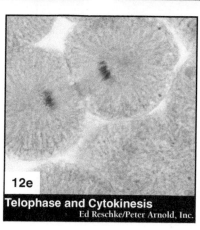

**12e**

**Telophase and Cytokinesis**
Ed Reschke/Peter Arnold, Inc.

Wild-type

Yellow-green

**15** Carolina Biological

Yellow-green mutant ***Brassica rapa*** seedlings in the right half of each quad (wild-type with anthocyanin in the left half).

**16** Eloise Carter

***Talinum,*** a succulent commonly found in shallow soils on rock outcrops.

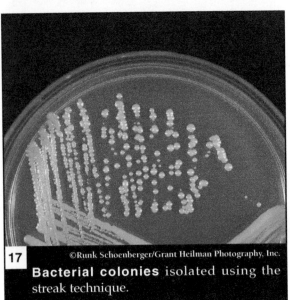

**17** ©Runk Schoenberger/Grant Heilman Photography, Inc.

**Bacterial colonies** isolated using the streak technique.

**18** ©John Durham/SPL/Photo Researchers, Inc.

**Fungi** growing on an agar plate. Note the filamentous fungal body, the mycelium.

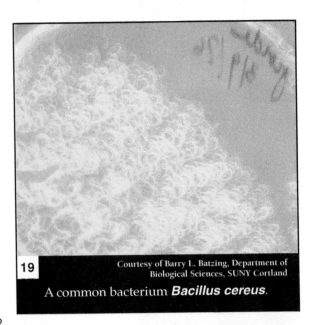

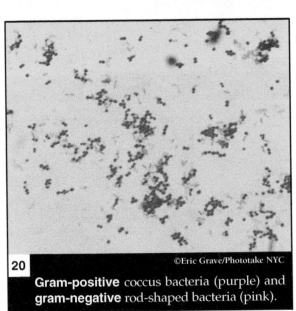

**19** Courtesy of Barry L. Batzing, Department of Biological Sciences, SUNY Cortland

A common bacterium ***Bacillus cereus.***

**20** ©Eric Grave/Phototake NYC

**Gram-positive** coccus bacteria (purple) and **gram-negative** rod-shaped bacteria (pink).

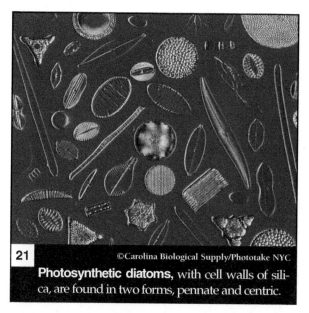

**21** **Photosynthetic diatoms,** with cell walls of silica, are found in two forms, pennate and centric.

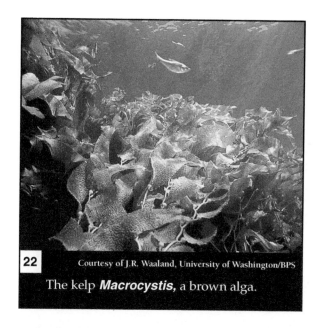

**22** The kelp **Macrocystis,** a brown alga.

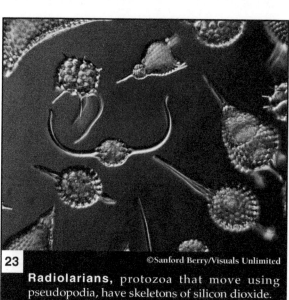

**23** **Radiolarians,** protozoa that move using pseudopodia, have skeletons of silicon dioxide.

**24** **The slime mold Physarum.** The vegetative plasmodium is a multinucleate mass of protoplasm.

**25** **Fruiting bodies of a slime mold** are shown magnified about 50 times.

**26** A red alga, **Palmaria,** found in deep marine waters.

27 ©Laurie Campbell/NHPA

***Ulva,*** sea lettuce, is an edible green alga.

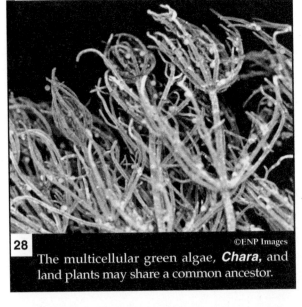

28 ©ENP Images

The multicellular green algae, ***Chara,*** and land plants may share a common ancestor.

29 ©Science VU

**Ecuadorian poison frog in cup fungus.**

30 ©Pat Lynch/ Photo Researchers, Inc.

In a **moss,** spores develop in sporangia at the end of the sporophyte growing out of the leafy gametophyte.

Gemmae cup

31 ©Jane Gushow/Grant Heilman Photography, Inc.

**Liverworts.** Gemmae cups on the surface of this bryophyte function in asexual reproduction.

32 ©D. Newman/Visuals Unlimited

***Lycopodium.*** This club moss is a living member of the division Lycophyta.

**33** ©Glenn Oliver/Visuals Unlimited

This *Selaginella* species lives in moist habitats, but other species may survive in a desert.

**34** ©William M. Partington/ Photo Researchers, Inc.

Sporangia, small spherical structures, are seen on stems of the **whisk fern**, *Psilotum*.

**35** ©Visuals Unlimited

**Horsetail stems** are seen here with strobili containing sporangia.

**36** ©Grant Heilman/Grant Heilman Photography

**Fern fronds** are the sporophyte stage of the life cycle. The fiddleheads in the inset are young fronds ready to unfurl.

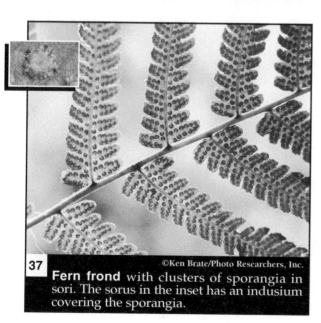

**37** ©Ken Brate/Photo Researchers, Inc.

**Fern frond** with clusters of sporangia in sori. The sorus in the inset has an indusium covering the sporangia.

**38** Eloise Carter. inset: Bill Morgan

**Coniferophyta.** First, second, and third-year cones of bristlecone pine. Some bristlecone pines are more than 4,000 years old.

**39** ©Biophoto Associates/Photo Researchers, Inc.

**Cycadophyta.** Pollen is produced in male cones, seeds in female cones in cycads.

**40** ©Keith Gunnar/Bruce Coleman, Inc.

**Ginkgophyta.** These ginkgo leaves are shown with ovules.

**41** ©M.E. Warren/Photo Researchers, Inc.

**Ginkgophyta.** Male strobili, pollen-producing structures, cluster at the base of leaves.

**42** ©D. Wilder. inset: Gerald and Buff Corsi/Visuals Unlimited

**Gnetophyta.** Mormon tea occurs in the deserts of North and Central America. Inset, enlarged male cones.

Stamen

Pistil

**43** ©Anthony Mercieca/Photo Researchers, Inc.

Close-up of a **tulip** showing reproductive structures stamen and pistil.

**44** Jerome Wexler/Photo Researchers, Inc.

**Wind pollinated flowers** are inconspicuous and produce enormous quantities of pollen.

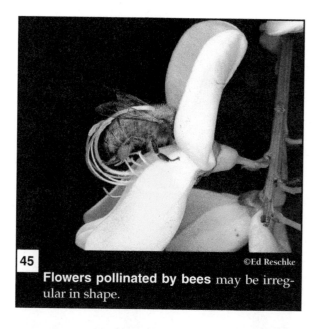

**45** ©Ed Reschke

**Flowers pollinated by bees** may be irregular in shape.

**46** ©Robert Brons/BPS

**Hummingbirds** pollinate red tubular flowers.

**47** Merlin D. Tuttle/Bat Conservation International

**Bats** pollinate night-blooming flowers with pale sepals and petals.

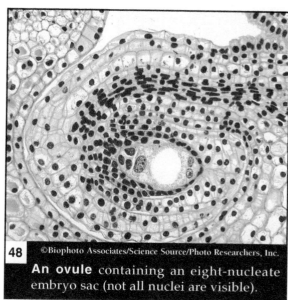

**48** ©Biophoto Associates/Science Source/Photo Researchers, Inc.

**An ovule** containing an eight-nucleate embryo sac (not all nuclei are visible).

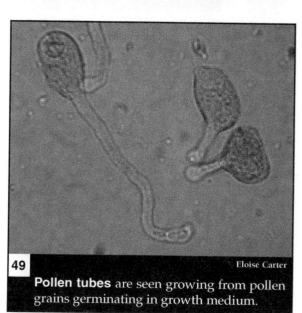

**49** Eloise Carter

**Pollen tubes** are seen growing from pollen grains germinating in growth medium.

**50** ©S. Stephanowicz/SPL/Photo Researchers, Inc.

**Sponge.** Needlelike spicules of calcium carbonate protrude from the osculum and the surface of the sponge body.

51 ©Robert Dunne/ Photo Researchers, Inc.
**Red finger sponges.**

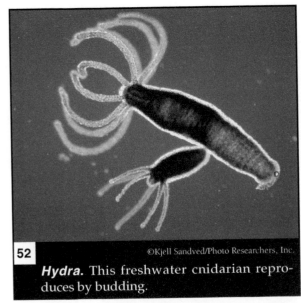

52 ©Kjell Sandved/Photo Researchers, Inc.
***Hydra.*** This freshwater cnidarian reproduces by budding.

53 ©Kjell Sandved/Bruce Coleman, Inc.
***Dugesia,*** a freshwater planarian with two pigmented eyespots between the two auricles on its anterior end.

54 ©Runk-Schoenberger/ Grant Heilman Photography, Inc.
***Nereis.*** This segmented clamworm is an annelid that bears fleshy appendages called parapodia.

55 ©Ed Reschke/Peter Arnold, Inc.
***Donax,*** a molluscan species, seen here with the foot and two siphons extended.

56 Courtesy of Gregg Orloff
**Roundworm,** in the phylum Nematoda, has a smooth body with no segments.

57 ©George J. Wilder/Visuals Unlimited
***Cambarus.*** The freshwater crayfish is a member of the phylum Arthropoda.

**58**
©Grant Heilman/Grant Heilman Photography

The segmented body and jointed appendages are visible in this **grasshopper,** a terrestrial anthropod.

**59**
Norbert Wu/Minden Pictures

**Sea star.** The radial symmetry of echinoderm adults is evident in this Deuterostome.

**60**
Judith Morgan and Eloise Carter

*Branchiostoma.* The lancelet is a small chordate that lives in coastal waters.

Sclerenchyma

Parenchyma

Collenchyma

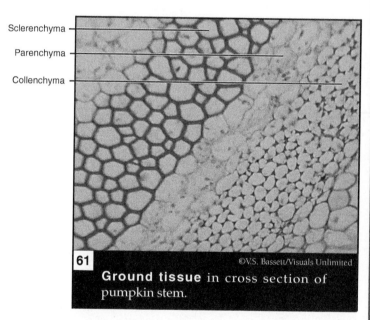

**61**
©V.S. Bassett/Visuals Unlimited

**Ground tissue** in cross section of pumpkin stem.

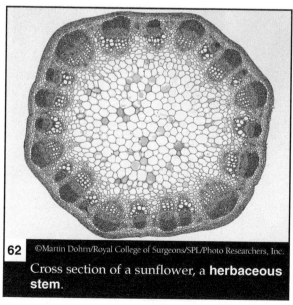

**62**
©Martin Dohrn/Royal College of Surgeons/SPL/Photo Researchers, Inc.

Cross section of a sunflower, a **herbaceous stem**.

**63**
From David L. Bassett, MD, *A Stereoscopic Atlas of Human Anatomy*

This **woody stem,** seen in cross section, is more than 2 years old.

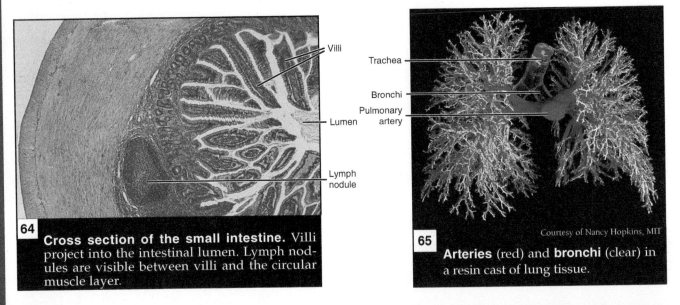

**64 Cross section of the small intestine.** Villi project into the intestinal lumen. Lymph nodules are visible between villi and the circular muscle layer.

Villi

Lumen

Lymph nodule

**65 Arteries** (red) and **bronchi** (clear) in a resin cast of lung tissue.

Trachea

Bronchi

Pulmonary artery

Courtesy of Nancy Hopkins, MIT

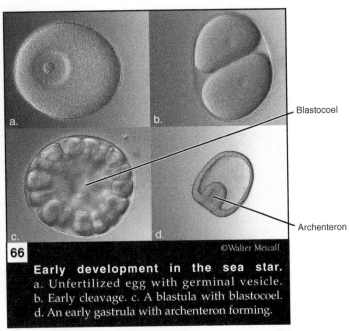

a.

b.

c.

d.

Blastocoel

Archenteron

©Walter Metcalf

**66 Early development in the sea star.**
a. Unfertilized egg with germinal vesicle.
b. Early cleavage. c. A blastula with blastocoel.
d. An early gastrula with archenteron forming.

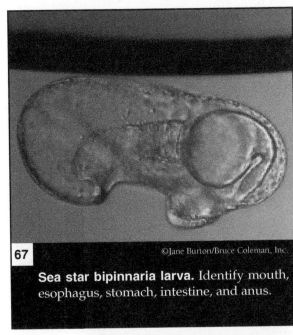

**67 Sea star bipinnaria larva.** Identify mouth, esophagus, stomach, intestine, and anus.

©Jane Burton/Bruce Coleman, Inc.

**68 Zebrafish** are important organisms for developmental studies.

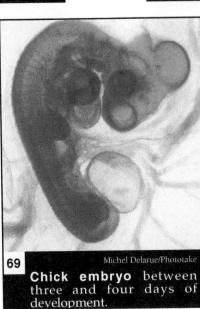

Michel Delarue/Phototake

**69 Chick embryo** between three and four days of development.

**70 *Betta splendens.*** The male Siamese fighting fish displays agonistic behavior.

# Index

Blood, 4-5, 96, 106, 108-110, 113, 124, 126-127, 133,
   140, 171, 231, 233-236, 238, 241-242,
   244-245, 253, 255-268, 272, 275-277, 286,
   296, 314, 319-320, 364, 370
   circulation, 96, 124, 126, 133, 140, 238, 255-257,
      261, 263-264, 266-268
   components, 231
   functions of, 296
   movement of, 171, 242
   plasma, 231
   pressure, 171, 242
   types, 96, 370
   vessels, 96, 108-110, 140, 233-236, 238, 244-245,
      255-257, 259, 261, 264-266, 268,
      276-277, 286, 319-320
Blood cells, 4-5, 171, 231, 234, 370
Blood vessels, 96, 108, 110, 140, 233-236, 238,
   244-245, 255-257, 261, 265-266, 268,
   276-277, 286, 319-320
   of heart, 256
   structure of, 277
Bloom, 7, 250, 295
Blue-footed boobies, 348
Body cavities, 97, 364
Body plans, 115
   animal, 115
   insect, 115
Body temperature, 232, 235
Bog, 144
Bolting, 216, 222
Bonds, 303
Bone, 173, 228, 231, 240, 248, 254
Boron, 88
Bowels, 239
Bowman's capsule, 277
Brachydanio rerio, 311, 326
Bracts, 50, 72, 75
Brain, 97, 101, 104-105, 108-109, 123-124, 127-128,
   147, 232, 275, 288-289, 291-292, 301,
   313-314, 319-320
   components of, 289
   development, 128, 147, 301, 313-314, 319-320
Bread mold, 21
Breasts, 168, 347
Brine shrimp, 152-155, 330-333
Bronchi, 267-269, 380
Bronchioles, 268-269
Bronchitis, 271
Brown algae, 3, 8-11, 33
Brownian movement, 171
Budding, 24, 378
Buffer, 61
Bugs, 152, 156-158, 330, 334-337, 348
Bulbourethral glands, 279, 281
Bulbs, 100

C
C3, 202
C4 plants, 202
cabbage, 197, 206
Caenorhabditis elegans, 118
Calcium, 12, 16, 88, 98, 377
Calcium carbonate, 12, 98, 377
Cambrian period, 93
Cancer, 248, 271-272, 294
   cells, 248, 271
   lung, 271
   prostate, 294
   skin, 248
   stomach, 272
Candida, 28
Canopy, 50
Capillaries, 133, 245, 263-265, 268, 277
   blood, 133, 245, 263-265, 268, 277
   structure of, 277
Capillary bed, 263-265
Capsule, 84, 277
Carbohydrate, 9, 182
Carbohydrates, 21, 249, 316
Carbon, 45, 96, 129, 191, 253, 268, 321
   nutrient, 253
Carbon cycle, 45
Carbon dioxide, 96, 129, 191, 253, 268, 321
   in blood, 96
Carbonate, 12, 98, 377
Carcinoma, 248
Cardiac, 68, 173, 231-232, 242-243, 256, 272
   muscle, 173, 231-232, 242, 256
Cardiac muscle, 173, 231-232, 256

Cardiovascular, 272
   system, 272
Cardiovascular system, 272
Carnivores, 44, 244
Carotid, 260
   arteries, 260
Carrageenan, 15
Carrots, 187
Cartilage, 133, 228, 231, 236, 240, 248, 255, 271
Casparian strip, 189
Cataracts, 293
Cavity, 84, 93-94, 96-101, 105, 109-110, 112-113,
   118-121, 123-124, 129, 140, 142, 147, 236,
   239-245, 251, 254-256, 261, 263, 266, 268,
   276, 280-281, 283, 298, 301-302, 305, 321
Cecum, 243-244
Cell, 2, 4-10, 12-17, 19, 21, 24, 52, 66, 71, 79-81, 99,
   102, 171, 173-177, 179-180, 182-184, 186,
   189, 191, 194-195, 198-200, 204, 208-209,
   212, 214, 216, 229-232, 248, 288-290,
   297-300, 303, 305, 312-314, 317, 357,
   369-370, 373
   characteristics, 2, 5, 7-8, 10, 12-17, 19, 21, 102
   origin, 15
   primitive, 317
   structure, 2, 4, 8, 13, 17, 21, 24, 99, 173-174,
      176-177, 179-180, 184, 186, 191, 194,
      198-200, 204, 209, 288-290
Cell body, 12, 232, 288
Cell differentiation, 179
Cell division, 177, 179, 200, 214, 297, 300
   in meiosis, 300
   overview, 179
Cell membrane, 5-6, 10, 189, 303, 370
Cell size, 179-180
cell structure, 2, 180, 184, 194
Cell wall, 7-10, 14-15, 171, 175, 179, 212, 369
   bacteria, 14-15
   diatoms, 8-10
   fungi, 7-10, 14-15
   of algae, 15
   oomycetes, 8
Cell walls, 9, 14-16, 21, 52, 174, 179, 183, 195, 373
Cells, 4-5, 7, 9-10, 17, 20-21, 23-24, 42-43, 48, 54, 60,
   66-67, 71-72, 79-80, 96, 99, 101-102, 105,
   125, 133, 136, 140, 171, 173-177, 179-187,
   189-191, 194-196, 199-201, 203, 208, 216,
   227-229, 231-234, 245, 248, 253, 271, 277,
   288, 291, 297-298, 300-301, 303, 305-306,
   309, 312-315, 317-318, 322, 326, 369-371
   classification of, 298
   cleavage, 297-298, 300, 303, 305, 309, 312-315,
      317, 322
   functions of, 99, 184, 186-187, 189, 200, 248, 271
   morphogenesis, 297
   size of, 67, 208, 300, 305, 309, 315
   structure and function, 173-174, 177, 190, 199
   types of, 96, 174, 185, 187, 194, 232, 288, 370
   vesicles, 303
Cellular slime molds, 14
Cellulose, 7-8, 21, 212
Central canal, 135, 289
Central nervous system, 130, 232, 275, 289, 328
Central vacuole, 369
Cephalization, 128, 147, 239
Cephalochordata, 131
Cerebral ganglia, 105
Cervix, 283-285
chain, 343, 347
Charophytes, 17
Cheese, 27
Chemical messengers, 205, 212
Chemicals, 60, 114, 144, 222
Chemistry, 14, 115
Chemotaxis, 30, 60-62
Chestnut blight, 24
Chicken eggs, 325
chickens, 315-316
Chicks, 319
Children, 26
Chitin, 21
Chlorophyll, 10, 15, 114
   structure, 114
Chlorophyll a, 10, 15
chlorophylls, 17
Chloroplast, 17, 369
Chloroplasts, 4, 10, 191
Chondrocytes, 230-231
Chorion, 286, 313, 321, 325

Choroid, 292
   function of, 292
Chromosomes, 298, 315, 370
   human, 370
   maternal, 298
   paternal, 298
Chrysophyta, 8
Cigarette smoking, 270
Cilia, 6-7, 96, 103
Ciliary body, 291-292
ciliated cells, 133
Ciliates, 5, 7
Circulation, 96, 118, 124, 126, 133, 140, 238, 255-257,
   261, 263-264, 266-268, 274
   fetal, 238, 256, 261, 264, 266-267, 274
Circulatory system, 96, 108, 113, 130, 133, 136, 140,
   142, 244-245, 253, 255, 261, 266, 268, 276,
   301, 319
   clade, 2-4, 8, 13, 33, 60, 93-94, 103, 106, 111,
      117-118, 121, 144
Clams, 94, 111
Class, 32, 37, 100, 103, 135, 147, 149, 153, 156, 159,
   164, 168, 172, 206, 218, 221, 225, 251, 274,
   331, 334, 337, 342, 346, 353
Classification, 2, 4, 14-15, 17, 35, 37, 41, 94-95, 117,
   298
Claviceps purpurea, 25
Clay, 207
Cleavage, 128, 297-300, 303-305, 307-310, 312-317,
   322-324, 328, 380
Cleavage furrows, 299
Climate, 201, 211
Clitellum, 109-110
Cloaca, 119
Club fungi, 26-27, 32, 34
Cnidocytes, 101-102
Coal, 49, 56
Coccus, 372
Coelom, 93-94, 96-97, 108-110, 113, 115, 118, 120,
   124, 126, 133, 147, 236, 239
Coelomates, 115
Cold, 9, 211, 233
Collar cells, 99
Collecting duct, 277
Collenchyma cells, 174
Colon, 243-244, 246
Colonization, 20, 39
Colony, 14, 347, 369
Coloration, 160, 338
Communication, 148, 331, 343, 351-361
Communities, 324
Community, 4, 351
Companion cells, 176, 183, 194, 200
Complement, 298
Complex carbohydrates, 21
Compound, 4-6, 8, 11-12, 17, 21, 23-24, 26, 37, 53-54,
   61, 79, 81, 84, 98, 100-101, 103-104, 108,
   110, 117, 120, 125, 131-132, 153, 179-180,
   184, 186, 191, 194, 232-233, 245, 288-290,
   303-304, 311-312, 315, 318, 331
Compound eyes, 153, 331
Compound microscope, 4-6, 8, 11-12, 17, 21, 23-24,
   26, 53-54, 79, 81, 98, 100-101, 103-104,
   108, 110, 117, 120, 131-132, 179-180, 184,
   186, 191, 194, 232-233, 245, 288-290,
   303-304, 311-312, 315, 318
   first, 6, 12, 54, 98, 303-304, 315, 318
Compound microscopes, 37
Compounds, 3, 17, 61, 68, 347
   organic, 3, 17, 61
Conclusions, 32, 128, 149, 153, 156, 159, 164, 168,
   171-172, 206, 221, 225, 236, 238, 331, 334,
   337, 342, 346, 351, 354, 356, 360
Conduction, 187
Cones, 50, 70, 72, 291-292, 375-376
   function of, 292
Conidia, 24, 26
Coniferophyta, 40-41, 68-69, 86, 375
Conifers, 40-41, 44, 68, 70, 85-86
Connective tissue, 128, 228-234, 245, 250, 256, 281,
   364
   types of, 232
Conservation International, 377
Contractile vacuoles, 6
Contrast, 102, 173, 180, 305
Controlled experiment, 187
Controlled variables, 223
Convergence, 3
Coral reefs, 16